# Mammals,
# Amphibians and Reptiles
# of Hertfordshire

Other titles on Hertfordshire wild life:

*The Birds of Hertfordshire*
*The Breeding Birds of Hertfordshire*
*Birds at Tring Reservoirs*
*The Butterflies of Hertfordshire*
*Wild Flower Habitats of Hertfordshire*


Future titles in this series include:

*The Fungi of Hertfordshire*
*The Dragonflies of Hertfordshire*
*The Hoverflies of Hertfordshire*
*Hertfordshire Landscapes and Wildlife*
    *- a pictorial survey*
*The Cuffley Story*
    *- people and wildlife in a Hertfordshire village*

*Watercolours: 'Dormouse and guelder rose', (1996) facing page, by Daphne Baxter (studio: Wormley West End, Hertfordshire) and title page 'Harvest mouse' (about 1949) by Eileen Soper (1905-1990), (studio: Harmer Green, Hertfordshire, with her father George Soper and her sister Eva). Both author's collection.*

# Mammals, Amphibians and Reptiles of Hertfordshire

*Michael Clark*

*With distribution maps compiled by
Dr.Jennifer Jones*

*Introduction by Ralph Newton*

*Published in 2001 by
The Hertfordshire Natural History Society in association with
Training Publications Limited, Watford, Hertfordshire*

*To the memory of the great Hertfordshire naturalist,* **Ralph Newton**, *who sadly did not live to see this book which he did so much to inspire, in its finished form. Also for my parents,* **Joan and Bernard Clark**, *who allowed me as a child the free run of the countryside around our home in Cuffley.*

**Ralph Newton surveying bats at a Hoddesden house using a licensed bat net (1976).**

*First published 2001*

© text & pictures Michael Clark 2001 (except where otherwise stated)

Published by Training Publications Limited on behalf of Hertfordshire Natural History Society.

ISBN 1 84019 012 4

ISBN 1-84019-012-4

9 781840 190120 >

**British Library Cataloguing in Publication Data**
Clark, Michael
Mammals, Amphibians and Reptiles of Hertfordshire
1. Mammals - England - Hertfordshire
I. Title

*Set in 9pt Times and printed in Great Britain by Training Publications Limited, 3 Finway Court, Whippendell Road, Watford, Hertfordshire WD18 7EN*

# *Foreword*

Hertfordshire is a small and overcrowded county, with diminishing countryside and increasing urbanisation of many parts. As farming has become more intensely arable, field ponds have been filled in and many miles of valuable hedgerow habitat has been lost to the detriment of the small mammal, amphibian and reptile populations.

Many once familiar country scenes and sounds have become increasingly uncommon - a grass snake slipping away into a pond, the spine-chilling scream of a vixen at dead of night and the eerie flight of bats at dusk flitting among the trees along a country lane. Nevertheless, now that I have read Michael's manuscript, it is encouraging to find that there is still a surprising wealth of these animals to be found in the county.

**Ralph Newton.**

Owing to human activities, mammals are often very secretive creatures and largely nocturnal, as are amphibians. Reptiles hurry away from sunny banks at the vibration of our tread: unlike birds all these animals are not so immediately obvious, requiring more diligent searching and observation to record.

Michael Clark's book is the culmination of many years of patient work as County Recorder, painstakenly researched, with revealing past records of earlier writers and fascinating references to books on bygone Hertfordshire.

An authoritative account, it is also a major contribution to our knowledge of the county fauna. This is, however, no mere listing of species and dry statistics: here is a naturalist of the old school who brings the subject alive with anecdote and reminiscences, having an obvious delight in the whole spectrum of the natural world and the happy skill of communicating his joy in observation.

If we wish future generations to continue to enjoy the pleasures of watching our wildlife in the beautiful and varied countryside that remains in Hertfordshire, we must endeavour to protect and conserve our county heritage now by ensuring there is a place for nature, and thereby creating a richer environment for ourselves.

**Ralph Newton**

# Acknowledgements

It may seem odd to add amphibians and reptiles to the duties of the Mammal Recorder, but the *Hertfordshire Natural History Society* (henceforth *HNHS*) amalgamated the survey in 1945, when Bertram Lloyd was in this post, and it has continued to be a combined role ever since. It certainly seems to be logical to me when the vertebrates I most commonly note in my diary include frogs, toads, wood mice, foxes and badgers.

Having evolved into a largely crepuscular creature myself, I tend to record most observations on walks each morning and at twilight, or after dark when I do my round of closing up poultry sheds. I hope, therefore, that readers will find the range of subjects covered appropriate.

When Alan Ward and the editor for Castlemead's series on Hertfordshire's natural history, Tom Gladwin, asked me to write this book, they requested I *'add the amphibians and reptiles so that they are not left out, as there are not enough of them to fit into a book of their own'*.

By the time the *HNHS* had formed their Mammal Group in 1994 and taken over from Castlemead as the publishers of the book series, Dr Jenny Jones was up-dating all the distribution maps on Recorder software at the Hertfordshire Biological Records Centre (henceforth *HBRC*) based in County Hall, and I am indebted to her for taking on such a vital dual role in this aspect of the book.

Clive Herbert has also contributed an enormous amount to our surveys and, like Jenny, has kindly read the finished text. They have both provided extra material and helpful comments for which I am most grateful. Henceforth the *Hertfordshire Amphibian & Reptile Group* is referred to as *HARG*. Steve Kourik checked the proofs and both he and the then *HNHS* President, Ken Smith, have been particularly supportive throughout the project.

**Dr.Jenny Jones at the Biological Records Centre, County Hall, Hertford. Jenny is the new Recorder for all the species in this book and welcomes your records for the new survey. Contact her at:**
>    **HBRC Environment,**
>    **County Hall,**
>    **Pegs Lane,**
>    **Hertford SG13 8DN**

**or:**

**e-mail   jennyjones@hertscc.gov.uk**

8

Robert Campbell of Blackwells, Oxford, has generously allowed me reproduce the national distribution maps from the *Handbook of British Mammals* to give a comparison alongside the county maps, and Dr Deryk Frazer gave permission for me to use material from his and Malcolm Smith's *Reptile and Amphibians in Britain* Collins New Naturalist volumes from 1951 and 1983.

The modern survey began in 1970 when Phyllis Hager asked me on behalf of *HNHS* to become County Recorder. I published sets of tetrad maps in the *HNHS Transactions* (henceforth *Trans*) to encourage the contribution of more records. I have listed the names of the helpers who have sent in records, but my apologies to anyone who has been inadvertently left out. Please keep records (and additions and corrections to this book) coming in and they will be published both in future issues of *Hertfordshire Naturalist* as well as any later editions of this book. Emma Pitrakou has greatly helped in the design and preparation of the book, especially the charts, for which I am more than thankful. The first draft was prepared by Cathy Bibby and checked by Trevor James and Colin Fitzsimmons.

I have worked on the text, pictures and layout as the author/ editor with the help of many in the *Hertfordshire Mammal Group* (henceforth *HMG*), the *Hertfordshire & Middlesex Bat Group* (*HMBG*) and other organisations. I am indebted to Catherine Hockings for helping to scan in the typewritten manuscript when we revised the first draft. Anna my wife has also been a constant support to the project and, with our children, seems to have devoted just as much time as myself to wildlife interests throughout our married life, first in Cuffley and, from 1969, in Tewin.

David Anderson's *Bedfordshire Naturalist* 1985 summary is included with his *Bedfordshire Wildlife* book notes and Joan Childs has provided recent Bedfordshire information on bats. John Dobson has brought the Essex material up to date with his timely *The Mammals of Essex*. I have referred to the

Top: Trevor James, Chair of the Hertfordshire Natural History Society Recorders' Committee.

Centre: Janet and Tom Gladwin. The Rev. Tom Gladwin commissioned this book. As well as his records mentioned in the text, his remarkable study of a stoat is shown on page 156.

Left: Emma Pitrakou who carried out much of the design work at Tewin Orchard prior to the final editorial work by Diana Turner, Phil Farrer and Beryl Bowsher at Training Publications.

Herbrandt, 11th Duke of Bedford, (1858-1940), created a unique collection of animals at Woburn 100 years ago. He was responsible for saving Père David's deer *Elaphus davidianus* from extinction. He also gave the land at Whipsnade for London Zoo to have a rural park setting for part of its collection. Hertfordshire's black squirrels *Sciurus carolinensis*, muntjac deer *Muntiacus reevesi*, and Chinese water deer *Hydropotes inermis* are all descended from Woburn animals. (Picture reproduced by kind permission of the Marquess of Tavistock and the Trustees of the Bedford Estates.)

recorders throughout because it seemed relevant to compare records from the counties which have the longest boundaries on either side of Hertfordshire, plus references to Buckinghamshire, Cambridgeshire and London.

Paul Moxey took the trouble to research the mammal records from the *London Natural History Society* area for me and these findings are summarised in Appendix 6. The work and enthusiasm of the leading Hertfordshire historian Tony Rook has also been invaluable. My sincere thanks go to all these people, but especially so, now sadly only in memory, to Ralph Newton, who tragically died in 1999. It is lamentable to me that he did not see his introduction and the rest of the book published. He has been such a source of wildlife knowledge and patient advice to me and I particularly treasure memories of our pursuits of bats with Clive Banks all over the county on so many nights.

Bernard Nau spent a considerable amount of time helping me establish the first tetrad system on my Mac computer before the recorder software became the standard software in the *Hertfordshire Biological Records Centre*. He has been an inspiration to natural history study in Hertfordshire and Bedfordshire especially. Barry Norman has willingly got soaked helping to promote otters and water voles and my thanks also go to the author Diana Norman for supporting so many conservation projects with Barry.

Help with pictures and published material has come with generous permission to reproduce items and I am indebted to Aerofilms, Borehamwood, Hertfordshire, for aerial views; *HBRC* and Hertfordshire Archives and Local Studies Collections in County Hall, Hertford; Henry Arnold, John Catt, Chris Dee, Pat Morris and Ken Smith for maps; The Hon.Dr.Miriam Rothschild and The Walter Rothschild Zoological Museum, Tring, for pictures and references on Lord Rothschild and his collections.

The generalised soil map of Hertfordshire has been created from the national survey which ignores county boundaries. This is the first time it has been published in this way and I am indebted to Ian Bradley of the Soil Survey and Land Research Centre at Cranfield University for producing the map which also illustrates the extent of the urban areas.

My sincere thanks also go to all the recorders and other supporters who have contributed to the survey, especially those who have taken the trouble to go through their notebooks and complete annual reports, and to all other helpers including:

N. Agar, M. Ainger, M. Allen, P. Alton, S. Ames, D. Anderson, G. Appleton, W. Ashley, E. Askwith, W. Atkins, P. Attewell, The Earl of Arran & Lady Arran, C. Aybes.

J. Baker, M. Baker, R. Ball, C. Banks, B. Barker,

D. Barker, S. Barley, G. Baron, M. Barrett, B. & S. Barton,
J. Barton, R. Bateman, D. Baxter, S. Bearder, T. Bearder,
F. Bedford, M. & I. Bedford, L. Bengines, G. Beningfield,
G. & H. Bennell, T. Bentham, J. Birks, I. Bishop,
S. Bisserot, M. Bland, N. Bonner, R. Bono, D. & R. Boon,
L. Borg, H. Bott, C. Brackenbury, K. Bradbury,
B. & T. Brady, A. Brewster, B. & P. Briggs, S. Bryer,
W. Buckingham, P. Buckle, J. Burgess, D. Bushell,
A. Burton, C. Burton, R. Burwood.

J. & R. Card, P. Carne, S. Carr, A. Catchpole, P. Cawdell,
S. Cham, D. & N. Chapman, C. Cheeseman, A. Clark,
A. J. Clark, A. & P. Clark, D. G. Clark, E. Clayton, R. Cole,
M. Collins, P. Collins, A. Cook, R. Coope, A. Cooper,
D. Cooper, E. Cooper, D. Corke, F. Courtier, D. Cove,
D. Cowan, M. Crompton, M. & P. Craner, M. Crayford,
P. & S. Creasey, E. & J. Crew, A. Cummins,
P. Cunningham, D. Curry.

S. Dalton, G. Daneski, G. Dangerfield, O. Dansie,
W. Darling, S. Darton, K. & C. Davies, C. Dawes, C. Dee,
P. & P. Delap, M. Demedecki, R. Denton, C. Doncaster,
J. Dony, C. Dorken.

B. Eastcott, D. Eaton, P. Edwards, R. Edwards, J. Eldridge,
K. Eltringham, E. Evans, C. Everett.

E. Fairhead, H. Faure-Walker, R. & L. Favell, J. Fearnside,
D. Fennell, M. Ferrero, C. Ferris, C. Fitzsimmons,
G. & G. Fitzsimmons, J. Flowerdew, A. Folen,
W. Fordham, J. Foster, C. Fountain, D. Frazer, R. Freeman,
B. Frewin.

N. Gammon, K. & J. Gardner, G. & H. Gartside,
M. Gaved, M. Giffen, B. Gillam, R. Gillmor,
J. & T. Gladwin, T. Glue, F. Goetz, A. Goodall, S. Gorton,
D. Gow, D. Green, W. Green.

E. Haddow, M. Hadley, P. Hager, M. Hale,
R. & R. Hamilton, R. Hamilton-Peters, M. Hancox,
S. Hanley, L. & J. Harmer, G. Harper, S. Harris,
Sir N. Hawthorne, R. & S. Haydon, P. & V. Haywood,
F. Henning, J. Henson, C. Herbert, Hertfordshire Mercury,
J. Hickling, M. Hicks, K. Higby, D. Hills, D. & Y. Hodson,
M. Holden, T. Holder, N. Holmes-Smith, K. Hook,
J. Hopkyns, M. Hopkyns, A. Horder, D. & J. Hosking,
F. Hughes, W. Hughes, R. Humphreys, E. Hunter,
E. Hurrell, H. Hurrell, J. Huston.

B. Ing, M. Ingram, C. Irons, R. Izzard.

I. Jackson, O. Jackson, C. & T. James, D. James, O. James,
N. Johnson, B. Johnston, J. Jones, K. Jones.

A. Keith, S. Kelly, L. Key, P. Killey, J. & M. Killick,
A. Killingley, A. & M. King, P. Kingsbury, G. Kinns,

Walter, Lord Rothschild
(1868-1937), at the age of 24.
His museum at Tring (see pp260,
276 & 277) is world famous.
Research for this book illustrated
the enormous debt not only
Hertfordshire, but the whole nation,
owes to Walter for his scientific
approach to natural history study,
his collections and his museum.
Reference to his niece, Miriam
Rothschild, is also made from p276.
(Reproduced by kind permission of
Miriam Rothschild from her book
*Dear Lord Rothschild*.)

During an evening field meeting led by **Dr Jenny Jones**, Michael Warburg surveys ponds for newts at night on Chorleywood Common. The eggs of great crested newts are individually folded between the protective leaves of pond weed.

T. Kittle, S. & K. Kourik, Viscount Knutsford, H. Kruuk.

D. Laming, F. Lancaster, B. Lawrence, T. Lawson, K. Leah, J. & A. Lee, L. & R. Lennon, J. Leonhardt, L. Lewis, A. Ling, D. Livingstone, B. Loyd, T. Lording, P & V. Loughrey, C. Lucas.

J. McLusky, D. Manning, J. Manser, T. & S. Marks, J. Marsh, B. Marshall, A. Martin, D. Martindale, C. Mason, L. Masters, D. Macdonald, A. McDiarmid, J. McIlwain, G. McKenzie, R. McReady, C. Mead, F. & J. Meads, R. Miller, G. Millington, W. Mitchell, J. & R. Maley, D. Marriott, E. Maughan, P. Moles, J. & P. Morgan, P. Morris, P. Moxey, R. Murray, N. & S. Myhill.

B. Nau, E. Neal, G. Nelson, R. & M. Newton, S. Nichols, H. Nixon, B. & D. Norman.

P. Oakenfull, A. Ogilvy, A. Oliver, M. Osmond, A. Outen, C. Owen.

F. Page, W. Page, R. Paget, G. Parker, D. Parsons, M. Pearson, A. Petri, P. Petrocokino, C. Petts, B. Phillips, C. Plant, B. & A. Polydorou, J. Primett.

A. Randall, B. & D. Rands, D. Reed, M. Reed, M. Robbins, P. Roberts, A. Rook, A. Rowe.

B. Sage, G. Salisbury, J. Saunders, B. Sawford, J. Scivyer, P. Scrivens, G. & M. Shadbolt, P. Shott, K. Seaman, B. & H. Senior, K. Seymour, R. Sherriff, J. Shipman, D. Shirley, P. Sleeman, B. Smith, G. Smith, J. Smith, P. Smith, R. Smith, T. Smith, D. Snape, E. Soper, T. Soper, B. Staines, E. Stanley, J. Stapleford, R. Stebbings, G. Steward, A. Strawn, S. Summers, J. & M. Sutton, A. Swan, R. Symes.

R. Tabor, D. Talbot, P. Taylor, B. Teagle, N. Teall, R. Temple, C., M., J., J. & T. Thody, T. Thomas, G. Thompson, P. Thornton, J. Tomkins, G. & I. Torrance, B. Trevis, B. Trigg, A. Trotman, H. & D. Turrell, J. Tyler.

R. Uffen, Universities Federation for Animal Welfare.

V. Veal, T. Vine.

P. & S. Waine, K. Walton, P. Walton, A. Ward, R. Ward, R. Ware, B. Warren, D. Warren, S. Warrington, W. Watkins, A. & D. Watson, I. Watson, L. Watson, P. Watt, P. Wayre, G. Webb, R.Webb, D. Webster, G. Wellstead, R. Westlake, K. & J. Wheeler, A. White, B. White, G. White, A. Whittet, J. Widgery, K. Wilde, J. Willett, A. & B. Williams, A. & V. Williams, A., I & V. Williams, M. Williscroft, J. Wilson, L. Wilson, Z. Wilson, W. Wince, R. Wing, C. Woodard, R. Woolnough.

L. Young.

# Contents

*(Names in brackets = extinct in modern times in the county)*

**Common toad** *Bufo bufo*

**Great crested newt** *Triturus cristatus*

**Slowworm** *Anguis fragilis*

**Hedgehog** *Erinaceus europaeus*

**Common shrew** *Sorex araneus*

**Brown long-eared bat** *Plecotus auritus*

**Brown hare** *Lepus europaeus*

**Harvest mouse** *Micromys minutus*

**Western polecat** *Mustela putorius*

**Eurasian badger** *Meles meles*

**Order Artiodactyla**: even-toed ungulates
FAMILY CERVIDAE: DEER

**Order Primates**
FAMILY HOMINIDAE

**Roe deer doe** *Capreolus capreolus*

**Woolly rhinoceros**
*Rhinoceros antiquitatis*
**from Water Hall Farm, Hertford
(Hertford Museum).**

**Hand axe found near
Hitchin (Hertford
Museum).**

**Mammoth**
*Elaphas primigenius*
**(Hertford Museum).**

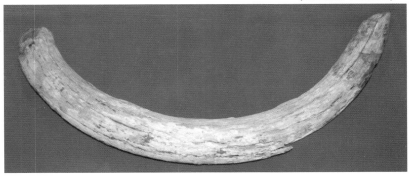

**Mimram river habitats, Archers Green near Tewin.**

# Setting the scene

The lives of all the animals described in this book are affected in one way or another by the human pressures exerted on them. We have at last come to recognise just how delicate and easily damaged the habitats are which surround us. All of us carry the chemical evidence of our modern food production and this is shared by each new generation of surviving amphibian, reptile and mammal.

The amphibians and reptiles are particularly sensitive to various pollutants and a considerable amount of research work is in progress into this subject. To review what is being done, I recommend the herpetology website which shows the extent of this work.

It is, therefore, impossible to ignore our own role in the distribution of our animals. I have included humans in the account to complete the picture of mammal distribution, but this section is not intended to compete with the long and distinguished tradition of history books on the county. The Hertfordshire Natural History Society (*HNHS*) has always covered the 'earthy' side of our past: the flint hand tools we may find as we investigate animal tracks or scratch around on the spoil heaps of the larger mammals.

The location and relative size of Hertfordshire compared with other English counties.

We are fortunate enough to have had one of the leading British archaeologists, Sir John Evans, as a member of the Society and I have reproduced illustrations from his first papers published by the Society in the 18th century and the beginning of 19th century.

Other distinguished members are listed at the end. A special feature is made of Walter, Lord Rothschild, who not only recorded a vast range of Hertfordshire material, but gave his Museum and priceless collection to us all to share through The Walter Rothschild Zoological Museum at Tring, (British Museum, Natural History). Henceforth references to these collections are abbreviated in lists to *Roth and Nat Hist Mus*.

I have tried to make the accounts more readable with the use of full names in places where they relate to personal communications and incidents. I have been told by a reader of my original text that I am being unscientific by so doing: a criticism which I find very encouraging. There is a bibliography of published material which is referred to in the text at the end of this book.

I involve the human role in the study of the natural history of the county and this book is only one of a series of studies on all aspects of the county published or to be published in the future. The most comprehensive account of the habitats is in *The Breeding Birds of Hertfordshire* (K.W.Smith, C.W.Dee, J.D.Fearnside, E.W.Fletcher and R.N.Smith, 1993) which is essential reading for all fauna studies. The text is illustrated fully with maps prepared for the book by Chris Dee with information from Hertfordshire County Council and the Ministry of Agriculture Fisheries & Food (*MAFF*).

The county includes part of the Ordnance Survey areas SP, TL and TQ as shown.

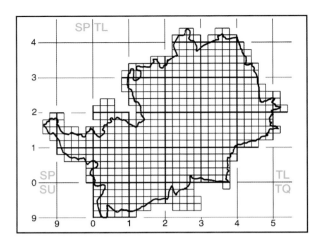

# Hertfordshire localities referred to in this book
*showing the boundary changes at Potters Bar, Barnet and Totteridge*

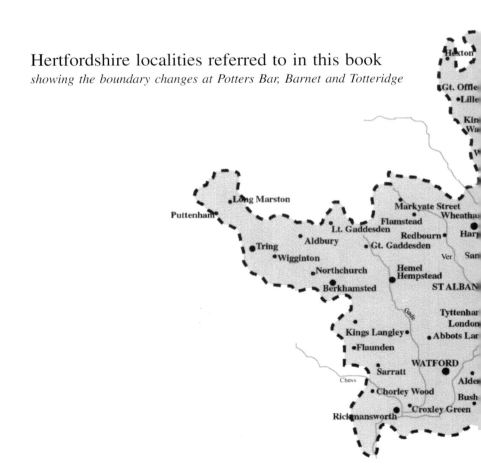

The maps which form the basis of our review of each species were originally filled in by hand from a tetrad grid generated by Dr.John Dony for his *Flora of Hertfordshire* (1965). The county boundaries were revised in 1965 with minor alterations to the border with Bedfordshire in the northwest and with Middlesex in the south: Potters Bar was added at the expense of south and east Barnet.

The 10km squares are shown with the 2x2km squares in the lighter weight of lines in the grids alongside one of the first survey cards with filled squares of the first published reports in the 1970s.

The county (163,415 hectares in area) is in the south of England immediately to the north of London and in the

metropolitan green belt of countryside. This planning law protected habitats from development which had in the past caused continuous suburban sprawl of human habitation, factories, derelict sites and roads at the expense of natural features.

Hertfordshire's towns are shown and about one million humans live in them or in village communities in the surrounding countryside. The county has contributed very generously to housing needs with the first garden city at Letchworth, another at Welwyn Garden City and the new towns at Stevenage, Hatfield and Hemel Hempstead. There has been large-scale growth around Watford, St.Albans and along the Lea Valley (Hoddesdon and Cheshunt) where green belt market garden nursery land was developed as housing land. Stevenage expansion is expected despite the green belt to the west of the town: a potent symbol of falling standards of integrity and lack of environmental concern amongst certain of the human species.

Tree types today show a welcome return to mixed and broad leaved plantings with fewer coniferous monocultures which were such a feature of the 1950s. Rackham's (1986)

**Ash / Maple woods**

**Beech woods**

**Oak / Hornbeam woods**

**Major woodland types (after Hinton 1978 and Sawford 1990).**

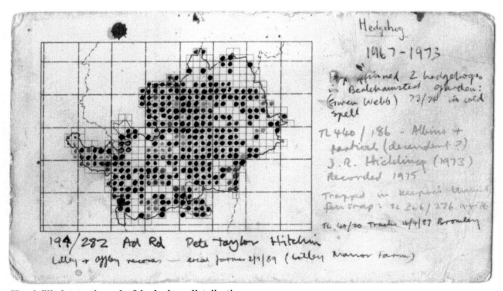

Hedgehog
1967 - 1973

Hand-filled tetrad card of hedgehog distribution.

remarkable study of the countryside estimates, by using swine records from the Domesday Book of 1086, that Hertfordshire was once 30% woodland, the fourth most wooded county along with Middlesex.

The distribution of ponds is also very significant for our amphibians in particular and the increase in garden water features is to be welcomed. An aerial view of Rickmanworth (p84) illustrates how we can know an area well yet still be unaware of the amount of foliage, cover and water habitats which exist within densely populated human settlements. In this case the habitat is related to Daubenton's bat *Myotis daubentonii* and the knowledge that they survive well here as a result of this water and vegetation is tempered by the recorded loss of over 80 of these bats caught and killed by a single domestic cat during an 8 week period (p81 *et seq.*).

The changes to the farming habitats are referred to with reference to a comparison made at Brook Farm, Cuffley, in south Hertfordshire (p229 *et seq.*). The status of livestock is related to the success or failure of certain species such as the serotine bat *Eptesicus serotinus* (p86).

Dr.Michael Benton wrote in his excellent *The Rise of the Mammals* (1991): '*As we look back over our evolution, the appearance of major advances seems to have accelerated*

# Administrative boundaries of Hertfordshire
*and boundaries of the surrounding counties*

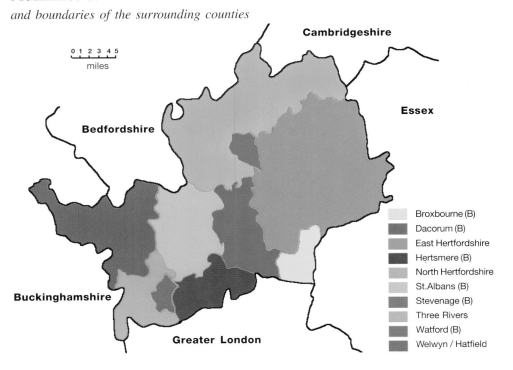

0 1 2 3 4 5
miles

Cambridgeshire

Essex

Bedfordshire

Buckinghamshire

Greater London

Broxbourne (B)
Dacorum (B)
East Hertfordshire
Hertsmere (B)
North Hertfordshire
St.Albans (B)
Stevenage (B)
Three Rivers
Watford (B)
Welwyn / Hatfield

*towards the present: bipedalism 10-5 million years ago, an enlarged brain 3-2 million years ago, stone tools 2 million years ago, wide geographic distribution 1 million years ago, fire 500,000 years ago, art 35,000 years ago, agriculture and global population increase 10,000 years ago, industrialisation some 200 years ago, tele-communications 100 years ago, and space travel 40 years ago. The rate of population increase follows a similar ever accelerating trend, rising from an annual rate of 0.1 per cent in Stone-Age times, to 0.3 per cent in the 18th century, to 2.0 per cent and still rising today.*

*The massive increase in our numbers has driven many*

# Generalised soil map of Hertfords

☐ Hertfordshire

☐ Shallow, well drained, silty soils over chalk
Moderately deep, well drained, loamy soils over chalk
Deep, slowly permeable, clayey soils over clay
Deep, slowly permeable, clayey soils in chalky drift
Well drained, loamy soils over chalk gravel
Well drained, chalk-free, light loamy soils over sand or sandstone
Deep, well drained, chalk-free, loamy soils over chalky clay at dep
Deep, well drained, chalk-free, silty soils
Moderately well drained, medium loamy soils over clay at depth
Moderately well drained medium loamy over clay soils in drift
Seasonally waterlogged, slowly permeable, chalk-free clayey soils
Seasonally waterlogged,
       slowly permeable, chalk-free medium loamy soils in drift
Wet, chalk-free, alluvial, clayey soils
Wet, chalk-rich, alluvial, clayey soils
Disturbed soils
Urban areas

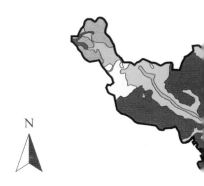

N

*mammalian species to extinction - if not in late Pleistocene times, then certainly in the past 300 years: Steller's sea cow, the Tasmanian wolf (thylacine), the quagga, the aurochs, the Arizona jaguar, the Caribbean monk seal, the Barbary lion, and dozens more. Indeed, 19 mammal species have disappeared in three centuries, and nine of these during the 20th century. At this increasing rate, we shall kill off another five species of mammals by the year 2002, and another 20 by 2100, until all wild species - except perhaps rats and mice have gone by the year 2500. This is evidence for the impressive success of Homo sapiens, but also a stark warning of the folly of the so-called "wise human"'.*

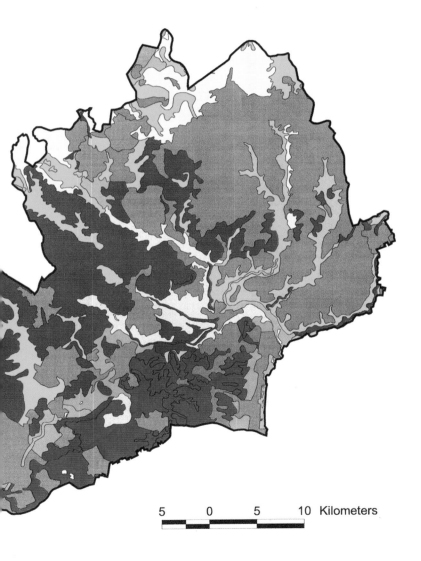

5    0    5    10  Kilometers

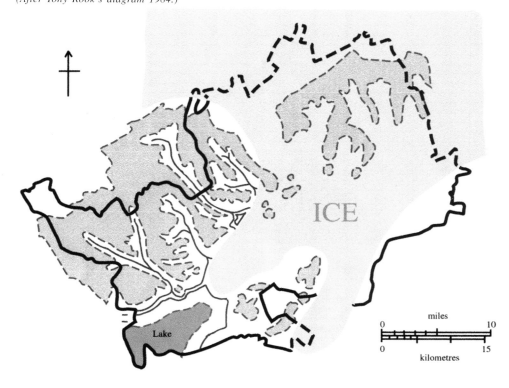

**Ice flow during the last Ice Age, about 10,000 years ago, across Hertfordshire. A diagrammatic representation to illustrate where the ice broke through and diminished the Chiltern Hills in the northeast, and showing lake St.Albans where the proto-Thames was diverted.**
*(After Tony Rook's diagram 1984.)*

ICE

Lake

miles
0                    10

0                    15
kilometres

I frequently refer to Bertram Lloyd's 1947 list of the vertebrates (see full details in the bibliography) because it is the last significant list and summary for the county. This reference is abbreviated throughout to *Lloyd (47)*.

I give each species an historic introduction (usually for the period prior to 1970) and set this in italic to distinguish it from what the modern survey has revealed.

I retain the imperial measurements in places to be faithful to original references. Names which relate to published material listed in the bibliography have the date in brackets next to them.

**Hertfordshire showing the Chiltern Hills, rivers, roads and settlements in the Roman period up to 406 AD. Based on Rosalind Niblett's map in** *Roman Hertfordshire* **(1995), drawn by Alex Thorne and reproduced by kind permission**

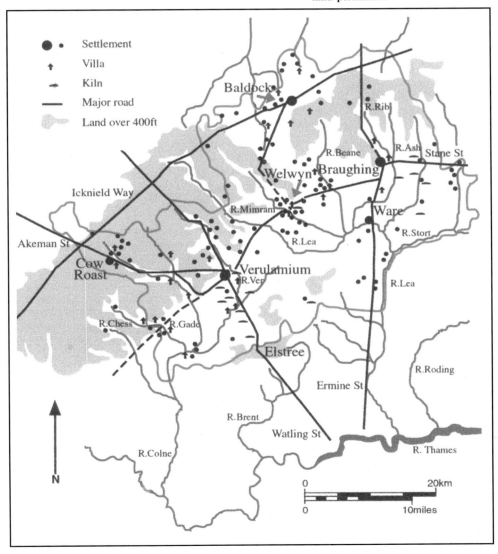

**Birch Green typifies the traditional village community surrounded by farmland. Cole Green bypass appears at the top of the picture.** *Photograph courtesy of Aerofilms, Borehamwood, Hertfordshire.*

Most of Hertfordshire's human population lives in towns and uses transport systems illustrated in this aerial view of Berkhamsted, west Hertfordshire, *viz.* London Road, the Grand Union Canal and the London to Rugby railway line. Bulbourne River is in the centre and Aeofilms picture represents the increasingly popular transport by aeroplane.    *Photograph courtesy of Aerofilms, Borehamwood, Hertfordshire.*

**The typical beech woodland of the Chiltern Hills at Aldbury Common, 1993, showing Ashridge Monument (top, right).** *Photograph courtesy of Aerofilms, Borehamwood, Hertfordshire.*

As farmland is more intensively cultivated, garden habitats with ponds, shrubs and trees, such as at
Braughing, become increasingly important for the survival of mammals, amphibians and reptiles,
especially bats.    *Photograph courtesy of Aerofilms, Borehamwood, Hertfordshire.*

# Amphibians and reptiles

In keeping with taxonomy, amphibians and reptiles precede the mammals. With only 3 species of newts, 1 frog, 1 toad, 2 snakes and 2 lizards indigenous to the county, these much maligned and rather neglected animals are worthy of a brief summary before the status of each species is discussed. It is hoped that this book will encourage more records for the Hertfordshire and national surveys as well as increase the general interest in these animals. The 9 in our county represent only a fraction of the some 4,000 amphibian, 3,750 lizard and 2,700 snake species described so far for the world.

**Woolmer Green village pond, near Knebworth, during cleaning work with earth-moving equipment.**

**The long pond in Tewin Orchard Nature Reserve created by Patrick Loughrey for the *HMWT* in 1989.**

During my annual survey in the nature reserve at Tewin Orchard, I shine a spotlight into the ponds night after night to monitor events. In 1988, for example, due to a mild winter and spring, the frogs and toads had assembled at virtually the same time (toads usually arrive 2 or 3 weeks later than frogs) and I was able to see a toad in tandem with a frog.

Unless you monitor their presence nightly you may miss the essential difference in lifestyle between newts and the frogs and toads.

By regular observation you will notice how newts keep their territories and remain in the ponds month after month. Although newts turn up on land throughout this time many of

them live a pond life until the cooler days of autumn when they seek hibernation sites on land.

In contrast frogs and toads leave the ponds promptly after the appearance of their spawn and, although during the summer they return to the water to find food, they are not as aquatic as newts.

Most of my viewing takes place when I do the rounds closing up poultry sheds. These are good retreats for the amphibians and many live underneath to emerge when the poultry have gone up to roost. (I have noticed one of these many toads emerge from a retreat as I closed shed doors at about the same time on several nights in July in different years.) There are marked fluctuations in populations of amphibians: male great crested newts held territories along the length of the large Tewin Orchard pond in 1998, for example, were virtually absent in 1999, yet back to the same high density in the very wet spring of 2000.

A herpetological group was established in Hertfordshire in 1988 to encourage their study. This resulted in an increase in records received and reports on their status followed. When Colin Fitzsimmons, the driving force behind the group, left to work in Dorset, Clive Herbert and the *Trust* continued to pursue this neglected area of study with the *Hertfordshire and Middlesex Herpetological Standing Committee*. Members, which

**A woodland pond near Hertford shaded out and with stagnant water for want of management.**

**In contrast an ancient pond on Upper Green, Tewin, flourishes despite tree cover due to management work in 1976 and 1996.**

**The distinctive profile and markings of an adult frog** *Rana temporaria.*

Phil Farrer

**The male frog clasps the female during mating in spring: note the blue tinge to the chin in the male at this time.**

included Dr.Jenny Jones, Martin Hicks, Keith Seaman and the writer, prepared registers of reptiles and amphibians and papers on their status. These were particularly helpful when dealing with management issues which arose at the *HBRC* and planning offices. The *HMHSC* ceased operation in 1994 with the formation of the *London Amphibian & Reptile Trust* and the *Hertfordshire Amphibian & Reptile Group*. Both organisations are part of the county network of *Herpetofauna Groups of Britain and Ireland*. They merged under one administration in 2000.

In one project in 1989, Colin Fitzsimmons used the local media to launch a survey in the county to find adders, but without any news of the species. Apart from W.H.Fordham's 1962 unconfirmed report of an adder near Ashwell, the species was something of an enigma in the county until the 1990s (see p57 *et seq.*).

Many people dislike amphibians and reptiles because of an unjustified fear that they will be unpleasant to touch, but the quality of the scales of our grass snakes, for example, is remarkably beautiful to see and to handle if the need arises. Under no circumstances should they ever be killed and all are now protected by law.

Amphibians and reptiles are entirely useful and attractive in their own right. To grow, reptiles shed their skins periodically and this can alter their appearance significantly. Eyes become opaque and the usual patterns or colours may become distorted. A grass snake may darken to look rather like an adder as the familiar yellow patch on the back of the head becomes less obvious. There often seems to be confusion over the differences between the life cycles of amphibians and reptiles. A summary of identification and general points should be helpful before I report on their known status:

*1 **Herpetology** is not the study of infectious skin conditions but of things which creep (herpeton in Greek) and it covers all amphibians and reptiles. (Thus our local group became 'Herts Herps'.)*
*2 **Like mammals and birds**, all species have vertebral columns, but unlike mammals and birds, they are cold-blooded.*
*3 **Hertfordshire** has 9 of the 12 indigenous and 2 of the introduced species in Britain. There are several alien types established nationally, including Alpine newts (Triturus alpestris) and Midwife toads (Alytes obstetricans), both present for over 30 years at Chorleywood and Ashridge*

respectively. Odd transplanted pets include red-eared terrapin (Pseudemys scripta elegans). The reason there are so few native species when compared with mainland Europe is due to our cool climate and position as an offshore group of islands.

**4 All species must hibernate** to survive our winter months and find retreats from October, but break torpor if warm spells occur. In southwest England frogs may spawn before Christmas, with little or no real hibernation, but in Hertfordshire conditions are rarely mild enough until the end of February or early in March. Our lizards may appear on warm sunny days during the year.

The warty look and markings of the adult toad *Bufo bufo* (**Tewin Orchard**).

When there have been very cold springs, sometimes after a mild January, large losses of frogs have been found in ponds. It is now known that frogs which hibernate in the mud and soft detritus at the bottom of ponds are usually males. They become active if the water warms up, but risk death from lack of oxygen if freezing temperatures commence in February. The ice on the water will not kill them and as long as they remain in torpor their oxygen requirements will be very slight. Once active, however, and eager to find the female frogs arriving to breed, they risk using up all the available oxygen under the unwelcome ice. A sad, foul mixture of rotting frogs and pond weed will present itself as the warmer spring temperatures return in March.

Frogs survive amazingly well, however, against all the odds, and the same pond will recover its frog population as others arrive to breed. Many garden ponds may not be deep enough for survival in cold winters or have sufficient depth of mud at the bottom. In mild springs the males which hibernated in the ponds will claim the females as they approach. They mount and grip the first to appear with the help of nuptial pads on the front toes. During this time temperature is very influencial on activity. Humidity is also a factor for toads, which governs the end of torpor, and their commencement of migration for breeding.

Part of a large group of toads mating in a pond in spring.

Perhaps the most basic differences between amphibians and reptiles are that amphibians have skin and deposit their eggs in water, whilst reptiles have scales and lay their eggs on land.

**5 Fertilization varies between species.** In amphibians fertilization is usually external. Frogs do not feed during the time when males grasp females in the nuptial embrace. This can last hours or days. They prefer shallow water and the spawn laid by the female is fertilized by the males in the water. The spawn floats and can form large masses. **Toads** also embrace and the nuptial pads on the males extend to three digits. The female lays her eggs in double strings, one from each oviduct. They prefer deeper water

*Leapfrog: frogs jump with consummate ease and have moist skins. In contrast, toads walk, can hop short distances and have dry, warty skin.*

**Smooth newt** *Triturus vulgaris* **heavy with eggs (aquarium, Tewin Orchard, 1977).**

*than frogs. The strings are wound round underwater plants and the male deposits sperm over the eggs as they appear.*
**Newts** *court without any gripping but the males may whip, wave or fan scents with their tales in excited movements in front of the females. After the display, if the female is receptive, a male will deposit spermatozoa which she picks up by the lips of her cloaca and absorbs into the oviduct to fertilize her eggs. She can keep part of this for future use and egg laying in British newts occurs over a period of several months even after courtship has ceased. Fertilization is thus internal in newts but external in frogs and toads.*
**Snakes and lizards** *reproduce by internal fertilization and after courtship displays. The grass snake mother may show protective behaviour towards her eggs in the first week of incubation. Young female grass snakes have fewer eggs than older ones. Because they are cold-blooded they cannot incubate eggs in the same way as a bird, so sites which generate their own heat such as compost, hay or manure heaps are chosen and about 30 flexible shelled eggs are left in clusters linked by a sticky film.*

*Colin Fitzsimmons found grass snake eggs in a tree stump in Northaw Great Wood in the summer of 1987, and more recently John Card has photographed a female laying eggs near Much Hadham, see p245. After 8 weeks the 190mm long young snakes hatch through slits in the leather-like shell made by their egg tooth, shed a few hours later. Common lizards have 5-12 young which break from transparent capsules at birth and are fully formed minute lizards. Slowworms (legless lizards) have their young in much the same way, but on breaking free of the egg on birth, are a glossy golden yellow with a black underside. They hunt very small food items after a few days.*

**6** **Reproduction** *and longevity can be summed up as:*

| | |
|---|---|
| **Grass snake** | *Lays about 30 soft white eggs; breeds from 3-4 years old; fully grown at 5 or 6 years, usually 1,200mm, occasionally 1,500mm or longer. Long specimens (2.5m or more) now rarely found, and may have taken many years to grow to that size.* |
| **Common lizard** | *4-10 young live from birth (but can spend up to 12 hrs in egg sacs) in late July; mates May, breeds from 2-3 years old; fully grown at 4-5 years, up to 180mm. May live up to 13 years. Also known as viviparous.* |
| **Slowworm** | *Up to 22 live young from birth late August/ September; spring mating, breeds from 4-5 years old; continues to grow for 3-4 years more; 400mm, longest slowworm recorded in Britain 489mm; may live to 55 years plus if protected from predators.* |
| **Newt** | *200-300 eggs (200-400 in palmate newts)* |

34

laid individually, wrapped neatly in pond weed or aquatic plants, March-April; fertilization from externally deposited sperm; hatches 2-3 weeks; breeds from 3-4 years old; fully grown at 5 years (still in larval stage from May for much of first year). No growth in hibernation; very hardy. Palmate newts may live over 12 years, smooth newts over 20 years and great crested newts over 29 years, although this is unlikely in the wild.

**Grass snake** *Natrix natrix* **(Welwyn Garden City).**

**Frog** 1,000-2,000 eggs laid in a mass; external fertilization; tadpoles hatch in about 21 days; tadpoles take up to 3 months to develop into young frogs and move onto land; breeds from 3-4 years and lives over 5 years.

**Toad** 2,000-3,000 eggs laid in strings; external fertilization; tadpoles hatch in 8-10 days, June-July young toads go on land; breeds from 4 years (males) or 5 years (females); known to live from 18 to over 40 years if protected from predators.

**7 Metamorphosis** of amphibians, ie the transformation from egg to larval and then adult stages, takes place in all our British species in water. A tadpole is the water stage of any amphibian and they breathe by internal or external gills. Newts usually return to water when ready to breed but Colin Fitzsimmons has seen an overwintering palmate newt in a pond in a mild winter. Adult frogs will often stay in and around water in late summer long after the breeding season. Males may hibernate in the mud under water.

Newt tadpoles resemble their parents, but their legs develop early, front pairs first, and they have external gills for 3-5 months during the larval stage. They may overwinter as tadpoles and there is an incomplete form of metamorphosis called neoteny when the adult size is reached and breeding might occur whilst the individual retains its larval gills. Great crested newts are now known to breed in this condition. Neoteny in smooth newts is commonly combined with albinism.

Frogs briefly have external gills, but these are lost and replaced by an internal set. Water is passed over the internal gills to absorb oxygen and exuded through the left side of the body via the spiraculum. The mouth is made up of a black beak or mandible with rows of minute horny 'teeth' arranged differently in each species. In the common frog there are about 640. They feed on algae and flesh if they obtain any: a carcase that has fallen into a pond will be picked clean in time. Hind legs appear first and the front pair only when the young frog is about to leave the water. Final development is

**Common lizard** *Lacerta vivipara* **basking on a grassy bank.**

*The throat of the smooth newt is usually spotted whereas the palmate is free from speckling. In the field, the spotting on the palmate newt appears much finer and the tail tip is very obvious in the male in the breeding season. In winter it is easy to confuse the two species.*

rapid and it is rare for frogs to over-winter as tadpoles.

Frog tadpoles are dark olive, speckled and spotted with black. They lack skin defences and must rely more on camouflage. Toad tadpoles are smaller, black, distasteful to predators and have a rounded tail tip whereas that of the frog is more pointed.

**8 Adult** *amphibians and reptiles in Hertfordshire are all carnivorous and swallow food whole. They have powerful and rapid digestive juices. Amphibians and reptiles typically take live food because a prey item must move to be seen, although great crested newts regularly dine on frog spawn and can have a significant impact on frog numbers if their population in a pond is large. They have also been known to eat fully-grown smooth newts, but normally concentrate on smaller prey and can take the entire tadpole production of a female frog in a season. Snakes can take meals 25%-50% of their own weight, by way of their elastic skin and jaws which have ligaments attached to each other and their skull. (It is hard for us to imagine eating half our weight of fish and chips at one sitting.) Tame reptiles may take dead items.*

Reptiles do not feed every day and can live for long periods without another meal. (Boas and pythons captured abroad have been known to refuse to eat and the record delay before taking food is 33 months.) The snakes probably have little sense of taste – at least one has been known to swallow a blanket – but all have a good sense of smell through their tongue. Scent particles are picked up and transferred to a special structure called Jacobson's organ in the roof of the mouth between the nostrils. We all know of the flickering tongue of a snake which is completely harmless, even in cobras.

Amphibians do not drink because all the liquid they require is absorbed through their skin. Much of their breathing is also done through their skin and no British frog or newt can survive long in a dry place.

Toads, in contrast, have a dry epidermis and can endure arid sites much longer. Death is caused as much by lack of oxygen as by lack of moisture. Salt is also fatal to amphibians, but snakes can swim in the sea unaffected. Snakes have a unique skin pattern, like our fingerprints, but their marks grow fainter in old individuals. Frogs show more than 6 varieties of colour hue, but the patterns are almost always distinctive. In their skins and those of toads, smooth and palmate newts the pigment in their cells can change position to help merge with a particular background, but great crested newts appear able to change their colour least.

*The male newts, which perform dances in
courtship, grow and display more distinct
colours and higher, decorative crests each
breeding season.*

**9 Voices** *are not remarkable and newts,
for example, only squeak when squeezed
or hurt, but frogs make the distinctive
croaks with their throat sacs - a sound we
all know if not from field observation, from
fairy story or music hall: the traditional
're-bbit, re-bbit'. (This is the sound June
Crew reports that some passing motorists
make at frog and toad lift sites as they
come alongside the naturalists who give up
their time to save as many amphibians as
possible on the roads. Another friendly shout of support is
'Get a life!'.) Both male and female frogs croak: males call to
establish territory and attract females; male toads croak
(deeper in older individuals) in courtship combat. Female
toads are mute; snakes hiss to bluff or threaten.*

**Face of toad** *Bufo bufo* **(Tewin
Orchard).**

**10 Cold-blooded** *lizards and snakes cope with our climate
through hibernation when the sun is low in the sky and cold
temperatures prevail. They bask in the sun whenever they
can for the rest of the year. If their body temperature rises to
between 25°C and 30°C, lizards and snakes will become
active and they all seek warmth in a variety of ways.*

*A compost heap creates its own internal heat as it breaks
down and grass snakes exploit this to increase their own
body temperature, lay their eggs and have them incubated in
such sites. Older snakes lay more eggs – up to 40 – which
hatch in about 8 weeks depending on the heat of the compost.
The female may travel over a mile to find a suitable active
heap and may also stay to defend the eggs. Other females
may find the same site and add their eggs to produce a
sudden snake boom in late summer.*

**Eggs of grass snake** *Natrx natrix.*

*Another source of heat for basking is stone, and the fact
that we lack stone walls and have few warm, sandy heaths in
the county, must have had an adverse effect on reptile
numbers. As land in the home counties has become so
valuable, 'waste land' gradually ceases to exist, although
embankments to roads and railways may sometimes
approach this sort of category of habitat. One of the best
known of these is the Cuffley railway embankment which
became the only reptile reserve in the county thanks to the
efforts of Colin Fitzsimmons. (All embankments should be
surveyed to ascertain their biological value.)*

*It is interesting to note that the estate around Hatfield
House was a heath before a country house with parkland
was created. Nomansland Common and Hertford Heath are
also examples of historically good herpetological sites, if
rapidly losing this interest through lack of consistent
management now. Basking exposes a lizard to predators, but*

*they gain the muscular activity with the heat to respond at once to attack and dive for cover. (This behaviour is easy to observe abroad in the Mediterranean where geckos, for example, live in abundance on walls and dart into crevices by the roadside as you pass by.) The slowworm will seek shaded places and bask half-hidden to exploit reflected as well as direct heat.*

*Abandoned corrugated iron sheets allow reptiles to bask underneath, out of sight, and the gain in temperature enables them to hunt for food, reproduce and develop the juveniles inside their bodies as rapidly as possible. The young are born inside a thin membrane rather than within a true eggshell and break out at once.*

*Sunbathing is, therefore, far from being just idle pleasure to reptiles: it is life itself. Cold summers as well as habitat loss in the late 1980s did not encourage our reptiles, but the warmer years in the 1990s were more helpful to them.*

100 Km

# Common frog
## *Rana temporaria*

*The earliest note on the species I have been able to find in the Trans is by Edward Mawley (Vol **VII**, 3: 86 1892) who noted that frog spawn had been seen as early as 1st March in 1891. Generally too familiar to be recorded in any detail in the county, frogs are known to have large population swings from year to year, when abundance one spring can change to a marked reduction in another year. They are described as 'declining' by Burton (1974) for the London area and he felt that the collection and transportation of spawn might drastically reduce their distribution. Frogs were reported to be 'widespread and fairly common' and to be breeding in many garden ponds in Beds Wildlife (1987). A century ago Laver said they were 'extremely common' in Essex.*

Garden ponds have saved many local frog populations which would have otherwise died out during the last century. During this time about 80% of village and farm ponds were filled in (*Hertfordshire Countryside Forum* figure).

It is easy to be critical of farmers and landowners and say that it was wrong to replace so many ponds with water troughs or to abandon them altogether as arable cultivation became more lucrative, but there has been a constant emphasis on health in farming, never greater than today. John Wallace, who now manages his Hertfordshire farms with his daughter Diana Colingridge,

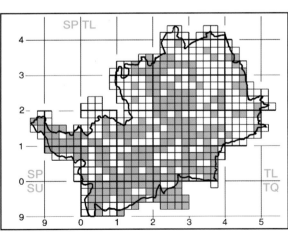

**Common frog** *Rana temporaria* **distribution is still widespread, but has become more localised to garden ponds and lakes.**

**Widespread, declining**

is one of our most conservation conscious farmers. He has pointed out to me that there were very important disease considerations associated with ponds and having standing water in high troughs is considered much safer for livestock.

In fact, the decision to fill in village ponds in many places had nothing to do with farmers, but came from lack of local interest. If unmanaged, ponds quickly deteriorate, choke up, may smell foul to householders living nearby in hot, dry summers and there is always the fear that children may drown in them. This fear causes many garden ponds also to disappear, commonly when people with infants move to a new house.

How many people who may criticise farmers for clearing wilderness areas in the name of economy, do not give a thought for the frogs that have bred in their garden pond for 30 or more years, but which turn up one spring and find the ground levelled. How often are these householders criticised? June Crew, who has organised toad lifts, has shown in her own garden that ponds can be safely wired round until children are older and this also helps deter herons from removing the vertebrates present.

Gradually frog spawn sinks into the pond water and the egg cases become the first meals for the hatching tadpoles.

Although the translocation of frogs and toads does not need a licence the best practice is never to do so because of the risk of spreading disease. Ideally, communities should recognise the importance of ponds and manage them properly. I would rather a garden pond be turned into a sandpit for a few years as a safety measure until children are old enough to enjoy them restored as ponds, than have them levelled completely. The anxious parents would then give their children a treasure for life and may even turn them into naturalists.

In the last 30 years much greater public concern has been shown for frogs as they have declined nationally due to pollution of ponds as well as loss of suitable sites.

As road traffic has increased, conservationists now organise toad lifts where spring and summer migration routes take the amphibians across roads to and from their breeding sites. (See the details given in the next section.) Frogs leap and are faster on tarmac, but still suffer large losses on the wet nights which trigger the migrations.

Simultaneously across the county the roads can suddenly be invaded by hopping frogs (this is where they are most obvious), but they will also move unobtrusively in dry weather. I compared notes with Trevor James in September 1986 after most of the summer movements had taken place, and both of us found frogs crossed roads on our separate journeys in different parts of the county on

Frog tadpoles cluster in a mass after hatching.

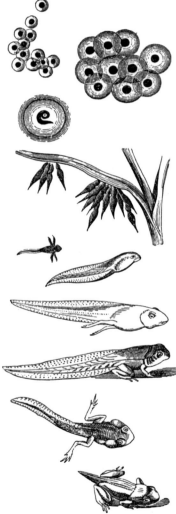

Frog development from Vol.5 of Lydekker's *The Royal Natural History* (1896).

exactly the same wet night.

Evans (1983) recorded albino and also part-albino tadpoles from her pond in Berkhamsted (*Trans* **29**, 1:14) and noted slower development in these when compared with the normal coloured ones. She knew a local man who, when a boy, collected tadpoles regularly and thought the white ones 'useless' because they grew slowly and died before maturity. Frazer (1983) explains that albino adult frogs normally appear yellow with pink eyes because of the lipophores (one of the 3 types of skin cell in frogs) carry lymph even in the absence of pigments. Camouflage is very important to the survival of amphibians, but Beebee (1985) records a pond in Reading with a population mainly of this albino variety.

Frazer discusses colouration at length and includes a particularly interesting section on how they select breeding sites and colonise new areas. He quotes Savage who studied frogs near to the southern border of Hertfordshire in Totteridge (now part of Greater London) 50 years ago. (Malcolm Smith credited Savage with much of his frog reproduction data in his book, published in 1950.) Although many frogs hibernated in his experimental area of London clay ponds, Savage found that they left them in spring to spawn in ponds on other geological formations.

Some 92 ponds were observed over 80 square miles (1929-1938) and he found 11 out of 78 contained visible spawn in 1936 and 1937, but 22 out of 86 showed spawn present when visited in 1938. Twenty years later spawn was found in only two. Considerable fluctuations in numbers were also found by Frazer's cousin, O.H.Frazer, working on the Isle of Wight in the 1960s.

Savage also discovered that frogs were attracted to new ponds by the odour of algae, which would not only be a guide to water but would provide food for the tadpoles in the weeks after spawning. He found that frogs were attracted to ponds which were high in potassium and low in phosphates. In laboratory research he finally traced the chemical substance involved as glycollic acid which was produced by the algae. Even in dilutions as low as 1 part to 80 million this attracted adult frogs in the breeding season and he thus demonstrated that glycollic acid was the lure that brought frogs to a certain pond in spring whilst they ignored others.

Spawn has been seen as early as 28th February in Garston near Watford, Hertfordshire (C.M.Everett, 1999) but it is usually noticed in early March. New batches may appear into mid-April. The temperature of the water influences spawning and they seek the warmest, usually most shallow, parts of the pond where algae will reproduce more rapidly. When the eggs are released and the male has fertilized them in the water, both relax and the female can swim away to make her way out of the pond. With the risk of predators ever present adults quickly leave. The familiar croaking of the frogs in the breeding season is a serenade to the females. Spawn shows above the water surface initially, but will sink and melt away as the tadpoles eat their way out of their egg shell jelly.

Maturity of the tadpoles is used in textbooks as the classic example of amphibian metamorphosis (see opposite). Hibernation commences in October, but you can see frogs enjoying a late, sunny autumn day in the water, heads up as if sunbathing. Birds (particularly herons), grass snakes, hedgehogs, polecats, foxes, domestic cats and humans (by their vehicles as well as their pets) are the major predators.

# Marsh frog
## *Rana ridibunda*

During annual pilgrimages down to the Romney and Dungeness areas of Kent, Michael Russell has often heard marsh frogs calling and only associated them with this region of England.

However, over the past three years he has been hearing the same call emanating from an expanse of water used to irrigate greens at the Aldwick Bury Golf Club, TL 155/147, adjacent to the River Lea near Harpenden. Investigations resulted in sightings which confirmed that they are indeed marsh frogs.

After a brief search at least 6 individuals were located including a large 180mm long adult with bright emerald green coloration, sporting a yellowish-green stripe and very yellow bulbous eyes.

# Common toad
## *Bufo bufo*

*Toads were clearly considered to be too common to receive much attention in the Trans, but many were seen on Berkhamsted Common during a dawn chorus walk (1949) and when toad lifts commenced in the 1970s Norman Gammon noted (1975) that 932 were saved and 239 run over at the Stevenage Titmore Green and Redcoats Green Ponds; 1,573, including some frogs, were saved and 300 run over at Hamperhill, Bushey; 2,227 were saved and 130 killed at Bourne End.*

*This conservation work is now an annual event at many sites where a rota of devoted people with plastic buckets transfer as many toads as possible from one side of the lethal roads to the other so that they can reach their breeding ponds. Beds Wildlife (1987) reports them to be common with several breeding sites of many hundreds of toads each year. Burton (1974) found them to be more widespread than frogs in the London area.*

The enduring memory of my first visit to Tring reservoirs was not of the wild birds I had gone there to watch, but of the dozens of toadlets walking across the exposed shore line. The mass movement from water to land in June and July is

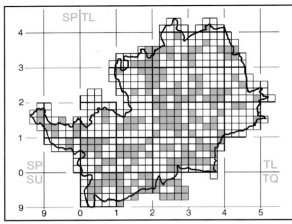

**Common toad** *Bufo bufo.*

**Declining**

**June Crew's pictures of the construction of the barrier near Ware which prevents amphibian road casualties at an annual migration site.**

dramatic to witness, but only about 1 in 20 will live to be adults. They develop a protection from predators shared with great crested newts, however, which is the poison from glands on their head and back. The distasteful flavour of toads will discourage many, but whilst some grass snakes pass them by, others regularly catch them. The defensive posture when approached as the toad raises itself up on all fours is quite dramatic. A toad does not hop but walks, and if you see an amphibian on the road ahead it is possible to distinguish whether it is a frog or a toad by the way it moves.

The migration of adults in March and April finds hundreds or thousands on the move from hibernation sites to breeding ponds. They are much more concentrated than the intermittent movements of frogs to the water. Signs are now erected in many places to warn motorists that toads are crossing, and sponsored diversions have been designed to keep toads from crossing (see illustrations).

Although toads have very different skin from frogs, their 150mm tongues are similar: both are rooted at the front of the mouth and are long enough to flick out at invertebrate prey and catch the animal on the sticky surface. Prey varies slightly, with ants a favourite of toads and slugs or snails preferred by frogs. A wide variety of flies, beetles, bugs, worms, woodlice and moths are caught by both. They are a very welcome guest on farmland and garden alike. Feeding takes place mostly at night in the safety of darkness.

Despite their enthusiasm for company at breeding time, adults live alone away from the ponds in summer. Toads are often seen on roads in the autumn during mild, damp evenings, especially near woodlands. Colin Fitzsimmons found over 50 next to Northaw Great Wood, for example. Hibernation begins from around October with the first cold spells and lasts until the start of warm spring nights in February or March. Toads rarely hibernate underwater: they prefer to hole up somewhere secure such as in piles of logs, under stones or inside a tunnel made by a mammal.

I frequently find toads in bark mulch heaps during winter work in the orchard and I carefully place these where they will not be disturbed. I also find many toads under sheets of corrugated iron which I have put down in grassland over a long period to study small mammals.

With much greater interest in herpetology in recent years the future for toads away from the vast arable field areas is better in Hertfordshire, especially since many colonies now come under 'neighbourhood watch' schemes to help give them safe passage to breeding ponds.

There are 12 or so sites which have, or need, annual toad lifts. June Crew has organised and provided the results for 1998 and 1999 to illustrate the recent work at one such site: Hollycross Road, Amwell, but *Herpetofauna News* published the following records in the 1980s:

*'The spring 1988 toad migration schedule included the following sites: Bourne End, near Hemel Hempstead; Great Wymondley; Hertford; Hoddesdon; Redcoats Farm; St. Ippollitts; Stotfold; Taylors Mill, Potten End; Tring; Welwyn Garden City; and Wheathampstead. The toad lift at Bourne End in 1983 had been 1,273 toads between 10th March and 23rd March with 122 newts (T. vulgaris) also moved'.*

*In 1986 the following records had been made:*

Frog spawn.

| Date | Number of dead toads | Toads rescued | Newts rescued | Weather | Notes |
|---|---|---|---|---|---|
| 18 March | 12 | 6 | - | Mild & wet | 11.30pm |
| 25 March | 10 | 70 | - | Cold & dry | |
| 3 April | | | | | First toad spawn |
| 4 April | | | | | Potter Bar |
| 14 April | 10 | 77 | 31 | Cold & dry | |
| 15 April | 4 | 89 | 1 | Dry | |
| 5 April | | | | | Frog spawn |
| 16 April | 5 | 129 | 1 | Dry | Hatfield Herts. |
| 17 April | 6 | 222 | - | Wet | |
| 18 April | - | 41 | 2 | - | |
| 19 April | 5 | 307 | - | - | |
| 19 April | | | | | Toad spawn |
| 20 April | 20 | 132 | - | Wet | Welwyn |
| 21 April | 15 | 71 | - | Dry | |
| 22 April | 3 | 52 | - | Wet | |
| 23 April | 15 | 190 | 2 | Dry | |
| 24 April | 6 | 59 | 2 | Dry | Animals now leaving site |
| 25 April | 10 | 50 | - | Dry | |
| 26 April | 5 | 17 | 2 | Warm/Dry | |
| 27 April | 6 | | | | |
| 28 April | 24 | | | | |

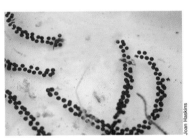

Toad spawn.

**Totals   156 killed; 1,512 toads and 41 newts moved**

June Crew's 1998 and 1999 records show identical main surges in the successive years (2nd/3rd March), considerably earlier than the 1986 data. Numbers, however, showed typical large amphibian fluctuations:1,600 moved across the road to the spawning grounds in 1998, but only 733 in 1999. Air temperature was only 8°C, but rain triggered the movement from cover. The next major migration was between 25th and 28th March (700 toads).

With the permission of the farmer a new design of barrier was fitted alongside the road edge, funded through the landfill tax scheme by RMC Aggregates (Greater London)

43

Limited and by Hertfordshire County Council. This stops the amphibians reaching the road and they assemble at the ends where the collection buckets temporarily retain them. They can then be taken across to their breeding ponds in Amwell Quarry. In 1998, 3 frogs, 2 smooth newts and 1 grass snake were also collected for safe transfer across the busy road. In 2000 a further reduction in numbers was recorded and 2 grass snakes were found.

# Smooth newt
## *Triturus vulgaris*

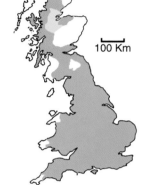

100 Km

*Although they have appeared in our distribution maps in the Trans since 1973, this species is so widespread (also known as the common newt) that they have barely been referred to in the past and, like the rabbit, were clearly felt to be too common to attract written accounts. This is a pity, for these hardy little amphibians frequently seem to turn up during field work in all parts of the county. Their distribution map should be filled with records one day.*

*Lloyd (47), whilst describing them as fairly common throughout the county, noted that their presence varied locally and observed that they were 'noticeably scarce in the vicinity of Elstree Reservoirs'.*

*Sage (1966) found no records of the species in Northaw Great Wood at that time, although there were 2 ponds on the western edge. Following the construction of a new pond next to Cuffley Brook in the School Camp, on the eastern tip, they were quickly established by the 1970s. A great crested newt had been recorded under a log on the edge of the conifer plantation, part of the Hatfield Estate, on 18th May 1959, and they were present in a pond on the southern edge of the wood, by the Ridgeway in 1999 (R. Miller). No surveys had been made in the wood specifically for newts prior to the 1966 Northaw Great Wood book; they had clearly been overlooked.*

*Beds Wildlife (1987) reported them locally frequent and Burton (1974) noted that it was the commonest species of newt in the London area.*

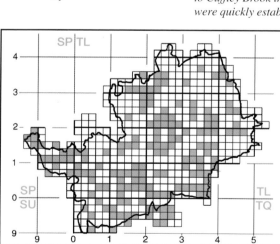

**Smooth newts** *Triturus vulgaris* **are familiar in ponds throughout the county in contrast to the more northerly distribution for the palmate newt.**

**Widespread**

Frazer (1983) reported two breeding periods in the same season in suitable conditions: early in February and later during April and May. Because they breed in shallower water than that required by great crested newts, their continued abundance in suitable habitats suggests that they have been able to benefit from the proliferation of garden ponds as other sites have diminished.

Another encouraging feature of their life cycle in the face

of so many adverse modern conditions is flexible breeding behaviour, which has been known to be interrupted by drought for 3 months and then resumed (Mertens, quoted in Smith, 1954).

A good time of year to see active pond life is mid-August. At night-time shine a strong torch into the water and you will usually see many young smooth newts in their adult form, but still with their external gills.

During August adult newts return to a terrestrial life after the three aquatic months when they are so fish-like. They feed on land, hiding during the daylight in shallow surface retreats.

As the autumn advances smooth newts will seek out more secure underground refuges to protect themselves from freezing temperatures. Moisture is important to them during winter torpor and, as with toads, many may be found together at the most successful hibernation sites.

At Tewin Orchard we find smooth newts frequently under sheds, log piles and heaps of chipped bark. They are so adaptable that human habitation does not deter them and on wet nights they sometimes enter the house.

**Adult male smooth newt** *Triturus vulgaris* **with breeding crest.**

# Palmate newt
## *Triturus helveticus*

*Records in the survey of the distribution of palmate newts in the county are probably the most interesting for any species described in this book. They have never been reported in Bedfordshire and the national distribution indicates a distinct absence from The Fens and Midlands to the immediate north of the county.*

*We now know that they prefer water conditions in the more acid soil areas than the smooth newts and their range reflects the distribution of this type of pond. Apart from the undesirable release of captive specimens at Oughtonhead (recorded by N Herts Mus in the 1980s), our known genuine presence is very much to the south of the county. No other indigenous vertebrate reflects such a clear demarcation of distribution in Hertfordshire.*

*Oldham (Trans XV 4:207, 1915) exhibited specimens from Ashridge Park (where they survive to this day) and pointed out that they had not been previously recorded in the county. He thought it underrecorded, but had found them in a pond at Cross Oak, Berkhamsted, near Marlin Chapel, and in*

**Detail of speckled head of palmate newt** *Triturus helveticus.*

**Palmate newt showing filament on tail tip and webbed hind foot.**

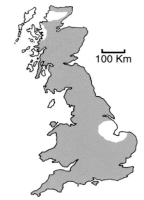

several ponds on Berkhamsted Common. In nearly every case they were in association with great crested and smooth newts.

He described the species again in a paper read at Watford in 1933 (Trans **XIX**, 4: 209, 1934) and suggested that it was more a species of uplands, mountains, moorlands and 'swampy places on sea cliffs and hillsides where one would not expect to see either of the others. It is said to be more resistant of cold and it certainly occurs at higher altitudes than the others. I have found it in two places in the Lake District between 1,600ft and 1,700ft; at 1,950ft in Llyn-y-Fan Fawr, Brecon; and at 1,750ft and 2,250ft in tarns on Snowdon'. He also recorded it 'up to 2,900ft in the Swiss Alps'.

Oldham noted the local distribution gaps, but although he thought that it had not been found in Bedfordshire, he considered that it was 'hardly credible that it is not there'. This has yet to be proved and E.S.Brown (Trans **XXIII**, 2: 73) makes the point that 'in the Hertford area it must be scarce, if present at all, for a great deal of pond collecting has failed to reveal it, although I have found it just over the Essex border in Epping Forest (1947)'.

It appears therefore that there is a gap in its distribution, which to judge by its occurrence in other parts of the country, may be associated with alkaline conditions.

Lloyd (47) noted Oldham's discovery of the species in the county in 1914 and reports that it 'occurs all over the Berkhamsted district'. Foster (1934) commented on the absence of the species from the chalky Hitchin region and the Hexton book (1936) confirms that whilst great crested and smooth newts had been brought to the village school, no palmate newts were found.

Laver (1898) found the species in several parts of Essex and knew Baker who first described them for Britain via Thomas Bell (1849). In 1846 he had seen some of the first examples Baker had caught. It is not listed in Beds Wildlife (1987), but Burton (1974) reported a restricted distribution around London, even 'common' in Epping Forest, Essex.

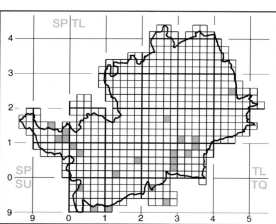

**Palmate newts** *Triturus helveticus* **are confined to the more acid ponds which they require.**

In the past I have seen a few individuals in garden ponds in the north of Hertfordshire chalk areas such as Pirton where they have been translocated by home owners. This is no longer legal; nor is it helpful to the species.

Local

More recent records have not changed the picture of central Hertfordshire as the upper limit for its range. On 15th May 1988 I was able to visit the gardens of Amersfort, Potten End, Gaddesden, to see a long-established walled breeding pond with all three species of newt present.

My first encounter with the species had been in the late 1950s when I saw a dehydrated, flattened male in the dust

46

and pebbles at the then unmade end of Tolmers Road, Cuffley, by the Scout Camp entrance. The thin filament which extends beyond the tail tip in the male during the breeding season was retained in death and very characteristic. (There are slow backwaters and garden ponds along the Cuffley Brook here and the spot was also personally memorable because I fell off my bicycle trying to stop at the specimen.) Colin Fitzsimmons recorded these newts elsewhere in Cuffley from the 1970s and reported them present in Audrey Ogilvy's garden pond at Garston, near Watford (1977).

Ralph Newton and Colin Fitzsimmons reported them from Bencroft Wood, near Wormley West End (1980), and Clive Herbert has confirmed to me that they were still present there in 1999. A sighting also came from Andrew Catchpole at Hertford Heath in the early 1970s.

The species is distinctly smaller than the smooth newt with sooty webbed hind feet, pale orange belly, extended tail filament in the male and lack of obvious spots on the throat in the female. Frazer gives the larger feet of the female in the smooth as the best guide.

Smith (1951) reported that the palmate newts were more aquatic than the other species and said that they are in and out of water at any time of year according to conditions. In the more stable lowland pond conditions they show a similar departure time from the water as the smooth newts when the breeding season is over.

Their courtship and egg-laying pattern is much the same as for the other newt species, although the body of the male is curved in front of the female to create more of a hollow. Ironically, therefore, as far as our county is concerned, they are far more local than the great crested newt: the species which is often in the news when matters of protection and the law are concerned. Exchanges of tadpoles would only be considered by English Nature where reintroductions to historically known sites are proposed and after the original cause of their extinction has been identified and rectified.

*In 1982 Ralph Newton noted in his field diary:*
*'At the pond in Bencroft Wood numbers of newts, both smooth and palmate, were clustered round the frog spawn, biting off the jelly to eat. The palmate newts always seem to outnumber the smooth newts there.'*

# Great crested newt

## *Triturus cristatus*

*Great crested newts have rarely been referred to in our literature and apart from Lloyd's glib 'not uncommon; widely distributed', in his 1947 report, the Trans only make reference to their presence at Park Street in 1945.*

*Sage (1966) found 'a male beneath a log by a damp path near the southern edge of the coniferous plantation' in Northaw Great Wood, 18th May 1959, but no evidence of breeding in the very*

**Male great crested newt** *Triturus cristatus* **in breeding condition.**

Male great crested newt (in an aquarium), Tewin Orchard, May 1977. The belly patterns are specific to individuals and have been well illustrated in a *British Wildlife* magazine article, see Macgregor (1995).

**Widespread, declining**

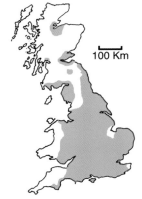

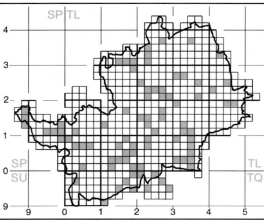

shaded ponds on the western edge of the Wood.

*We now know that Hertfordshire is a stronghold for these striking newts which I found relatively easy to locate in the streams on the Theobalds borders of Northaw Parish at the time Sage wrote his chapter in the Northaw Great Wood book. Fitzsimmons also found them in Nyn Park and they were still present in 1999. They also breed in a pond on the edge of the Great Wood, as described earlier.*

*Laver (1898) reported them as common throughout Essex (with the delightful local name of 'water swift') a century ago and they survive in Bedfordshire as 'a few sizeable colonies'. Burton (1974) found them in 'odd places' throughout the suburbs of London, but 'rare in Epping Forest, Essex'.*

*I saw them in high brick-sided garden ponds at Balls Park in my school days during the 1950s (where they are still present, Herbert & Atkins 1999) and saw an almost identical site at Amersfort (see the reference in the previous section on palmate newts). Between these times they have turned up in woodland ponds, small temporary water in old tractor ruts, backwaters of streams, garden ponds and at refilled gravel working ponds.*

Great crested newts do not like to share a pond with fish and this may be another reason why fewer locations for them are found nationally these days. I have seen many at hibernation sites when gardening and they can be easily watched without disturbance in clear pond water. The spectacular breeding colours and the crest in the male as well as the size rewards the attention of the pond watcher. It is now illegal to disturb them, capture or keep them without a licence.

The adults enter the water in February or March and the males soon start to pursue the females with rapid tail movements. The courtship culminates with the deposit of a bag of sperm which drifts down onto the detritus at the bottom of the pond. If the highly coloured and crested male has succeeded in inflaming the female's passion, she will drift down to pick up the small package with her cloaca and the eggs are fertilized inside her.

The female wraps each egg individually in a piece of pond weed and although a few hundred ova may be laid, it has been found that 50% are infertile due to a genetic defect at the second stage of myotic division. Like their parents, the tadpoles are carnivorous and are as big as adult smooth newts by the end of the summer, with external gills still very obvious when they leave the water.

Hibernation is on land as a rule, in a radius of up to 500m from the pond, depending upon the habitat.

# Common lizard
## *Lacerta vivipara*

Common lizards are locally found throughout the county. Foster (1934) gave Weston Hill, Norton Common (scarce), Knebworth Woods, Pegsdon Hills and Lilly Hoo (frequent), Hexton and Barton Hills (frequent), Ickleford, Wilbury Hill, Wain Wood, Rowney Warren, Southill and Flitwick. (There is a reference to a basking lizard in the Trans **XII**, 8: IX iii seen by members of a 1905 ramble to the Flitwick Mineral Springs, Bedfordshire.)

100 Km

The Hexton book (1936) gives a little more detail: 'The common lizard is rarely seen on the hills and is difficult to catch, but is far more common than the average country person would believe. One specimen was recently captured in a frame in the school garden'.

Fordham (1938) noted that: 'The colony of common lizards which has had its home for at least the last 50 years on both sides of the Icknield Way, halfway between Baldock and Royston, is still flourishing. Quite a number of lizards have been seen thereabouts lately'. The 1930s are the best documented period for the species which certainly favours dry, hot summers.

Lloyd (47) gives the Hitchin and Icknield Way records and adds that they were 'about Elstree Reservoir, near the Middlesex border (where they also occur on Stanmore Common), and in the unspoilt parts of the gardens at Bushey Heath I have several time seen individuals between 1928 and 1938'.

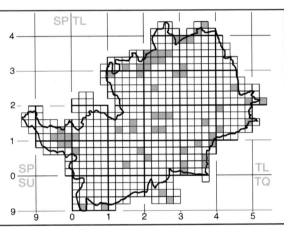

Our largest numbers recorded were over 20 under gorse on Ashridge after the two very dry summers of 1975 and 1976, by Peter Scrivens who observed them in 1976 and again in 1977. Harold Nixon (1971) had seen them over several years on ant hills at Marshalls Heath, Harpenden; Enid Evans and Philip Kingsbury have recorded them from Berkhamsted (seen with young by Philip Kingsbury, 3rd September 1988); John Leonhardt and David James have sent records from the Ivinghoe Beacons and there are modern reports from Hoddesdon, Wormley, Smallford, St.Albans, Welwyn, Pirton and Cuffley. Colin Fitzsimmons recorded a female with 11 young (late July 1980) from the railway embankment at Cuffley and it is this kind of site and the newer motorway embankments which may provide sanctuary for the species.

Beds Wildlife (1987) reported that the species was 'uncommon, but widespread' and Laver's (1898) brief

**The common lizard** *Lacerta vivipara* **has a known distribution which reflects the rarity of the undisturbed and neglected habitats (such as railway embankments) they prefer.**

**Scarce, declining**

49

**Common lizard** *Lacerta vivipara.*

*'common in all parts of Essex' must be tempered with the contemporary loss of heaths and neglect of commons since he wrote this, although I can vouch that they still prosper down to the tideline along the sea wall, from Walton to Felixstowe. As with the adders there, it is the soft-footed approach and silent observation which allows you to approach basking sites with greatest success. ('Sea wall' sounds very municipal, but the sea defences along the east coast here are in fact beautifully overgrown sanctuaries stretching for miles where grasses cover most of the soil and stones. Small areas of exposed concrete are particularly favoured for warmth by the reptiles. They are the nearest coastal sites to us where summer lizard watching can be guaranteed.*

*Burton (1974) considered these lizards to be common in the countryside around London and to survive 'in pockets' throughout the suburbs. As well as including Epping Forest, Essex, he mentions Brent reservoirs, Middlesex.*

**Young common lizards with adults in Thomas Bell's classic work** *A History of British Reptiles* (**1889**).

Colin Fitzsimmon's record of 11 young is high: they usually have 5-8 and the perfectly formed young lizards may escape from the egg membrane at once or over the next 48 hours.

The species is able to scamper up apparently flat surfaces and can be seen basking on gate posts, walls and banks. Although they vanish with amazing speed, if a habitat has produced one lizard it is likely to have others basking nearby. Young and males emerge from hibernation around March, ahead of females (Frazer 1983), and after mating in April the young are born in midsummer. In the autumn they seek out hibernation sites and adults retire ahead of the young. The skin is sloughed in pieces and this may take place 6 times annually until fully grown, when 4 times each year is normal. Despite their speed, few will live more than 5 or 6 years and they are taken typically by snakes, birds and weasels. Young may also be eaten by frogs, toads, hedgehogs and shrews. The ability, like the slowworm, to shed the tail will save the lives of many and a short replacement tail can grow.

'Forked' tails are known where a tail has only been partly lost, but a new one grows alongside. Pregnant females look much fatter than the males, as you might expect, but the females are generally broader in the body.

Conservation of our oldest, well managed commons and heathlands, especially in sandy areas, will ensure their survival in the county, and particular attention should be paid to 'no-go' areas for humans along major roads and railways. It may take many years for the motorway banks to become as favourable as our less cut-back railway embankments have become. The irony of the highly dangerous and noisy intrusion of major roads into the countryside is that they may be the saving of some of our more unusual species, provided that populations have not become too fragmented to allow colonisation.

# Slowworm
## *Anguis fragilis*

Despite the widespread distribution shown on maps of Hertfordshire and the national surveys (which are almost interchangeable with that of the common lizard) this shiny, legless lizard has never attracted much attention in the county. It appears to be increasingly local, confined to undisturbed sites such as railway and road embankments, churchyards, the older neglected gardens and village greens that are still allowed to retain a natural character.

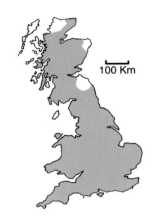

Lloyd (47) had more to say about slowworms than any other reptile or amphibian: 'This common reptile is by no means common in Hertfordshire and is even decidedly scarce in some parts of the county. The author of the list of reptiles in the Victoria County History (1902) knew of only one reliable record - from Watford in 1886 (*Trans, **IV**, 119*). In the west it is uncommon. I have only once seen one at Elstree (southwest). Charles Oldham tells me that during his 35 years' residence in the county he has only twice seen slowworms - namely 2 near Harpenden in 1927 and 1 at Hudnall Common (Ashridge) in 1914.

'Stanley Flower FRS informs me that he has twice found them at Spencers Green, just over the Buckinghamshire border, near Tring. Mr.A.L.Goodson, of Tring Museum, says that there were slowworms in that district (e.g. near Hastoe) up to 1925, but he has seen none of recent years. In May, 1942, A.L.Goodson found one (seen by R.B.Benson) in Stubbings Wood, near Hastoe. Benson recalls seeing dead ones at Berkhamsted occasionally up to about 1914, but has seen none there since then'.

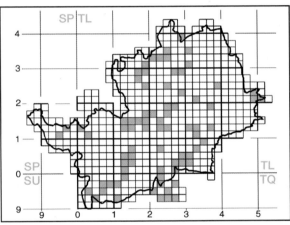

The slowworm *Anguis fragilis* distribution in Hertfordshire suggests a preference for the brown earths and London clay over the boulder clays of the west and northeast.

**Scarce, declining**

Sage (1954) noted that Lloyd had not listed them for the south of the county and reported them from the more sandy parts of Northaw Great Wood: in the School Camp and the main car park in particular. He added that a number of individuals 'have been found suddenly and quite by accident, and have generally escaped by rapidly disappearing down a hole in the ground'. Likewise, Lloyd's report prompted Hager (1955) to give two records for Barnet gardens, both during September 1954.

At Sandon it was felt to have become less common in 1972 when management of the churchyard changed and 'the grass was cut very short on a regular basis'. (Thankfully, many churches now take habitat conservation into account in the maintenance of the graveyards and any surrounding

The 'legless lizard', an adult slowworm *Anguis fragilis* coiled in grassland.

lands, most of which are very valuable refuges for wild life.)

Brown (1949) noted in the Trans that he found several hibernating together in the winter of 1939/40: 'The apparent scarcity of this reptile in the county prompts me to record the discovery of 3-4 in my Hertford Heath garden. They were exposed when raising turf'.

There is no record of them in the Hexton survey (1936), but Foster (1934) in the Nat His Hitchin Region had noted that the species was found all over the district, but was never common. 'Slowworms', he wrote 'are usually mistaken for snakes and are usually killed in consequence. In Hitchin the sloping grounds on the south side of Hitchin Hill and of White Hill seem to be favourite localities. Ray Palmer reports a very large specimen from Weston measuring 17 inches (433 mm) and tells me he has found several in the same district. I have seen them from Offley Park, Offley Holes, Preston, Wain Wood, Pirton, Holwell and Ickleford. No doubt they occur all over the district. A specimen in Letchworth Museum came from Walkern.'

Laver (1898) reported a widespread status in Essex and sadly noted that its strong resemblance to a snake induced country people almost universally to destroy it. Since the Wildlife & Countryside Act amendment of 1988 they are protected.

In both counties the modern distribution has probably been greatly reduced as neglected dry and damp areas between which they move have been lost. Beds Wildlife (1987) lists them as uncommon and local, especially in the north of the county, with most records from the Dunstable and Whipsnade areas. In contrast, Burton (1974) reported them to be 'widely distributed, found in many of London's suburban parks and often common in outer suburbia'. He included Epping Forest in his list of sites.

Although the distinguished author on our amphibians and reptiles, Malcolm Smith, felt the name slowworm appropriate because the Anglo-Saxon wyrm became worm in Middle English and was applied to any snake-like creature (even by Shakespeare) it seems misleading now. Certainly when compared with the snakes their actions are slower and more considered, but in modern usage the word worm is confined to invertebrates.

Their carefully measured activity is ideal for their feeding habits and includes the capture of various appetizing slugs and snails, particularly the small grey species, spiders, worms and insects. On warm, wet late summer and early autumn nights they will eat an abundance of these foods prior to hibernation in October.

The birth of young, which varies according to temperature around August or September, might seem late because there is such a short time to winter torpor. However, the greater availability of food at this time of year as well as the high ground temperature and strong sunlight during pregnancy probably explain this: after a week not feeding the juveniles will begin to eat very small, moving animals at a time when young slugs abound. We tend to forget what happens in the hours of darkness as, for example, crane flies hatch from their leatherjacket pupae, like hundreds of little towers across a lawn in heavy autumn rain, and earthworms come out to feed and mate. They grow rapidly until frosts force torpor on them.

At first they look quite different from their parents, appearing in a rather fancy two-tone metallic finish. They are a golden ochre colour above and gloss black below, with a black dorsal stripe from a triangular patch on the head which continues back to the tail. It will usually be four years before they are able to reproduce, having doubled their length in each of the first two years. All reptiles have spectacular glistening skin, pleasant to the touch, and all have complex life histories.

Although the slowworm has the look of a snake, there are a number of differences, the most obvious of which is the blink of the moveable eyelid. Snakes do not have this facility and permanently stare. Whilst the slowworm's tongue flickers out in a snake-like way, it is with a slower action performing the same functions of smell and taste, but possessing only a short notch. (Snakes have a gap through which the tongue can exit and return without the mouth being opened, but all the lizards must open their mouth to use their tongue.) The ear holes are invisible, unlike other lizards.

The Latin name *fragilis* is from the phenomenon of tail-loss, when the animal sheds the end of its body if bitten or snatched. A stump regrows if they survive such an attack and the confusion caused by leaving part of its body with the predator must be a strategy which allows many to escape. Colours vary from dark to pale and there is a distinctive blue spotted variation. Females produce more young the older they get, from a few in the first litters to over a dozen later.

They have been known to live for over 50 years protected in captivity, but there are many animals which will catch them, tail or no tail. The birth is about the nearest thing to live as possible because the young have developed in the oviduct and break the thin shell of their egg with an egg tooth at the moment of birth or very soon afterwards. In very cold summers and autumns the pregnancy may be delayed right through hibernation until milder conditions in the following year.

Pregnant slowworms bask in the sun whenever possible to aid development of the young in the oviduct. About four

The striking appearance of a juvenile slowworm (top) and a detail of the adult (Tewin Orchard).

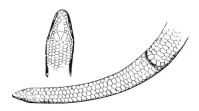

Details of head scales and underpart of tail from Bell (1889).

times annually the skin will be shed to allow for growth, as in other reptiles. In this species it is usually sloughed complete. They can be encouraged near human habitation where they favour damp areas with stones to sunbathe on. A rockery built around a compost heap would be ideal, if eccentric in traditional gardening terms.

The modern distribution maps suggests a bias to central Hertfordshire and when I mentioned this to Trevor James *(HBRC)*, he felt that this was a genuine indication of survival in the more favoured boulder clays and gravels and where there are more old woodlands. This area has always been the least successful for farming because of the difficult soils.

The older, undisturbed habitats, especially where there are damp areas (for feeding) combined with gravel banks (for dry sheltered retreats), are likely to retain their slowworms. The *HARG* survey of allotments has shown this to be an important habitat. The western tip of Hertfordshire, with far-ranging woods and valleys, is similarly favourable.

# Grass snake
## *Natrix natrix*

**A 1m long grass snake** *Natrix natrix.*

*With so few reptiles in Britain, members of HNHS have been keen to document them in the Trans. In fact, the first colour plate published in the Journal was of Margaret Pelly's painting made on the spot when a batch of about 20 grass snake eggs was found in manure at Bentley Priory, by Stanmore Common just over the Hertfordshire border in Middlesex, 14th August 1936. (One egg was opened and the 80mm long red embryo painted and also reproduced, Vol XXI:1, p 64.)*

*Lloyd made several references to the snake in the Trans (1934, 1939 and 1941) and concluded: 'this snake must be considered rare in the north, northwest, and east of Hertfordshire, and in the Chilterns, although relatively common all across the south of the county and over the Middlesex border'. He gave the earliest known county date for emergence from hibernation as 6th March1938 when he came across a dark one, probably about to slough its skin, basking on dry leaves at Bridge Street Coppice, Hilfield, near Elstree.*

*Lloyd (47) called them 'widely distributed' and lists records from Bishop's Stortford, Tring, St.Albans, and Elstree. There are specimens in Tring Museum from that district (1912 and 1928) and in St.Albans Museum (from London Colney 1940). See 'The Distribution of the Grass Snake in Hertfordshire'; 'Further Notes on the Grass Snake*

100 Km

in Hertfordshire' and 'New Grass Snake Records', by Bertram Lloyd, in Trans, **XX**, 30 1934, **XXI**, 64 1939, and **XXI**, 277 1941 respectively. A grass snake was seen in Letchworth, August 1941 (W.P.Westell) and R.B.Benson saw one at Bricket Wood (where he had observed others) on 21st May 1944. It was said by a local keeper that this species is often seen thereabouts.

Sage (1966) reported them to be more frequent than slowworms in Northaw Great Wood and in the damper parts of the woodland. As a child I made the usual mistake of picking one up too vigorously (always avoid any sudden movements) and was annointed with the foul milky fluid they discharge from their vent when disturbed. (Frazer [1983] describes this as a 'foetida mixed with faecal matter from the cloaca'.) I found them on walks in the 1950s in The Dell in the Northaw Fields, in Home Wood at the Cuffley Scout Camp east end, and swimming in a pond by Cuffley Brook in Theobalds Park, which confirms Lloyd's view of their survival in suitable habitats in the south of the county.

They are very much a water snake and John Baker gives a detailed description of a frog being taken by one at his fish pond in Park Street, St.Albans (Autumn 1987 newsletter of the Herts Nat His Soc). Although Foster (1934) confirms their rarity in north Hertfordshire by reporting just a few records, Fitter notes the patchy abundance in south and southwest Hertfordshire at suitable habitats (1949). On 23rd April 1978 Ralph Newton observed a pair mating in Balls Wood, near Hertford Heath. I have had grass snakes brought to me by Tony Williams from his garden off London Road, Hitchin and two from the Watford area in the 1980s.

It is unfortunate that the enormous growth in human population in the south will not have been matched by an increase in sympathy for these harmless snakes in what remains of their habitats. The combination of sand and ponds is ideal for the species and the vast amount of gravel extraction has left lake areas which should continue to provide suitable habitats as long as there is enough food for the snakes to live on at these sites.

Despite a strong presence in Hertfordshire and Burton's record of grass snakes as 'fairly widespread in rural areas around London, but very

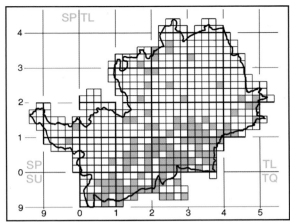

The grass snake *Natrix natrix* distribution has a distinct bias to the south which has always been noticed in records. They particularly favour sandy soil and ponds such as worked-out gravel pits which have filled with water.

**Local, declining**

**Margaret Pelly's watercolour of grass snake eggs at Bentley Priory, August 1936.**

**A grass snake has a circular pupil to its eye.**

**A grass snake feins death in characteristic pose (top) and swims with ease.**

*rare in the suburbs' (1974), Beds Wildlife (1987) notes that they are unknown apart from 'along the Great Ouse River and one Toddington record'.*

Despite Christine and Denis Shepperson's record of 11 seen on one day near Amwell (24th April 2000), observers who live in north Hertfordshire feel pleased to see one or two grass snakes in as many years, but those out walking and watching regularly in the centre or south of the county continue to record them. Bricket Wood Common, for example, continues to be a stronghold with several clear sightings by one recorder (C.Everett, 1999): one in scrub in a recently coppiced area on 25th May, one there also on 22nd June and one again on 23rd August. One was seen swimming in a pond on 25th May and one crossed a path ahead of the same observer on 5th September.

In 2001 Christine Shepperson reported 2 coiled together at a sheltered sunny part of Hilfield Park Reservoir, seen by Steve Murray. Peter Oakenfull has found as many as 13 grass snakes and one slowworm together at one site between Welwyn Garden City and Hatfield (May 2001).

The loss of pond habitats must have influenced their distribution, although interested and sympathetic garden pond owners and the lakes left after gravel workings help them survive. They hunt in ponds and streams for tadpoles, small fish, frogs and both smooth and palmate newts. One large meal may be sufficient for over a week.

Distinguishing a grass snake from an adder is not always straightforward especially if the usual yellow neck patches of the grass snake are absent. In such cases look for the circular pupil of the grass snake eye which is protected by a transparent skin. An adder's pupil is usually a vertical, narrow diamond shape, unless in very poor light.

When shedding their skin, the green shade of the grass snake can appear drab brown and their eyes become opaque. Recognition can then be confusing to the novice and care should be taken at such a time. They are, however, much more aggressive and threatening when discovered, whilst adders slip away as quickly as possible if approached.

They both sense vibrations instantly and adder bites usually occur if for some reason they have not detected, for example, a footfall by someone, a dog or a farm animal. If you jump down onto a sunny spot amongst cover, perhaps from a high bank, this might take a snake by surprise. In thick ground cover the slightest tremors to the ground normally send them away.

To encourage our grass snakes we should construct more ponds, particularly where there is gravel, and position one or two compost heaps close by because the heat generated by dead, compacted vegetation incubates their eggs. It is a good management policy to mow to create different depths of grassland, short, medium and long, and always pile up the cut grass in undisturbed mounds in the warmest south-facing corners of a site. This gives a variety of retreats for the snake.

Grass snakes mate in April and May and lay eggs in June and July. Eggs hatch, depending on conditions, from August to September and the young fend for themselves at once. Hibernation commences in October inside secure retreats such as tree roots or crevices in old walls. Their main predators are humans (including those using mowers), birds of prey, hedgehogs, foxes, dogs and badgers.

My longest view of a hunting grass snake was not in Hertfordshire but in one of my favourite nature reserves: Wicken Fen. On a bright sunny day I was able to watch one slip out of sedges and swim across a small pool. It waited, half-submerged for several minutes and I noticed a small pike in the water. I wondered who was hunting who. It did not catch anything, but slipped away into cover. Such moments can almost make you feel you are in a tropical wilderness.

National surveys show that there has been a significant decline of grass snakes in the last 30 years and they have been lost from many places which used to have them.

*The most recent report of a snake bite was given in the Hertfordshire Mercury on 13th July 2001. An Alsatian dog was treated by local vets for an adder bite received in Balls Park, Hertford.*

# Adder

## *Vipera berus*

*The adder is our only venomous snake in Britain and whilst I have been able to watch this species close-up on numerous occasions on the Essex Marshes and managed to approach them on the cliffs near Salcombe, south Devon, between Bolt Head and Bolt Tail, I have never come across one in Hertfordshire. As well as sunbathing on warm cliff turf, they love to lie up under any available discarded, corrugated iron sheets which warm up in the sunshine. On the grassy sea walls, if mowers approach, they slip into cracks in the ground whilst the blades pass above.*

*Adders are reported from time to time from Hertfordshire, and there have been two bites to humans in the last decade: a child near Hertford, who recovered when treated with adder serum, and an adult near Welwyn Garden City who was twice bitten and treated successfully. I have never traced releases to anyone, but this may be an explanation for the case at Hertford. Tom Gladwin recalled that they were released at Mardley Heath, near Welwyn, over 30 years ago from Essex specimens, but there is no evidence that they survive on this Heath.*

*Laver (1898) observed: 'This (species) is common in woods throughout Essex, but is most frequent on the marshes... I do not think it is so plentiful as it used to be before the large hedgerows were reduced in size.' He devotes a good deal of space to the 'stings' to livestock which were rarely fatal; noted 17 adders and 2 grass snakes found together in hibernation on Saltcote Farm, Goldhanger and*

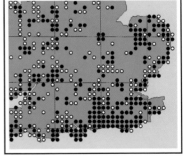

● **1970 onwards**
○ **1901-1969**

**The adder has no yellow neck patches and shows more scales than a grass snake on its rather blunt head. A distinct 'V' can be seen.**

**Adder** *Vipera berus.*

reported a dark form in the Epping Forest Museum, caught at Loughton in 1883.

Why should the species have appeared to have been absent from our adjacent county, Hertfordshire? Westell (1931) describes a tomb in the north wall of St.Mary's Church, Brent Pelham, attributed to Piers Shonks, 'a serpent-killer' of the time of William I, 1086. Clearly he was considered a very important local personality and was recognised with such a significant burial site that his job must have been considered a vital form of pest control. He may well have reduced the adder population greatly, even to the point of local extinction, from a very early time.

Foster (1934), considered that the species had been present, but 'of late years become nearly or quite extinct. At one time the area between Offley Holes and Preston, especially that portion near the rifle butts, had the reputation of containing adders; the writer and others used to see them there fairly frequently.'

He goes on to list various other sites including Clothall, Weston, Preston, Knebworth, Offley and Shefford, but the Bedfordshire naturalist Ray Palmer considered at least one of these reports to probably have been of a slowworm.

On one occasion I have been initially fooled by a short, fat female grass snake which had the dark adder colouring of those I have seen in Essex and no yellow on the neck as she was about to slough her skin. However, grass snakes and adders are different in shape and behaviour. It is best to look for the adder's blunt head, the different pupil shape to the eyes and more scales concentrated on the head on specimens which are unusually coloured.

Foster's final record which is from the diary of Joseph Ransom, of Hitchin, reads: '1808, 11th August. One of our men killed an adder which measured 2ft 2ins long; it had 5 young ones in its body which measured 7ins long'.

Foster commented: 'An interesting note, showing that in those days killing adders was not a very extraordinary event. In this case it seems that the size of the adder and of its young was the particular point of interest, not its mere occurrence'.

Lloyd (47) described adders as very rare, if indeed still found in the county, but gives a record from Duncombe Terrace, near Ashridge, (1940), 'about 1 mile over the border into Buckinghamshire', where J.R.Norman, a one time keeper of the Tring Museum, found one curled up in an old bird's nest.

Malcolm Smith's map (1951) shows the distribution as very doubtful for Hertfordshire, and Fitter stated in his check *list for Mamms Reps & Amphibs of the London Natural History Society area (1949) that it had become very rare north of the Thames. Smith adds: 'Its distribution in Central Europe is sporadic - its occurrence in some areas and absence from others having no apparent relation to geographic conditions.' Burton (1974) gives Epping Forest, but supports Fitter's observations generally for the adder in the London area. Beds Wildlife (1987) gives: 'local and rare; Rowney Warren has most records, also known at Kings Wood (Heath & Reach) and in the Everton/Potton area'.*

*The 1808 record seems to be accurate on every count: the description of the adult, its young and the time of year. Grass snakes would have laid their eggs by then and it is the peak time for female adders to carry well developed young. The transparent egg membranes would easily break and allow Ransom's workman to distinguish the young snakes.*

*Perhaps a very small, precarious population was finally eliminated across most of the county by human destruction following incidents like this one during the 18th and 19th centuries, but I now suspect adders have always survived near Welwyn Garden City, although specimens and photographs still elude the survey. Jennifer Ruby (1999) records from her research here that in the week ending 13th August 1847 'five dozen sparrows, two adders and 33 rats' were killed.*

*In the 1979 Trans I reported that 2 contemporary records had been received and it now seems certain that adders have always survived in central Hertfordshire where sandy, heath conditions survive. Reliable recorders have also reported sightings.*

*The BHS produced a leaflet 'Being kind to snakes' which points out that deaths from British adder bites are extremely rare. Wasp stings have killed about 200 people during the last 100 years whereas only 14 people have died from adder bites over the same period. (One of these people, author on reptiles Tony Phelps, is still alive - serum was injected into him and he was revived 4 minutes after his heart beat ceased - although he remains in the statistics as being 'dead by snake-bite', BBC Wild Track, 10th September 1999.)*

We can therefore now record that adders survive in the sandy areas near Hertford town and seem to have always survived near Welwyn Garden City. In 1999 Simon Scull reported that he had seen adders since he moved to the area and Derek Martindale disturbed one from his bicycle on the old railway line path. The first sighting in 2000 was basking in the bucket of an old earthmover in cover on 6th April at 10.30am.

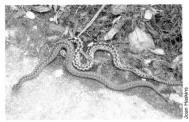

**A courtship pair of adders showing the greater tendency to brown colouration in the female.**

*Why didn't the viper vipe 'er nose? Cause the adder 'ad'er 'andkerchief.*
Traditional

**Midwife toad** *Alytes obstretricans* **photographed at Ashridge. This male is carrying eggs on its back and thighs.**

**Natterjack toad** *Bufo calamita.*

Phil Farrer

**A young marginated tortoise** *Testudo marginata* **in its natural habitat in Greece.**

# Introduced species

An introduced species which survived in at least one garden pond for more than a decade in southwest Hertfordshire is the midwife toad *Alytes obstetricans*. (It has such a descriptive Latin name!) There is doubt about its presence there now because of lack of maintenance to the pond. I was originally told of the colony by Clive Banks and was able to photograph a male carrying eggs there in the 1970s.

Ray Palmer wrote about the colonies of these toads in Bedfordshire in the April 1950 *BNA* journal *Countryside*. He describes how this small species from Europe had been naturalised in a nursery garden about 1878 (probably introduced by accident with foreign plants), which was then left undisturbed and flourished. When the nursery was sold and built over in the 1920s the toads were re-established in two Bedfordshire gardens. Both sites are kept secret by their owners to avoid disturbance or collection. *Beds Wildlife* (1987) reports: *'several stable colonies in and near Bedford, all traceable to an original Bedford site'*. (The reintroduction of natterjack toads *Bufo calamita* to the RSPB headquarters at The Lodge, Sandy in 1980 is also noted.)

The national picture has been given by Lever in *The Naturalized Animals of the British Isles* (1977). The spring croaking of the males is a loud bell-like call and the name comes from the behaviour of the male which attends the female as she spawns in the pond, manipulating the string of eggs in jelly around his body. Eventually he ends up with a belt of about 50 bright yellow eggs on his back and thighs. Incubation is on land in a retreat from which he feeds and occasionally returns to the pond to moisten the eggs, usually at night. After 4 weeks the tadpoles are well advanced in the eggs and the diligent single parent enters the water so that they can hatch and the egg cases fall away.

Our once familiar garden pet reptile, the tortoise, has become quite a rarity due to the controls on importing them. Most died in transport and the trade resulted in the gross over-collection of Mediterranean populations. Despite some long-lived specimens (such as 'Timothy' who Gilbert White observed into its 54th year in the 18th century) they do not breed outside warm captive conditions in Britain because our climate is too cold and damp.

Fitter (1945) reminds us of a warmer period in our history when he reported that the remains of a tortoise *(Emys)* were found during excavations by Abbott in 1892, which revealed the traces of mammoth, hippopotamus, rhinoceros, red deer, wild horse and bull at diversions to the Thames which later also produced wild bull, horse, sheep, wild boar, fallow deer and hare. (He adds that the gravels of the Lea valley show a much more Arctic fauna, including mammoth, reindeer, bison, rhinoceros and lemming which were 'considered by Warren to be typical of the northern tundra'.)

The species usually kept as a pet in modern times is the spur-thighed Mediterranean tortoise *Testudo graeca* and Hermann's tortoise *T. hermanni*. It is far better for those interested in tortoises to visit them in correctly heated zoo enclosures or, ideally, in their natural habitats in Greece, for example, and observe them under the conditions of temperature and terrain they prefer. I have photographed the marginated tortoise *T. marginata* while walking in the countryside beyond the monastery on the Island of Poros and elsewhere in the Aegean. They retreat into their shells when threatened but may still be killed by small predators which deftly extricate the head, tail and legs.

Much as I enjoyed seeing tortoises that wandered into our garden in my childhood (some trailing cord from a drilled hole in the corner of their shell and others defaced with a large name painted on them), I cannot think it appropriate to keep a reptile which loves warmth, hates the rain (which drums on its shell), will not breed (unless kept in an indoor vivarium), hibernates from November to April and does not even relish food for some time after waking or before returning

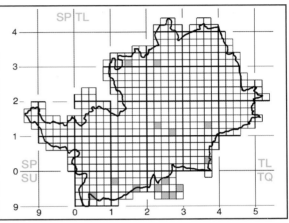

into torpor. The way Gilbert White's 'Timothy' would prop his body up against the garden wall to absorb as much of the weakening autumn sunshine as he could, seems to say it all and suggests a creature that should be somewhere else.

Records for released pet red-eared terrapins *Pseudemys scripta elegans* first came from Norton Pond, Letchworth on 12th August 1980 (Sawford) and then in 1982 from a pond in Park Lane, Cheshunt (Fitzsimmons) and another in Hertford Heath (Newton). There followed one observed in Blackthorn Wood, Welwyn Garden City, which survived over the winter from 1989 to 1990 and beyond (Boucher), and three were present at an artificial pond in successive years in Watford town centre, April-August 1998-1999 (Everett).

Additional *HBRC* localities are from Broxbourne Woods, Pirton Pond and the Lea Valley, 2000 (Jones).

It is illegal for anyone to deliberately release into the wild any non-native species of amphibian or mammal. It may, like certain forms of genetic engineering, permanently disrupt the ecology of the countryside and is quite likely to cause the local extinction of native species.

**The red-eared terrapin** *Pseudemys scripta elegans* **became a popular pet after films and comics created a craze for turtles. As they grew too large to keep many were unfortunately released by their owners. Their presence may cause the reduction or disappearance of indigenous pond species where they have been established.**

Water habitats including studies of the River Stort, Hunsdon Meads (above), and a restored gravel pit near Hoddesdon (below) which is now ideal for aquatic wildlife, both photographs by Ralph Newton.

The conversion of a derelict chicken shed with underfelt and a liner to create a pond (Tewin Orchard).

David Bellamy (below and facing page) leads a pond dip during a *HMWT* Wildlife Safari (Tewin Orchard).

Woodland pond near Broxbourne
(Ralph Newton) and Morven Park
pond, Potters Bar.

Before the ground and ponds freeze
hard, it is essential that reptiles and
amphibians have retreated into safe
sites for hibernation (winter scene at
Tewin Orchard).

Hertfordshire was named after the red deer and the war memorial in Hertford town centre displays a fine sculpture of a hart, based on a model by Alfred Drury RA. The memorial was designed by Sir Aston Webb and was unveiled in 1921. It now commemorates the dead of both World Wars.

# Mammals

Partly because we are mammals ourselves, I considered that this part of the book required less space by way of an introduction than I devoted to the amphibians and reptiles. Of the 48 species of wild mammals present in the county, the barbastelle bat *B. barbastellus* has just been detected for the first time since 1922; red squirrel *S. vulgaris* and black rat *R. rattus* have become extinct within the last 50 years; pine martens *M. martes* were trapped or shot until extinct about 125 years ago; polecats *M. putorius,* otters *L. lutra* and red deer *C. elaphus* disappeared and then reappeared, first due to human persecution and then as a result of human reintroductions; coypu *M. coypus* appeared as a fur farm escapee and then disappeared within about 40 years due to trapping campaigns, leaving just a few reports from a brief appearance in the county.

The wild mammals in Hertfordshire survive in habitats dominated by human structures and cultivation. They must compete with domestic livestock and pets maintained by the humans present. Domestic dogs *Canis familiaris* prey upon thousands of rabbits, hares, deer, livestock and small mammals, particularly if they are allowed to roam illegally unsupervised, whilst the toll taken of bats, birds and the smaller mammals (as well as amphibians and reptiles) by the domestic cat *Felis catus* runs into hundreds of thousands of items in the county annually.

The 48 mammal species now found here represent just a fraction of the million and more animal species known, of which the mammals make up just 5,000. All mammals show ancestral links with amphibians and reptiles and humans are the only British mammal to progress from walking on all four limbs to two.

All mammals are also highly advanced vertebrates which

Hedgehogs *Erinaceus europaeus* are one of the best known and popular wild mammals. Michelle Hart, *née* Williscroft, was pictured at Marden Heath, near Welwyn, in the 1970s. Photograph by kind permission of Nick Watts.

exploit their common characteristics in different ways. By regulation of our body heat we have obvious advantages over the amphibians and reptiles, but we do this at considerable expenditure of energy in cold conditions. The need to feed, almost continuously in some cases, imposes limitations on mammal life cycles. We should not belittle the amphibians and reptiles as being merely cold-blooded and limited by climatic conditions. Whilst all of them hibernate in Hertfordshire, as do some of our mammals, when temperatures are warm they are far from cold and sluggish as anyone who has handled a grass snake will testify.

Mammary glands, featured widely as photographic illustrations in certain types of printed ephemera circulated between humans, are the most obvious distinguishing features of mammals. The name of the Class refers to the females which feed their offspring with milk secreted from glands in the skin. These glands are even found in the egg-laying species which secrete milk for the newly hatched soft-shelled young so that they are able to lick the thick, yellowish fluid as it trickles from the hair next to these glands (Grzimek, 1972).

Temperature is regulated by sweat glands and hair: although the wild species look more hairy than we do, we too are covered in sparse hairs, apart from extra growth concentrated in certain areas of the body for protection and preservation of scents. Species without sweat glands reduce body heat by panting rapidly through the mouth until cool.

Theories abound as to why humans are like the marine mammals, which have developed fatty insulation under the skin with almost invisible hair which does not impair swimming, instead of remaining as hairy, for example, as an otter which also lives in and out of water. The need to float about in the warm water of southern seas and lakes, safe from large predatory animals (if that is why we developed in this naked form) has long since gone, but we now wear clothing to control our body temperature.

There have been certain places in the county this century, notably three near Bricket Wood, where squirrels, rabbits and other diurnal mammals may have been surprised by free-ranging naked apes in pursuit of naturism.

The same keratized material which gives mammals their hair provides the horns of goats, the hooves of deer, and gives us our nails or claws. Our teeth - incisors, canine, premolars and molars - are just as vital to survival as nails and claws. Martin Hancox wrote in our joint paper on the *Longevity of a Hertfordshire Badger, Meles meles*, (1992):

'*The evolutionary success of the mammals is attributable in part to their adaptive radiation in dentition for diets ranging from herbivore to omnivore to carnivore. The full functional division of labour amongst tooth types (heterodont condition) is achieved after the milk teeth and weaning in the second permanent dentition; but unlike their fish/reptile ancestors,*

Ironically, wild badgers live almost entirely on earthworms but domestic cats, which are fed by their owners, also hunt and kill about 275 million fellow mammals, birds, reptiles and amphibians each year.
Useful predation includes this example of rabbit control near Hertford, but nationally 4 million frogs, 170,000 newts, 370,000 lizards, 700,000 slowworms, 1.5 million harvest mice and 230,000 bats are killed each year (Mammal Society survey 2001).

*there is no further tooth eruption to replace worn or broken teeth, which sets a finite limit to longevity... and it has hence been said that mammals "dig their graves with their teeth".'*

Humans have the most complex nervous system of all the mammals, but olfactory organs, hearing and vision have been developed to varying degrees of sensitivity according to different mammal species and their behaviour. Our sense of taste has probably come about to help us distinguish poisonous fruits (usually bitter) from safer types (usually sweet).

Mammal skeletons can be distinguished by features such as the transformation of the lower joint of the jaw, the bones of the middle ear and the shape of the teeth. Mammal-like reptiles from the fossil record make it difficult for us to classify these animals, but the teeth and articulation of the lower jaws are the main guides. Which goes to show that including amphibians, reptiles and mammals in the same volume makes a certain amount of sense.

# Hedgehog

### *Erinaceus europaeus*

*Although hedgehogs are now one of our most popular wild mammals, this has not always been the case. Oldham's*

*analysis of Hertfordshire vermin payments (Trans **18**, 45-50) from church wardens' accounts between 1639 and 1820 was dominated by hedgehogs, along with such species as polecats. These had disappeared from the county by the 1930s. Chas Oldham wrote:*

*'The hedgehog's life is forfeit today when the gamekeeper traps it or crushes it to death with his boot-heel, as it was when head-money was paid for it by churchwardens, but whilst the fierce and agile polecat has gone under, this slow-moving creature, endowed with only a passive means of defence in its spiny coat, has survived the former and the latter persecutions and is perhaps as abundant as it ever was. The first particular mention of it is in the accounts for 1690:*

|  | £ | s | d |
|---|---|---|---|
| For 6 hegd hoges . . . . | 00 | 00 | 04 |

*It occurs many times between 1767 and 1791-2, but if any hedgehogs were paid for thereafter they were accounted for under the term '&c.' The price, where detailed, was, with the exception of the payment in 1690, always 4d, the same as for*

66

a polecat - a comparatively large sum, but probably an indication of the malevolence with which the creature was regarded.

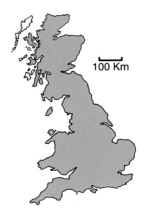

|  | | £ | s | d |
|---|---|---|---|---|
| 1767-8 | Paid for 22 Hedgehogs | 0 | 7 | 4 |
| 1768-9 | To sparrows, Pol Catts & Hedgehogs | 0 | 9 | 2 |
| 1791-2 | Paid for 2 Hedgehogs | 0 | 0 | 8 |

*Hedgehogs were classified with stoats, weasels, foxes, mad dogs and sparrows. At Bushey, for example, the church wardens paid for up to 60 hedgehogs annually and they were the top species in Elstree, Berkhamsted, the Gaddesdens, Harpenden, Rickmansworth, Ridge, St.Albans, Sandridge and Welwyn.*

The earliest mention in the Trans is by Puller (1882) **2**:3, 136, for the Rib Valley, as being present between Standon and the River Lea at Hertford. Roberts (1893) gives the first account from a garden when he described 2 local hibernation nests and a female with young under a wood pile in a walled garden (1891). He had noticed that the species appeared to be partial to the gardens in Victorian Watford.

Lloyd's account of the mammals of Elstree reservoirs (1943) describes hedgehogs as 'fairly common' and, in his 1947 report, as 'widely spread throughout the county, despite the constant absurd persecution by gamekeepers'. Fordham had reported from Odsey near Ashwell in 1943 that 'they used to be comparatively rare, but now (possibly due to the cessation of keepering during the war) all the overgrown hedges are full of them.'

Laver (1898) reported hedgehogs as common in Essex and regretted 'the persecution it has long undergone at the hands of the game preserver.' Dobson (1999) also describes them as common in Essex, but 'declining'. Burton (1974) noted them to be 'very abundant in the outer suburbs' of London and Anderson (1985) shows the hedgehog in 63% of Bedfordshire tetrads.

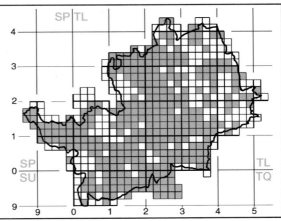

**Hedgehog** *Erinaceus europaeus* **distribution reflects the national picture; further survey work would be expected to complete all the tetrads. A native of grassland, scrub and woods, sub-fossil remains date back 9,500 years to the Mesolithic period.**

**Widespread, declining**

The persecution of hedgehogs is unusual now and concern is expressed for the species in some areas. They are popular in books and the media, and have their own preservation society. Sick or injured hedgehogs are helped by recovery work through volunteers such as Barbara Brady, who worked in Welwyn Garden City for many years, and large numbers are

A hedgehog in hibernaculum (top)
and a skin cleaned down to spines by
a badger. Hedgehogs provide a
variation in the staple diet of
earthworms for both foxes and
badgers.

*The British Hedgehog Preservation
Society provides fact sheets and
recent research shows that 59% of
mammals taken to British wildlife
hospitals are hedgehogs: 16% of all
intakes.*

*Morris (2000) points out that whilst
the slug pellets sold for garden use
which include metaldehyde do not
form a cumulative poison which
would harm hedgehogs, methiocarb,
the poison in agricultural slug pellets,
spread on arable fields by the tonne,
is both directly and indirectly
poisonous to the species.*

*The loss of food and potential lethal
content to invertebrates killed by the
pellets in fields may accelerate a
decline in hedgehogs and may also
explain why the large fieldfare,
redwing and other thrush flocks
appear to have also diminished.*

fed nightly in gardens. In Beatrix Potter books the facial
features of her hedgehog shows a moist nose, a dark face and
simple rounded ears and eyes. Perhaps this image remained
in the subconcious of the gamekeeper described by Morris
(1983) who:

> *'....killed them in June when he felt them harmful to game
> bird nests, but if he discovered them at other times of the
> year, when clearing brushwood in the autumn, for example,
> he would gently move them to a safe place'.*

Usually hedgehogs are killed during modern, often part-
time, keepering activities as just another animal which has
entered a trap set for weasels, stoats and rats along the
hedgerows near the pheasant rearing pens on estates or the
smaller shoots. Some deliberately trap for them and Morris
sensibly points out that if 2% of eggs are lost to hedgehogs it
would be much more cost effective on the keeper's time to go
out and buy a further 100 eggs to rear from the game farms.

Hibernation is the biggest threat to hedgehogs and the
susceptibility of undersized or late-litter hedgehogs to the
cold weather was illustrated by Walton (1979) when he noted
a young one active on mild and then frosty late autumn
evenings at his home near Welwyn on 13th, 17th, 26th and
30th November. Subsequently he found one of this size dead.
More obvious are road casualties which cause very public
deaths to many, often at regular crossing places used by
generations of hedgehogs.

On a drive from St.Albans to Codicote, for example, on
25th June 1986, I noted 5 hedgehogs dead on the road: two at
St.Albans, one at Sandridge Heath, one at Symondshyde and
one at Codicote. This observation on an 8 mile drive was
typical of midsummer motoring in the 1980s, but was less
typical in the 1990s as hedgehog numbers appear inevitably
to have declined. Remains of hedgehogs with their robust
spines survive longer on roads and are not washed away as
quickly as, say, rabbit or rat. We may thus imagine that they
are more frequent than other species. In 2000 I received
reports of the absence of hedgehogs from areas where they
have been regularly seen in the past, even in rural areas such
as the Pelhams.

Casualties can even be seen in winter when a sudden
change in temperature has roused a hibernating hedgehog. As
insectivores, they must rapidly find scarce invertebrate food
at this time. Records show that they are, in fact, active all
through the year.

Mild springs will give the best chance of early litters (and
therefore older, stronger hibernators) and one at Tewin I came
across was already lactating on 3rd May. In the last 20 years
they are rarely seen in Tewin Orchard because the badger and
fox population has grown, although there are good numbers
in the nearby village. They often drown in garden swimming
pools.

We once prepared a poultry run with woodshavings and

straw and left the door open until 6 chicks were ready to transfer from a heated brooder. When we put them in we failed to check the straw (21st July 1993) and next morning found all the chicks had been eaten by a hedgehog which had taken up residence unnoticed before we closed the door. Egg and chick losses are the result of poor husbandry and it would be absurd to kill hedgehogs for such natural variations to their diet.

Leonhardt noted from the field study area at Hudnall Park and Hudnall Common: *'never seen at Hudnall 1977-88'*. Badgers flourish there and Clements (1971-73) found that there was one casualty hedgehog for every 75 miles of roads in the well-populated badger areas of East Sussex, but one every 14 miles in West Sussex where he estimated the badger population to be a fifth of that of East Sussex.

Vehicle density on roads, the reduction of hedgerows and the increase in fox and badger populations generally has put more pressure on hedgehog populations in the last 10 years. They are much more familiar in our gardens. They retreat into compost heaps, untidy corners round sheds and seek deep leaf litter in undergrowth, after touring gardens in the neighbourhood at night. Welcome plates of (ideally) tinned pet food and water are readily eaten. Bread with milk is not appropriate for an insectivore, especially juveniles.

**Juvenile and adult curled up in defensive position.**

Nationally the popularity of hedgehogs has resulted in the foundation of the British Hedgehog Preservation Society. The high standing of the species is largely as a result of Dr.Pat Morris' informed writings and broadcasts, and the accounts by Les Stocker of the Aylesbury Wild Animal Hospital.

The Society produces excellent advice on hedgehog conservation and reported in August 1989 that a hedgehog monitored by a tracking device set a mighty distance record by travelling 3,744 metres in 7 hours 45 minutes - the equivalent of 3 hours 20 minutes a mile for the 2 to 3 mile journey.

# Mole

### *Talpa europaea*

**Mole** *Talpa europaea.*

*Lloyd (47) considered the species common throughout the county in all suitable situations. (Many gardeners would consider them common in numerous unsuitable situations.) He noted that colour varieties were common: cream, apricot and pied. Gibbs devoted a paper to the subject: 'Albino Moles in Hertfordshire', Trans XIII 14 (1908).*

*The Nat Hist Mus has several normal black coloured Tring examples, with Wiggington and Hemel*

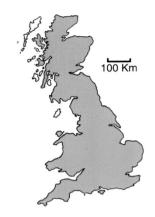

100 Km

*Hempstead albinos. Described from Elstree Reservoir (Lloyd 1943), but generally too familar to have been given attention unless a colour variety turned up.*

*Mole catchers worked from farm to farm: Hertfordshire has always been famous for its stones and flints, so that most farmers considered it an expensive county to cultivate. This was due to the damaged ploughs and the need to frequently replace shears and tines from harrows. Thus moles, which tend to bring deeply buried stones to the surface, were particularly unwelcome. Many a fine willow tree next to a stream began life as a mole snare support, pushed in, set and left to take root as the catcher moved on.*

*Anderson (1985) records moles in 79% of tetrads in Bedfordshire and this is probably typical of all surrounding counties, although Burton (1974) considered their London status as 'rare in the suburbs: confined to large parks in the outer suburbs and to rural areas'.*

Moles have many predators, although most of them find the mammal distasteful and having once killed and rejected one, they avoid the species. Exceptions are herons and the owls, but at Hexton I found an untouched, dehydrated mole amongst pellets in a barn owl nest. No doubt it had been brought at a time of plenty. The skulls are very distinctive in pellets. Peter Walton found a mole alive and unscathed next to a freshly run over weasel near Codicote in 1979. It appeared to have fallen from the weasel's jaws as the predator

The mole *Talpa europaea* is found throughout the county and although it is a woodland species, almost all habitats have produced records from the distinct earthworks on the soil surface. They swim well and can escape from flooded tunnels to re-establish territories on adjoining dry land.

Widespread

Typical tunnel hills in pasture, Weston.

was struck and survived.

When moles cross roads they rush in a distinctive wiggle to the safety of the far bank. They swim in much the same way and flood meadows which provide such fertile sites for territories are vacated when water spreads across. The flood below Ware in 1969, which damaged some houses in Stanstead Abbotts, resulted in hills along the 'tide-line' on the higher ground above what has become the Amwell Quarry area. Damp pasture and grassland is favoured because this gives a plentiful supply of earthworms and there are always mole hills along our river valley meadows. In March 1972 Trevor James counted 68 mole hills in 52 square metres of field near Cuffley.

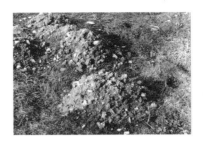

The large April breeding 'fortress' hill near Hertford.

If you wait silently next to a complex of hills and chance on an activity period, a movement on the surface turf will locate a busy occupant and you can move up to the mole as long as you tread carefully. I have knelt by a surface tunnel as it was being excavated and seen worms emerge frantically onto the grass surface - usually a suicidal activity in daylight due to local blackbird predation, but this is obviously a preferred option to being nibbled underground. Although very territorial, moles regularly use communal tunnels and David Stone (1986) recorded more than 10 moles captured using a single trap in the same tunnel over a period of only 24 hours.

# Common shrew

## Sorex araneus

*Despite their abundance, the common shrew did not excite the interest of collectors and only 2 from Hertfordshire are represented in the Brit Mus Coll. 1900 (no data) and 1929, both Roth, Tring. It is gratifying to know that they still qualify for their descriptive English name, whilst the common otter, common dormouse, common lizard and common long-eared bat certainly do not. Lloyd (47) sums up: 'Widely spread in all suitable districts'.*

*Laver (1898) says much the same for Essex, but coins a very apt description for their staccato squeaks,*

Common shrew *Sorex araneus* (Welwyn Garden City).

*which emanate from deep cover during disputes between shrews, when he says that hedge and coppice frequently resound with their 'shrill war-shrieks'. Dobson (1999) quotes Corke & Harris' 1972 review of small mammals found trapped in discarded bottles, where common shrews made up 51% of the 1,031 mammals identified from this source. Anyone who has carried out bottle surveys will*

71

100 Km

recognise this sort of figure from their results. Beds Wildlife (1987) gives them as 'widespread and frequent'; Anderson (1985) reports them from 44% of the tetrads in that county and Burton (1974) finds them 'confined to the outer suburbs and beyond, where they are abundant' in the London area.

Common shrews are well known for two features in particular: their incessant hunger (which results in hyperactivity, alternating with sleep, around the clock) and their pugnacious demand to be left alone. They are most familiar dead on paths in late summer or when cats catch them and bring them home without eating them.

Churchfield (1988) discusses the possible reasons why this species did not reach Ireland whilst pygmy shrews did. She points out that the land bridge may have comprised wet, peaty moorland not favoured by common shews because of the lack of their staple diet of earthworms. Pygmy shrews do not eat these and are less dependent upon burrow systems, so that the rarity of worms in the land bridge and the ability to live on the surface of land with a very high water table may be the reason for their greater distribution, rather than the age of recolonisation of Britain by the species.

Crowcroft (1957) and Churchfield show that few shrews even reach the comparative old age of 1 year and most die after breeding. Young shrews ensure continuity by remaining active over winter to breed the following spring.

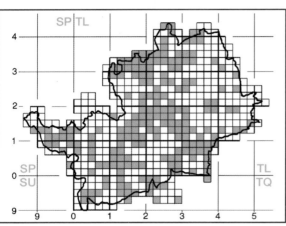

The common shrew *Sorex araneus* is found throughout the county and the map reflects recorder activity.

**Widespread, but in decline mainly due to habitat loss**

It appears that the musky smell of shrews which many predators find distasteful is principally from the pair of glands on their flanks. What discourages dogs and cats has little or no effect on owls and all the shrew species are an important part of the diet of tawny and barn owls, as examination of their coughed-up pellets of fur and bones of prey clearly shows. Birds are said to have little sense of smell and owls tend to swallow small mammals whole.

During my research into discarded bottle traps in the county, common shrews were the most frequent victims by far, but recent studies suggest they have suffered a decline and are less numerous. The bottle surveys in the county are illustrated on p279. All bottles left as litter are a potential hazard to small mammals.

**Common shrew *Sorex araneus* in a temporary vivarium at Tewin Orchard.**

# Pygmy shrew
## Sorex minutus

As with the common shrew, there are only 2 specimens for the county in the Brit Mus Coll. 1939, Jordan, Tring (Roth) and (no date) Montague, Bucks Hill, Kings Langley. Lloyd (47) gives the first county record as 1919, by Oldham, who also found a skull in an owl pellet in 1914, but reference to Oldham's paper (Trans **17**:3, 261-262) shows that there was an earlier Roth Tring Mus Coll. shrew from the town (no date) and a Bishop's Stortford specimen (May 1911, Grantham) before his 21st July 1919 shrew. Oldham's one was picked up dead from the canal towpath at Berkhamsted.

**Pygmy shrew** *Sorex minutus.*

He considered that because this shrew is the only type found in Ireland, it probably has a more ancient origin than our other 2 species. (See opposite. However, the material Oldham presents in his papers relates very well to the published material of his day and is always worthy of reference. He writes on owl pellet analysis, for example, which seems years ahead of its time and he was always up-to-date with the latest published knowledge of mammals.)

Lloyd reports on Letchworth, Hitchin, Elstree and Tring pygmy shrew finds and noted trapped specimens by Wilson from Batchwood, St.Albans (5th June 1938) and 3 Tring Mus skins labelled 'Tring, 1913, 1921 and 1939.' Laver (1898) found pygmy shrews ('lesser' shrews in his day) equally as often in Essex as the common species and correctly uses the tail length as the most obvious characteristic. Dobson (1999) quotes Corke & Harris' 1972 estimate that common shrews

outnumber pygmy shrews by about 5:1, but points out that in grassland surveys this ratio reduces to around 2:1 and in marsh habitats they outnumber common shrews.

Beds Wildlife (87) gives the species as 'widespread but uncommon' and Anderson (1985) notes that they were only found in 18% of the tetrads in the Bedfordshire survey. Burton (1974) knew it only from the outer suburban and rural areas of London, where it was 'much less abundant than the common shrew, although fairly widely distributed'.

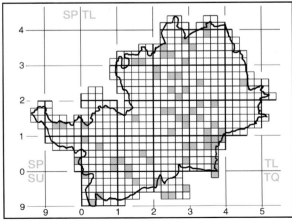

Our county survey suggests that the need for accurate identification has made the species under recorded. Where surveys have taken place with live trapping, owl pellet examinations or the analysis of discarded bottles, pygmy shrews are present at the density of about 1:6 compared with common shrews, as in the neighbouring county of Essex. Les Young's 1999 records from live trapping at Box Wood and Martins Way (Stevenage), Aston, Watton Road, Watton by-pass and St Ippollitts, sent in for the *HMG* mammal survey, show 7 common shrews caught and 5 pygmy shrews amongst the small mammals listed. The grassland habitats on roadsides certainly make the ratio of common shrew to pygmy shrew more even in a sample of this kind, although woodland sites were also trapped: 59 wood mice, 17 field voles, 5 bank voles, 1 yellow-necked mouse and 1 harvest mouse were also caught.

Our mixture of suburbs, gardens, hedgerows, woodland, grassland and scrub in Hertfordshire provides ideal cover, with ample food for this specialist catcher of spiders, woodlice, beetles and bugs. They race at high speed round our garden and I have even found a breeding nest in one of my bee hives where the young appeared to have been stung to death by the occupants, but not before the mother had gained access, built the nest and nearly weaned the juveniles.

# Water shrew

## *Neomys fodiens*

*The largest of our shrews is the least frequently recorded and it is worth noting past records of water shrews which began with T.V.Roberts' 1893 observations: one seen in a*

Peter Oakenfull

*small brook at Cassio Bridge, Watford, and another in the River Gade in Cassiobury Park. There are 2 Roth Coll. specimens in the Nat His Mus: a male at Wigginton (25th April 1910) and a female at Tring (1921).*

*Lloyd (47) noted these when they were kept in Tring Mus (with others) and considered the species as 'not uncommon in suitable situations'. He reported them from Hitchin, Berkhamsted and the River Gade and continued: 'In the Tring district I have only occasionally seen it, eg one watched swimming in the brook by the southwest corner of Wilstone*

**The sooty black fur, stiff hairs on the feet and silver white underside to the tail are the clearest features which distinguish the water shrew in the field.**

*Reservoir on 16th may 1920. On 6th July 1924 I found a freshly dead one by a conduited brook flowing out of Marsworth Reservoir not far off.'*

*He listed 4 found dead in Tring: one dead in the Museum grounds (A.H.Bishop), 4th May 1940; one dead on the road by Miswell Farm, Tring, November 1943 (A.H.Bishop); one dead in a mouse trap in the old brewery loft, Akeman Street, 8th April 1944 (R.B.Benson) and one seen by the canal on 21st April 1944, (R.B.Benson). They were often seen by Oldham in the Berkhamsted watercress beds in the years before 1935.*

*Laver (1898) found them throughout Essex, but 100 years on Dobson (1999) reported them more difficult to find, although 'fairly common'. Anderson (1985) describes them as 'rare' and from just 8% of Beds tetrads. Burton (1974) noted that in the London area they often occurred remote from water.*

Modern records include Letchworth, Hitchin, Weston, Tewin, Epping Green and Hoddesdon with a report from Fordham that a cat at Odsey brought in 6 in 10 days from 5th March to 15th March 1972. In all his many

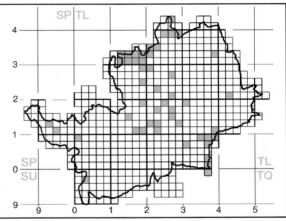

years recording the wildlife around Odsey, he had never seen them before and they were not found there again. Steve Kourik has also reported a water shrew caught by a cat at Watton-at-Stone (1997). Sara Churchfield, who has written so well on shrews, has surveyed at Lemsford and Rye Meads where water shrews are associated with watercress beds .

At Tewin I knew of a garden pond once owned by the Gaveds in Tewin Wood where a colony of water shrews lived in and around their woodland pool. The water has a rockery surround and ample cover.

Before there were ponds in Tewin Orchard I came across a water shrew when making a BBC TV programme with Tony Soper on small mammals: *Discovering Animals*. Nobody in the film crew believed that when I turned over a corrugated sheet to look for a vole or mouse I truly found 'on camera' the first specimen of this shrew to be recorded in the Orchard. I had already found in survey work in Epping Green and Weston that water shrews could turn up remote from obvious sources of open water. Benson (1944) made this point about finding the water shrew in Tring town.

I have even encountered these shrews from a tractor when mowing in the open grassland in the Orchard. They are so large and black that once you are familiar with shrews they are easily distinguished. There were many ponds close to Tewin Orchard that were filled in during the 1950s and the shrews may be a relic population from this time. There have been five ponds created here since the 1980s and the Upper Green pond close-by was renovated in 1976 and 1996.

**Some of the best pictures of water shrews have been taken by Peter Oakenfull at Welwyn Garden City (opposite and above).**

Whiskered bat *Myotis mystacinus*.

# Whiskered bat

## *Myotis mystacinus*

*Oldham, as well as being one of the leading ornithologists of his day, took a special interest in bats and wrote on the 'Whiskered bat (Myotis mystacinus) in captivity' in the Zoologist (1899) from a Cheshire specimen. However, he did not record the species during his 35 years of general natural history study in Hertfordshire (1907-1942) and Lloyd (47) makes no mention of the species. It is an illustration of how elusive some mammals can be, especially bats, that Oldham's favourite Hertfordshire haunt, Tring reservoirs, was probably then, as it is now, a stronghold for both whiskered and the almost identical Brandt's bat (Myotis brandtii). They must have flown over his gifted head on many summer evenings at what was then a lonely haunt of mixed reed beds and copses. (He also made studies of butterflies and molluscs.)*

*Newman (1896) found these bats rare in Epping, but Laver (1898) described them as common. Dobson (1999) has only had 1 modern record for Essex since 1980 and considers them as rare. Mickleburgh (1987) gives no additional Hertfordshire information for the LNHS area, but Childs (1998) recorded the first Bedfordshire information with a exceptional maternity roost in a house in Renhold of at least 300 bats.*

**Nationally the whiskered bat *Myotis mystacinus* is widespread, as in Europe and Palaearctic Asia, but our knowledge of the distribution of whiskered bats in Hertfordshire is limited to a few sites.**

All our efforts to record bat distribution in the 1970s and 1980s, which involved the examination and measurement of over 1,000 Hertfordshire bats, produced less than 15 whiskered bats (from Ashridge, Wilstone Reservoir, Wormleybury and Broxbournebury). This may explain why there were so few previous records.

Jenny Jones has reported active whiskered bats around the veteran trees of Brocket Park and along Mimmshall Brook. Although they have been located in hibernacula around Ware, Puckeridge, Potters Bar and Watford, the *HMBG* has found them in only 8% (4 sites in the county) of the known hibernation sites used by bats.

Ice houses and other winter sites will continue to produce bat records and there is great scope for their management. Access is only through licensed members of the *HMBG* and the locations of the 6 mines, 4 kilns, 1 air-raid shelter, 1 cellar, 1 well, 1 artificial cave and 17 ice houses where bat species of any type have been recorded remain confidential. Bat grilles have been installed in places and cave entrances are secured.

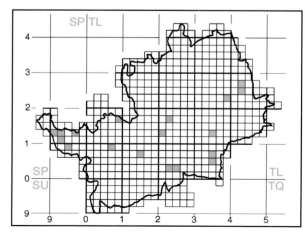

Other sites in the modern survey include the Champneys Estate, Tring Park, Aldbury, Ashridge, Hemel Hempstead, St.Albans, Water End, Gobions Wood, Watford,

Codicote, Ware, Hamels Park, Puckeridge and Furneux Pelham. The largest number of whiskered bats at any one site has been 3 at Tring and 3 at Wormley.

Briggs (1995) describes the valuable aid to modern bat surveys that electronic detectors provide and surprisingly found whiskered/Brandt's more often than Daubenton's bats in his east Hertfordshire study area, foraging at 7 locations.

**Right: part of a vast chalk and flint mine in south Hertfordshire where John Hutson (top) has fitted bat grilles for species like the whiskered bat** *M. mystacinus* **to hibernate.**

# Brandt's bat

## *Myotis brandtii*

There is no historical information for this species because whiskered and Brandt's bats were only described as being separate species in 1970, so that all previous records could be of either bat. The dentition is different and the male Brandt's bat has a club-shaped penis. Only at Wilstone Reservoir have we caught specimens and these were in association with the other species, including flying whiskered bats. We confirmed the records by use of photographs.

It is clearly a very local species in the county, but may be found increasingly in the future at the same water sites and old parklands where the few whiskered bats have been found. The first summer roost for the county was located in 1999.

**Upper right: the facial characteristics of Brandt's bat** *M. brandtii* **at Wilstone Reservoir near Tring.**

**Right: the distribution in Hertfordshire.**

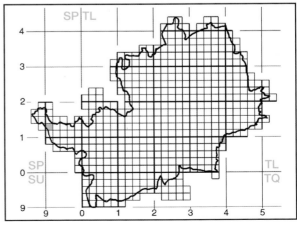

# Natterer's bat

## *Myotis nattereri*

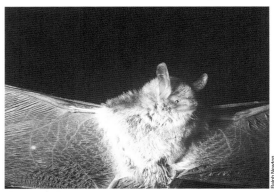

**Natterer's bat** *Myotis nattereri.*

*Museum material may take a long time to catalogue these days due to staff cuts and general shortage of funds in the area of research, but Lloyd (1941) records how a number of bats captured in April 1898 (listed by mistake as 1878 by Lloyd) from a hole in an old elm tree in Tring Park in order to study their parasites, were not identified and labelled until 1941. Amongst 6 brown long-eared bats and several pipistrelles, there were two Natterer's bats. This was the first and only spring roost for the species recorded in the county until the modern survey although Oldham found one in 1912 in Hockeridge Wood (only 100m inside the Buckinghamshire border) and Benson found another in Wendover in 1922.*

*It is of great interest that a mixed roost of the 3 species was thus found in an old elm in April, although it may have still been a winter hibernation site that they were all about to vacate. Lloyd (47) concluded that the species was possibly a 'scattered denizen of Hertfordshire'. He appears to have been right.*

*Anderson (1985) shows 4 locations for Bedfordshire and Childs records 10 for 1997 and a further 5 localities for that county in 1998. Mickleburgh (1987) and more recent records give at least 18 scattered locations in the Greater London area. Laver (1898) 'found them easily' in Essex, especially in Colchester where they hibernated under the castle, but 100 years later Dobson (1999) reports them as only 'fairly common, declining' in that county.*

**Widespread, local**

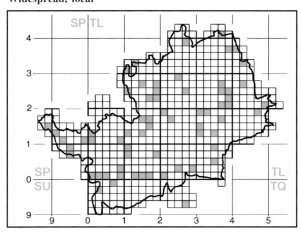

The hole in the old elm described above, located so conveniently next to Tring Museum, was an exceptional site and is a feature we miss in elms now. The loss of old elms over the last 30 years has greatly reduced the hollow roost sites available for bats. Despite the lack of previous records for the county, at the beginning of the present survey in the early 1970s, Tom Kittle photographed one he caught when ringing blackbirds going up to roost in the college house at Oaklands, St.Albans (1972). Terry Holder also reported one found dead in Tring (1974). We found after our first visits in January 1978 that this species hibernates annually in ice houses near Wormley in the Lea Valley and Hitchin in the northwest of Hertfordshire.

They also inhabit the brick crevices in ice houses close to the northwest Hertfordshire border in Bedfordshire and the only summer roost we surveyed was near Newport Pagnell, Buckinghamshire (via Alison Burton) where 3 and later 16 bats were measured from a colony of 22 in the roof of a farm shed under the ridge tiles along the warm apex.

Although there are now many known locations across the county, further colonies must remain undetected. They are elusive on the wing and it is possible to detect a distinct 'buzz' as they fly high around the tree tops.

They emerge about an hour after sunset from their roosts and are probably present in all the old parklands, farms and country estates with stands of old trees, especially where there are large ponds, lakes or rivers close-by. Over the last decade the *HMBG* records have transformed the survey and include 18 summer sites, with breeding in at least 11, and over 40 roosts or hibernation localities.

The *HMBG* is paying particular attention to the old barns favoured by Natterer's bats. They select cavities created by the mortise joints of the tie beams for roosting. Many barns have been converted to housing in recent years and if any conversions are planned, owners must by law determine if bats are present. A study by Patty Briggs (1995) showed that 15 of 40 barns examined (37.5%) had evidence of Natterer's bats. The Group can help with this essential first stage in the surveys. Barns and, to a lesser extent, stables make up a significant proportion of all the summer roosts. For hibernation they prefer undisturbed places such as ice houses, caves and mines. Unfortunately these sites become dangerous and are often closed up for safety reasons so the bats cannot use them or, even worse, they get trapped inside.

# Daubenton's bat

## *Myotis daubentonii*

*Oldham wrote a number of papers on bats and in his 1911 paper to the HNHS he gives a perfect description of this species in flight: 'The peculiar habits of Daubenton's or the water bat often cause it to be overlooked and it probably occurs throughout the county. It is certainly not uncommon in west Hertfordshire, and I have watched its unmistakable flight as it coursed to and fro like a ghostly sand martin, just above the surface of the water of the Grand Junction Canal at Grove Mill near Watford ('Zoologist,' 1907 p382); the Gade at Waterend, near Great Gaddesden, and in*

**Daubenton's bat** *Myotis daubentonii.*

Cassiobury Park; the Colne at Munden; pools at Aldenham Abbey; the village pond at Aldbury; and the Grand Junction Canal near Tring station.

'During the warmer months Daubenton's bat resorts to hollow trees, house roofs, rock crevices and the like, considerable numbers often sharing the same den. On leaving these retreats at dusk the bats apparently hunt for a short time at a moderate elevation and are then difficult to distinguish from other species, but as darkness closes in they settle down to the water. There is reason to believe that they spend the time until dawn flying, usually in the company of many of their own species, just above the surface, in pursuit of their insect prey.

'Quiet streams and tree-shaded ponds and lakes are its favourite haunts, but I have seen this bat flying over the incoming tide in a Norfolk estuary. In this country it is not active, so far as is known, during the winter months. It then retires to caves, old mine workings, and probably house roofs, where it spends the cold season in a state of hibernation. The specimen exhibited was found hanging by its toes to the wall of a chalk cavern at Abbots Langley on 4th February 1911. During hibernation Daubenton's bats, sometimes at any rate, abjure the social habits that obtain in summer, for I have also found them in other parts of England hibernating alone.'

Specimens of Nycteribia pedicularia parasites from this bat were exhibited by Oldham.

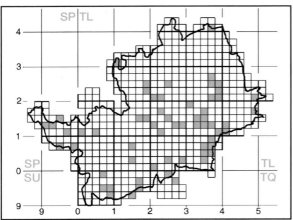

The distribution of Daubenton's bat *Myotis daubentoni* **reflects their presence along waterways and it may have increased in numbers as lakes and large ponds have been created in the county following gravel extraction.**

**Throughout, over aquatic habitats**

Lloyd (47) reported on Oldham's findings and noted that Dr.A.H.Foster had 'often seen it at Hitchin'. Bedfordshire has at least 6 locations known and London has a scattered distribution right across the area, especially on the outskirts. Laver (1898) found it 'not rare' and Dobson (1999) feels this to be a fairly common Essex bat, and, perhaps of all their bat species, has the best prospect of increasing its numbers in Essex in the 21st century.

Anderson (1987) only gave 6 localities for Bedfordshire and Childs (1997-8) gives a total of just 11 localities for that county, but Mickleburgh (1987) found it 'common' and scattered throughout the LNHS area.

Although the 'water bat' is commonly detected or seen in its distinctive flight at ponds, lakes, reservoirs, rivers and canal sites, very few summer roosts are known.

When handled, all 4 types of the *Myotis* genus, or the mouse-eared bats (whiskered, Brandt's, Natterer's and Daubenton's) have a similar light frame, broad wings and

80

distinctly mouse-like ears. But Daubenton's at once seem distinct because of their 'crew cut' hair, heavier neck, wide shoulders and very large feet. Like the other mouse-eared bats they have a distinctly thin inner ear, or tragus.

We found these bats at most open water sites in the early days of the modern survey and it is known that during a night they can fly up to 6km. However, they do not invariably turn up and despite past records from Digswell Park Lake, near Welwyn Garden City, two organised evening field meetings to survey the bats did not find any present. Open water may be important to them and excessive flora across a water surface can discourage regular use as a lake becomes overgrown. Our best views have been on clear, still, open water, but I watched one for some time on the River Mimram in Panshanger as it flew over the flowing, winding river where it narrowed by the old water pump, and caught the bat for confirmation of identity before I released it back into the air.

We have found that they tend to appear late when it is difficult to distinguish bat shapes, but the circling flight so close to the water surface, often in groups, is unmistakable and there is usually considerable reflected light on water surfaces, especially in Hertfordshire where a distant backdrop of artificial street lighting is now so widespread.

It is normal to find females lactating later than most species (well into mid-August) although their single young are born at the same time as other bats (end of June, beginning of July). Cold weather can, however, affect the pregnancies of all bats because they are able to control the development of their foetus to a certain extent so that births are delayed if necessary.

Whilst this species was found to be hibernating in all the ice houses we visited (plus Scott's Grotto at Ware) it was not until 1986 that the first summer roost was discovered. Work on the railway bridge at Stanborough, Welwyn Garden City, over the River Lea, meant that scaffolding was erected into the high, usually inaccessible arch and a colony of about 20 bats were seen.

I was able to visit and identify the species before they all moved to another arch. It was the first summer roost of any *Myotis* species found in the county, but in 1987 a second site turned up on the canal at Rickmansworth; we found that a colony was living under the canal bridge where the bats were being repeatedly caught and killed by a cat living at a private house. Patty Briggs described the help given to conserve this roost (in the low road bridge close-by) in the *HMBG* newsletter. A cat had found that by lying motionless in the branches of a willow overhanging the canal, it could catch the bats as they flew past or hovered around the tangle of foliage, securing them, with a swift swipe, in its claws.

How many it killed is unknown, but 80 plus were found dead or dying around the site before the reason for their high

**Daubenton's bat** *M. daubentonii* **in torpor in an ice house near Cheshunt.**

*Thanks to the use of the bat nets, we were able to see that this species easily takes off from the water surface and did so on many occasions during the surveys in the 1970s.*

*The Sunday Times, 23rd April 2000, illustrated the link between the food chain (of which the larger bats such as the serotine are a part) and the way livestock is now routinely dosed with avermectins to protect them from intestinal parasites. Chemical residues make cowpats, horse dung and sheep droppings, for example, uninhabitable for the insects which normally break these down into the soil. The larger bats depend heavily upon the capture of the bigger flying species, such as the dung beetles and cockchafers.*

The *Myotis* (mouse-eared) species of bats survive best in old, well-managed parkland with ponds and old trees such as the grounds of Hatfield House, central Hertfordshire.

*Photo: Aerofilms, Borehamwood.*

mortality was discovered. The cat is now living elsewhere and Patty's survey work here in 1988 located two more summer roosts: one in a drainage pipe under the railway bridge over the River Chess and another in the dry arch next to it, in a deep crevice of the bricks.

As at Stanborough, any repairs to brickwork must take into account the possible presence of bat roosts to avoid trapping them inside, whilst ensuring, of course, the future safety of the bridge. This area of south Hertfordshire, where the rivers Chess, Gade and Colne link with the Grand Union Canal, should produce much more valuable information on bats and is clearly a stronghold for Daubenton's. To have lost so many individuals to the one cat predator and yet still find them to be in good numbers over the waters here is an indication of a very old-established and healthy, if depleted, population.

A similar status must pertain in the Lea Valley where we have found the species at most of the water sites we were able to examine, including Church Lane, the New River at Wormley, Wormleybury Lake and Broxbournebury Pond.

The scattered distribution across central Hertfordshire shown on the map indicates a general presence in all suitable habitats, just as Oldham suspected 70 years ago. We handled over 30 in the 1970/80 survey work, had many injured ones to inspect due to the cat at Rickmansworth and noted them (at a safe distance without disturbance) as frequent ice house occupants. We discovered that all 3 of the Daubenton's bats caught on 5th July 1976 had the louse fly, or bat fly, *Nycteribia latreillei* in their fur and this is quite usual, rather like the highly specialised blood feeders found on house martins.

*HMBG* records show Daubenton's and Natterer's often associate in hibernation and they have been recorded from over 250 site visits. Twenty hibernation retreats are now known, with 2 bridge and 2 house roosts recorded. The largest numbers located in single hibernation sites are 13, 15 and 18. A roost of 197 was counted by Patty Briggs in 1992.

The flight of all bats is fascinating, but I particularly commend summer evenings by a large pond where these bats are flying for their displays of circling. One fisherman told us that he awoke with a start during the night when a 'water bat' picked up his float and carried it for a few metres before dropping it, enough to activate the alarm on his rod. Another fly fisherman caught one during a cast. It is the caddis flies, mayflies and other insects which hatch on the pond surface that they seek as they flutter around in wide circles just above the water.

In our bat research one mystery continued to bother us: despite the vast areas of water and insect life eagerly fed on by other species, we never found Daubenton's bats on the lagoons in Rye Meads. The same may be said for other apparently ideal sites; perhaps the lack of accommodation for roost sites nearby is the explanation.

The large feet of Daubenton's bat *M.daubentonii* have very sharp nails described as being like 'little fisherman's gaffs' by Clive Banks.

Daubenton's bat in torpor in an artificial grotto cave near Ware.

*Hatfield House and its estate (see opposite) are the jewel in the crown of Hertfordshire's heritage sites. The house and gardens are open to the public and the organic management practiced here ensures the most favourable environment possible for wildlife.*

A large roost of Daubenton's bats *M.daubentonii* near the bridge, centre left in this view of Rickmansworth, is referred to on page 81. The mixture of water and trees is ideal for the species.

*Photo: Aerofilms, Borehamwood.*

A note in the June 1965 report by the Rye Meads Bird Ringing Group describes the capture by mist nets of 4 species of bat: serotine, noctule, common pipistrelle and brown long-eared. All of the 56 bats were caught by throwing pebbles up to imitate insects and then long mist nets were swept overhead to capture the bats as they swooped. Of these, 46 were pipistrelles.

It is a difficult operation, but we refined the system for one person to control, as a hand net, and it is described in *Mammal Watching* (1981). They were designed by Clive Banks. (Arthur Whitaker describes catching several bats safely with a light fishing net, *Wild Life* **2**: 264-272 [1914] and J.G.Millais in *The Mammals of Great Britain & Ireland* **1**: 91 [1905] quotes W. Borrer's [1899] account of catching bats in a church with a butterfly net when they alighted on his white shirtsleeves.)

During the licensed study period in which we used these techniques, it was invaluable for survey work away from roosts as well as for sampling under bat exit flight paths before bat detectors became easily available. The bird ringers did not find Daubenton's at Rye Meads either and whilst there are some tall trees, the site is rather remote from older parkland habitats, buildings or bridges.

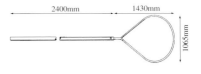

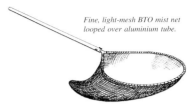

2400mm    1430mm    1065mm

Fine, light-mesh BTO mist net looped over aluminium tube.

See also pictures on pages 6 and 94.

# Serotine bat

## *Eptesicus serotinus*

*Lloyd (47) listed the first serotine recorded in the county, caught 12th June 1911 at Nortonbury, just north of Letchworth, by A.R.Thompson. (This area on the River Ivel, between two large open areas of water, is very similar to the Lea Valley habitats where most of the modern records have come from.) Fordham (1929) recorded the second specimen, shot by R.J.Buxton at the Manor of Groves, Sawbridgeworth 5th October 1927 (in what is, once again, an area near large expanses of water along Fiddlers Brook, above the River Stort valley.)*

*Barrett-Hamilton's 1910 observation of the species is worthy of note: 'The restricted distribution in Britain of a type of such wide range in the world is very remarkable, and must be regarded as one of the puzzles of British mammalogy, difficult or impossible to account for unless on the supposition that the species is either newly arrived or decreasing its range.'*

*Ralph Newton's modern observations at Stanstead Abbotts quoted below are very relevant to this point. Laver (1898) considered it a very rare bat in Essex with just 2 records and Fitter (1949) included only Welwyn (1937) amongst his few*

Ralph Newton

100 Km

**Most records of serotine bats have come from east Hertfordshire, especially the Lea Valley.**

**Declining**

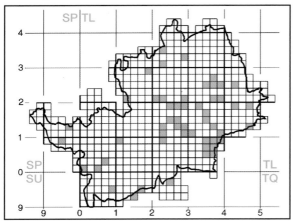

*records for the LNHS area, but Burton reported it to be 'a fairly widespread species occurring in many of the outer suburbs' and also makes the comment that it 'more frequently roosts in houses - the noctule bat prefers trees'. Mickleburgh (1987) shows scattered records for the whole LNHS area.*

*Dobson's (1999) review of the status in Essex reflects the experience in our county: a marked decline in the last 20 years as the food and feeding sites associated with cattle grazing outdoors in summer have diminished. He describes it, of all the mammal species found in Essex, to be the one which has shown the most marked decline over the last 25 years. Joan Childs has confirmed to me that the species is still not recorded for Bedfordshire (2001).*

*HMBG* surveys seem to continue to confirm the evidence that we are at the northerly limits of the range of this species which, within the county, has a central and eastern distribution very like that of the noctule bat. Hertfordshire had the only shared serotine and noctule house roost recorded in Britain and Ralph Newton wrote an account of his 10 year study of the site in the *Trans (1987)*.

From this fascinating study it is clear that the serotines present at the roost, unlike the more hardy noctules, are sensitive to prolonged cold, wet weather and are reluctant to emerge at such times, which may explain their lack of distribution in the north of Britain. The roost at Stanstead Abbotts showed greater use in May when both species were present. Neither hibernated there, but the serotines would stay until October whilst the noctules left to breed elsewhere in late May.

**Ralph Newton's photographs of serotine bats at the roof entrance in Stanstead Abbotts (above and opposite) were taken during his ten year study there. The roost was shared by noctule bats and one is shown opposite taking off from the narrow gap.**

As well as being sensitive to very windy, wet conditions, serotines are much quieter in their behaviour than the very boisterous noctules. When flying at sunset, both species fly high, rising to 30m, around tall, old trees typically and it is only the broader wings and reception of their distinct ultrasound on a detector which confirms the difference between the two. By dark, however, the steady patrol up the edge of pasture, particularly on the side of hedges sheltered from the wind where most of the insects concentrate, will give good views of the bats' silhouettes.

If Daubenton's bats are like little hydrofoils over water, serotines are like little jumbo jets, with steady, direct flight paths and intermittent soaring after initial high acrobatic feeding displays amongst the tree tops. We regularly watched and handled serotines which fed on the flying beetles around cattle at our most predictable site in Hoddesdon, at Admiral's Walk, by the large water-filled gravel pits.

Although they are very angry when handled and initially bite painfully, with gentle treatment serotines tame rapidly. Like all bats they become affectionate to humans if they have to be kept away from their normal roosts for any length of time because of injury, for example. Ten were seen by the Rye Meads ringing group regularly in the 1960s and they caught 5. We caught and measured over 40 in the Lea Valley after 1976, with a concentration around Rye Meads.

A juvenile found at the Node, Codicote (3rd August 1977) revealed the presence of a breeding colony somewhere here. *HMBG* have over 60 site records, including 17 bats in a single nursery roost, but numbers have declined: most of the observations are of individual bats, with a few of 2, 3 and 4 feeding together at dusk. Nursery roosts are still virtually unknown, but they have been present at 39 localities in the last decade and a major roost has been found since Ralph Newton's one in Stanstead Abbotts, at Chipperfield near Kings Langley.

**Noctule bat taking off from the roost shared with serotine bats. Measurement is shown on p270.**

# Noctule bat

### *Nyctalus noctula*

*Lloyd (47) considered noctules to be common and widely distributed with many to be seen at water sites such as the canal near Tring and over Elstree (Aldenham) Reservoir.*

*Of the 4 Tring specimens in the Nat His Mus, one male (20th March 1894) is albino and two were taken in hibernation (30th December 1895) in Tring Park. There is also one female from Tewin (8th July 1901) by C.H.Grant and W.E.Mayes.*

*Laver (1898) also considered it widespread in Essex, but Dobson (1999) has now found it to be scarce and in decline; just 4 recent records exist for Bedfordshire and there are a number of LNHS locations, especially to the north and west of central London. Burton (1974) found them widespread in the outer suburbs there and, as we later found near Luton, they often feed over rubbish tips.*

To complete my aeronautical similies, noctules, if not the Red Arrows display team of the bat world, are certainly one of the most dramatic and beautiful examples of 'fighter/dive-bomber' at sunset; common pipistrelles match the erratic crop-spraying techniques of the more exhibitionist light aircraft pilots and brown long-eared bats can resemble helicopters at times, especially when locating spiders on leaves of trees.

Despite their night-sounding name, noctules are usually the first bat we see as the swallows, swifts and martins take their final feeding flights of daylight, often over open water. They

**Noctule bats** *Nyctalus noctula* **at Hoddesdon.**

Noctule bats, local, usually near water.

Declining

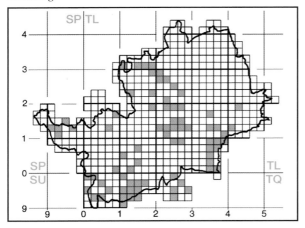

have long narrow wings which indicate an ability to travel long distances. Movements of up to 1,000 miles are known from Europe.

As well as the spring roost described in the section on serotines, Ralph Newton knew for 30 years a much more typical summer breeding roost at Broxbourne in an old beech tree. Whilst Daubenton's bats have been found to breed under almost constant daily traffic noise and vibrations (above them in Rickmansworth and below railways at two other sites), when the new A10 bypass at Hoddesdon began to be used the tree with the noctule roost inside could be felt to vibrate from the passing traffic and the noctules left, never to return. The road construction next to the site did not disturb them: it can only have been the effect of the ground movement on the tree that appeared to displace them after unbroken annual use for over 30 years. The long, narrow entrance hole to the roost had the telltale sign of bats in occupation: a dark staining to the bark at its base from urine and faeces over many generations initially building up inside the cavity and then spreading down the trunk. (In bird droppings, urine shows up as white and if this is not present beneath an apparently stained nest hole, it is likely that bats are present in tree hollows.)

The Rye Meads report (1965) indicated that over 30 noctules were regularly seen each summer and 4 were caught during April and May 1963. The bird ringers obtained one flea: *Ischnopsyllus elongatus* from a noctule on 27th April. Our modern records of noctules continue to confirm that good sites for this

Noctule roost in old beech tree at Broxbourne (see text) showing stain below entrance which is typical of bat roosts.

species also attract other types, including serotine. The River Lea in Brocket Park and at Stanborough are typical locations. Admiral's Walk in Hoddesdon has been a predictable place to see noctule and serotine bats and was a centre for rambles by Ralph Newton and, more recently, Jenny Jones. A hobby *Falco subbuteo* was seen hunting bats in the dark there during the 1999 walk, which featured pipistrelles, noctules and Daubenton's bats but, for the first time, no serotines.

*HMBG* records show noctules to have been present in over 78 localities and the 10 year study made of the unusual mixed serotine and noctule roost at Stanstead Abbotts is described in the *Trans* **28**: 3, 20-26 paper. Up to 8 have been seen in flight at Admiral's Walk feeding together at one time (Newton 1996). Old tree roosts are often only detected when it is too late and the tree has been felled. Jenny Jones considers the species to be in decline, but still finds them at Rye House Marsh.

# Leisler's bat
## *Nyctalus leisleri*

*There are no specimens of Leisler's bats for Hertfordshire in the Nat His Mus and only 1 record for the county prior to the modern survey; they were not mentioned in Lloyd (47).*

*There are no records for Bedfordshire (Childs 2001); a few scattered records for the London area, where Burton (1974) noted that they were recorded from 'Kew and Walton-on-Thames among other places'; and Laver (1898) made no reference to them in Essex. The modern Essex survey does, however, like London, show a scattered distribution, but Dobson (1999) describes them as 'scarce, declining.'*

On 23rd September 1972 I noticed a bat amongst leaf debris in a shop doorway in the centre of Welwyn Garden City. It turned out to be a female Leisler's with an irreparable wing injury, but she survived and responded to our voices with an eager chatter at feeding times.

For the first time I experienced how a bat tames almost overnight, whereas few other types of mammal, unless reared from before their eyes open or soon after, settle easily under human rescue and care. They are a remarkable group of animals and it is also surprising that this species, very local in Britain, replaces the noctule bat *N. noctula* in Ireland. The latter species is well able to fly across the Irish Sea, but remains absent.

In the Hertfordshire survey we have found that Leisler's, which are the smaller closest relative of the noctule in Britain, are present in at least 25 localities and many have been handled and measured. Four nursery colonies have also been recorded so far and the largest roost counts have been 11, 16, 17, 20, 30 and 41. They have also been found in bat boxes put up on the Hatfield Estate by Reg Chapman and Patty Briggs. However, the species must still be considered as rare in the county.

Nationally, one of these bats has been known to move 157 miles from where it was found 4 years previously. Their wings have the same thin shape for long distance flight as noctules. I have watched both species near where the injured bat described earlier was found, flying together by Digswell Lake and at a summer roost reported at Widford, near Much Hadham in 1976. At Widford, the Leisler's moved their house roost a short distance after initially staying in an eight year old house cavity wall and a loft, southwest facing. We saw 30 emerge during a visit (8th July 1976) and we caught

**Local, declining**

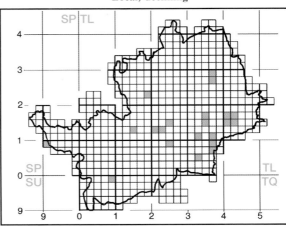

and measured 15 of them. They flew straight across from the houses to feed over the River Ash valley. The second house that they moved to was in the same road. Mobility of summer colonies has also been found in Essex (Dobson, 1999).

Individual bats were found in Stagenhoe, in the parish of St.Paul's Walden, where one emerged from a hidden site behind a chimney when we were examining a brown long-eared *P. auritus* and pipistrelle *P. pipistrellus* roost in parts of an old farm roof (31st July 1977), and at Barnfield Close in Hoddesdon where a juvenile was found clinging to a house wall after a night of heavy rain. It was given food and returned when fully active to the roost in the apex of the house, which was also shared by pipistrelles.

We have, therefore, locations for these bats over a wide area. They seem to like cavity walls or cavities inside roof spaces rather than open sites.

The lone Stagenhoe Leisler's bat only came out because it was angry at having my torch light shone in its face: I had no

Hertfordshire is something of a stronghold for Leisler's bats and they have been recorded flying with noctule bats over Digswell Lake near Welwyn viaduct (below). Robin Cole's other Mimram aerial views show the bat habitats around Tewin Bury Farm and Warrengate Farm.

idea a bat was there until it walked out onto the brickwork. This would suggest that they are difficult to detect because they prefer to hide away even within a roost where other bats are clustered very obviously in full view.

Jenny Jones has 2 recent east Hertfordshire reports: an established roost recorded by Anne Rowe in Buntingford and a house roost recorded by Roger Havard at Hammond Street, near Cheshunt.

**Insects over water are vital for bats and where trees and pasture combine with a clean chalk stream as at Archer's Green on the Mimram (left) or dense foliage surrounds large ponds and lakes, as at Gobions near Brookmans Park, bats find food in abundance.**

# Common pipistrelle bat

## *Pipistrellus pipistrellus*

**The pipistrelle bat** *Pipistrellus pipistrellus* **is our most familiar and widespread bat, now distinguished by ultrasound into two types (see text).**

*Lloyd (47) found Hertfordshire pipistrelles to be common and widely distributed. He makes reference to several preserved at Tring from the same hole roost in an old elm close to the Museum already referred to (April 1898) and the Nat His Mus has 6 Hertfordshire flat specimens all from Tring: 4 on 6th October 1908; 1 on 4th November 1920; and 1 on 28th July 1948 in the Museum grounds.*

*Laver (1898) found them abundant in Essex: 'Probably the commonest of the order' and Dobson still finds that this is true, although numbers are declining. He splits the species into two forms, the 46kHz and the 55kHz types and during our handling of hundreds of pipistrelles in the 1970s and 1980s we also felt there to be more than one type. The split is based on the two distinct ultrasounds shown on bat detectors which give two 'phonotypes'. DNA evidence also shows that there are two species.*

*Childs (1987 and 1988) also distinguishes the two forms and adds 19 sites to the widespread distribution in Bedfordshire recorded by Anderson (1985). Mickleburgh (1987) shows a widespread 'abundance' for the LNHS area, just as Burton (1974) had found, particularly to the north and west of the capital.*

*Clive Herbert and Alexandra Lang have described bat box use locally: see Herbert (1992) and Lang (1994), with*

*details of occupancy, numbers used, elevation and design.*
*Until 1992 only pipistrelles had been found in the boxes at*
*Oak Hill Nature Reserve, but 8 brown long-eared bats were*
*found together in one during August of that year.*

The pipistrelle is found in town and country and in many ways prospers from human habitation, especially in the river valleys where feeding sites are close to roosts. During our survey work this species so dominated the catch one night at Rye Meads (7th August 1976) that we had to give up at 69 and did not get home until 3.00am after taking the measurements and releasing the bats.

After emerging as one of the first active bats just after sunset from March to November, their rapid fluttering flight must be familiar to everybody. They settle to regular flight paths on sheltered sides of hedges, woods and banks. The Rye Meads ringing group reported them in large numbers in 1965 and descibed them as: 'Impossible to count; 40 were caught 12th April to 1st November; of these, 17 were recorded male and 23 female'.

They found females to be slightly heavier over this range at 5.7g compared with 5.1g for the males, but this would have covered the period of pregnancy, giving a bias as the foetus weight became significant. Rye Meads is the perfect venue for the species and we found a breeding roost in a maisonette (south facing) in Rye Road (7th September 1978), but there were odd nights when the expected appearance of pipistrelles at such a site did not materialise.

In the drought of 1976, on 26th June, we had just such an evening when we only caught one and noted the almost total absence of any bat species. This may have been due to abundant food being caught in previous evenings and feeding delayed to later in the night. Perhaps the bats just move to a favourite new breeding roost on such occasions, where all the bats would be concentrated around their new premises like bees round a new hive, rather than feeding out in the lagoon sites.

The mystery of how bats go from winter hibernation roosts to spring sites, then split up into separate sex breeding roosts and back to other roosts later, is still largely unexplained. Clearly all members of a colony seem to move at about the same time and we have house owners who note the excited activity of bats as they arrive, fly up to and flitter around tiny roost access points, pattering audibly onto windows, walls and tiles.

Blank nights have also occured at previously ideal sites in

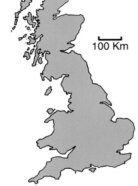

100 Km

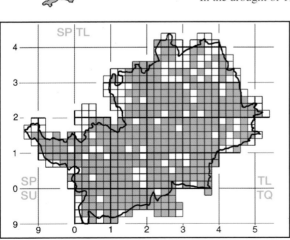

**Pipistrelles are common throughout the county.**

August in what seem like perfect hot and still weather conditions. Again, changes of roost site and temporary lack of activity in one place may be explanations. We devoted a paper to the work on summer roosts of pipistrelles in the county (1975-1980) in the *Trans* **28**:6, 59-62, (1982), when 51 of their roosts had been visited. Before all bats were protected by law, much of our work was involved in persuading householders who had complained to their local Environmental Health Department about bats in their homes to keep them. Complaints usually commenced in June when the female bats separated to form single-sex breeding colonies and these house visits peaked July to August.

This work continues with a very well organised *HMBG* helpline which responds to over 400 calls a year. For the up-to-date helpline telephone number readers should refer to current e-mail addresses on websites or seek *HBRC* advice via County Hall.

In places the colonies are very difficult to monitor because they move from roof to roof along rows of houses and then back again. Just as we found that the Leisler's bats moved from house to house in Waterford, much the same can be said of the pipistrelles there.

Ralph Newton's studies of pipistrelle bats at Hoddesdon in the Lea Valley. The largest counts of this species have been made here (see text).

The young leave their droppings more obviously outside the roosts as they learn to fly and may get inside the loft of a house from the preferred cavity wall and even end up downstairs occasionally. They get into cavity walls through gaps often left high in brickwork, especially under window sills or wooden panels. One Hertford loft had been converted into a photographic darkroom and I found that over 20 unfortunate juveniles, including one lactating female (presumably attracted by the calls of its young), had fallen into a wall-mounted sink below the roost and died, unable to climb up the smooth sides. A simple cover was fitted and the gap which allowed the bats to emerge into the loft from the brickwork was then sealed up.

As long as the exit from a cavity wall to the exterior is retained, the bats will return to such a site year after year. They always benefit from the warmth generated by sunlight on the bricks.

In our 1982 summary of roosts, a 12 year-old house in Ware was the most recently built property occupied and a 5 year-old bungalow had over 100 pipistrelles living under hanging tiles on both gable ends. Of the older properties, a roost of 60 in a 43 year-old house in Broxbourne and 30 in a 70 year-old house in Wormley were both found in new, flat-roof cavities of extensions only 3 and 2 years old respectively. Bats like clean draught-free places in which to live and raise a family. Most roosts were just below roof level, about 5-6m high, a few 2.5-3m and several higher with one at the top of a three-storey town house in Hoddesdon, 11m from the ground. I found that climbing a ladder to inspect this site concentrated my mind wonderfully.

Juvenile pipistrelle bat that was found in the roof of John McLusky's Datchworth home during building repairs. A safe exit to this breeding roost was left on completion of the work.

Clive banks involved with 'high church' pipistrelle survey work in Much Hadham.

Pipistrelle bats colonise modern houses, including all three of these in Hertford (above) as well as older cottages.

Below, pipistrelle bat roost at Wormley West End.

Although the female nursery roost is usually separate, we found a roost in Presdale Drive, Ware, with many lactating females, juveniles and adult males using the same access entrance (25th July 1978). At a detached house near Dunstable in Bedfordshire, there were three roosts in different sides of the same dwelling: south side, under hanging tiles, lactating females and juveniles; west side females and juveniles; north side only males. In cold summers the females sought the warmest possible parts of the walls or tiles.

Our paper was the first written material of any substance on the species in the *Trans* and it is a pity that very often the most common animals are ignored just because they are so familiar. To be (a) a flying mammal, (b) live in our climate, (c) an insect eater in modern Britain - yet still be numerous, deserves recognition, not neglect. Only in the dense alien conifer plantations established as a dreadful insult to our old woodland habitats this century do you find that pipistrelles (and all other bats) are rare or absent. Any you do see appear to be rapidly passing by, in a hurry to be somewhere else.

Of the more than 1,000 pipistrelles we recorded, some of the sites are worthy of particular note: a Todds Green roost (34 on 2nd August 1978) had been known for 19 years in the same roof; a Wormley West End boarded wall of a 300 year old cottage (3 caught 21st September 1978) was known to have been occupied for at least 16 years; 85 females flew from a Bunyan Close house in Pirton (6th August 1980) between 9.18pm and 9.47pm; 60 bats emerged in rapid succession through a 20mm gap in a bungalow wall, Buntingford (23rd June 1976); a roost of 30 left a house in Broxbourne on 5th September 1978, but when the now silent roost was visited on 8th September 1978, several bats flew past the entrance and one stopped, went inside and then left 5 minutes later with no other activity; mites and fleas were collected at various sites; at Rye Meads we recorded a flea *Ischnopsyllus octactenus* on 27th April 1963.

*HMBG* now have over 436 different site records listed, which represents a colossal workload for one species, shared by many people. Locations are visited several times in certain cases and the bats are widespread across the county. Thirty-eight roosts include over 100 bats and 11 have contained 300 or more.

There were 709 identified 55kHz brown pipistrelles, all roosting together at a site in Stanstead Abbotts and Jenny Jones holds the record for counting the largest total of 733 at a Broxbourne nursery roost in 1995. The Lea Valley still supports the largest numbers of pipistrelles and a roof not far from the regularly visited Admiral's Walk site included 400 bats in 1999.

# Nathusius' pipistrelle bat

## *Pipistrellus nathusii*

*There have been no previous records for Hertfordshire and our specimen was only the second individual bat of this species ever to be found in the British Isles. Because it was a bat not a bird, the occasion passed with little comment, but we published a paper on the event which took place on 17th August 1978 in the* Trans **29**:1, 15-18, (1983).

During the first decade of our survey work we took two RSPB wardens to Wormleybury to show them how we caught bats in flight. I stood in a gap in mature trees next to the lake and as one pipistrelle chased another I brought the net up between them and the second one fluttered into the mist net. 'A pipistrelle;' I said as the bat sank its teeth into the skin between my fingers 'they never draw blood', and blood dripped down my hand.

The bat was extremely angry which seems understandable after the interruption it had experienced during the mating season: it was a warm August evening ideal for bat courtship. I began to think this was not an ordinary pipistrelle and then looked for the post-calcarial lobe which, in a small bat, tells you at once in this country that it can only be a 'pip'. There was the lobe, but the bat seemed larger and stronger than most.

Later we examined the bat in detail and the truth began to dawn that it was a Nathusius' pipistrelle. Thanks to the help of Daphne Hills and Ian Bishop in the Mammal Section, I took the live bat to the *Nat His Mus* to confirm identification with the bat specialist there, John Hill. Amongst amusement on behalf of the staff that a live specimen actually made it into (and out of) the Museum, the identity was confirmed. The lower incisors are the best guide, but there are several other points, reproduced in our *Trans* paper. The bat was released alive at Wormleybury and from its behaviour there may be a resident colony. Dobson (1999) records the one Essex record from White Roding, near the Lea Valley (1985) and reports Hutson's record of this pipistrelle having now been identified on about 70 occasions in Britain, with 2 breeding colonies confirmed in 1997.

The Lea Valley is an important route for migration of birds and the species may have followed the sequence of

**Nathusius' pipistrelle bat is new to the county from 1978.**

**Range expanding**

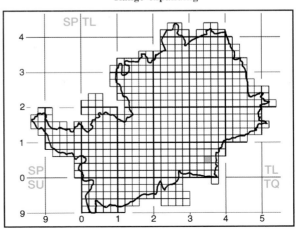

**Nathusius' pipistrelle bat during examination prior to release at Wormleybury.**

reservoirs and lakes, along a river and canal system north of the Thames in much the same way as birds do each year. Their arrival may also be linked with global warming. The previous specimen had been a coastal vagrant in Dorset, in a roost with other bats. It may be that ours, too, was alone, but chasing another *P. pipistrellus* in aggression.

The Nathusius had a less repetitive alarm squeak than a common pipistrelle; was more boisterous in the hand; was able to pierce the skin with a bite; had much larger buccal glands (in either side of the cheeks, visible when the mouth is wide open); had hair with a light tinge at the hair tips; had a longer 3rd digit, the third phalange of which folds downwards at an angle when at rest; its teeth were as in Saint-Girous (1973); its thumb is shown in A.Toschi & B.Lanza (1959); the proportion of its 5th digit to forearm length was about 130%.

Saint-Girous (1973) mentions that it is a difficult species to catch for examination and it is to be hoped that future evidence of these bats not only being present, but breeding here, will be found. They have been recorded on ships and oil and gas platforms in the North Sea. The increase in Dutch records also indicates an expansion of range. Movements of up to 1,600km have been recorded and they have now been added to the British species list.

*(see caption opposite)*

100 Km

# Barbastelle bat
## Barbastella barbastellus

*Although there have been no recent specimens, four have been found in the county this century and although only a few are ever located nationally each year, it has again been detected in the modern survey. The males are largely solitary and have a low, fluttering flight, mostly in wooded river valleys, but the species does form small female breeding colonies. They appear early, feed on flies over water and continental specimens marked with rings have lived for over 18 years. In Britain there have been only two recent breeding colonies recorded.*

*Our nearest specimen in the last 30 years was from Old Warden, Bedfordshire where one was found dead on the ground by trees, 16th May 1976. There are seven scattered LNHS localities recorded up to 1968 and Mickleburgh (1987) was unable to report further news of the species. Laver (1898) described one from Epping Forest (1843). Dobson (1999) gives a record for the Essex survey 1980-1999: 1 roosting at Finchingfield in August 1992.*

*Our only Hertfordshire records were 1 male at Willian (just south of Letchworth), by A.R.Thompson, 21st September 1920, preserved with skull and measurements in the Nat His Mus; another, 25th August 1922, by E.Sharpe at Oughtonhead, near Hitchin, which is preserved in N Herts Mus along with another from the Hitchin Mus Coll. lacking* data; Oldham found 2 early in the century in the mature woodland of Frithsden Beeches, Berkhamsted Common, in 1908 and 1909. He wrote in Trans **17**: 4, 295 (1923) of the Thompson specimen: 'The bat was picked up at 4pm, alive and apparently uninjured, with its wings folded, in the middle of a dusty road. It lived for a week and was then sent to the British Museum. On 6th September 1908 I took a female that was sleeping behind a piece of loose bark on a beech tree at Frithsden. On 27th June 1909, I found another barbastelle under the same circumstances in the same clump of beeches'.

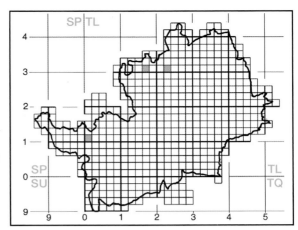

**Barbestelle bat** *Barbestella barbestellus.*

**Very rare**

**Opposite: detail of the two colour forms described from the watercolour by George Lodge in Millais (1906). The species was first described by Daubenton.**

Oldham studied the first of these rare bats in captivity, described its flight, its voice, including 'a curious subdued buzzing' and its appetite for house flies taken in his room. The species has been described feeding on flies over a mill pond and it is worth noting that there is just such a site at Oughtonhead.

Old woodland and river valley sites are clearly the most likely places for the species and a modern extensive survey of possible roosts in Frithsden Beeches would be worthwhile. They have been identified on detectors: in Surrey in their wet woods and in Norfolk along very wide woodland rides.

# Brown long-eared bat

## *Plecotus auritus*

Lloyd (47) described this species as being common and widely distributed, with several preserved from Tring Park in April and May 1898 and records them from across the county, including one for Bushey Heath 'where Wilson caught one in a butterfly net in August 1935'.

There are 4 Nat His Mus, Tring and Boxmoor specimens: 1st May 1895, 2nd February 1897, 15th September 1897, and 19th July 1921, all males; two female Hitchin specimens in N Herts Mus in 1943 and 16th August 1968. Laver (1898) described them in Essex as 'very common in the Colchester district and

usually have their haunts in buildings, although it has been brought to me from hollow trees....' He also gives Doubleday's 1843 record for the species in Epping.

Dobson (1999) shows wide distribution in modern Essex and describes the successful use of 'bat-bricks' fixed in

100 Km

*wartime bunkers with the entrances partially blocked, at Coggeshell.*

*The bats are found in torpor in ice houses during winter in both east and north Hertfordshire and are recorded across Bedfordshire, Essex and the LNHS area, but they are not as common in Central London as one might expect, perhaps from the lack of areas with old trees that have high moth populations.*

*In analysis of tawny owl pellets from Kensington Gardens I have found noctule and pipistrelle skulls, but no remains of brown long-eared bats. Only the rural areas of London figured in Burton (1974) and he found the bat to be 'fairly widespread, but nowhere common'.*

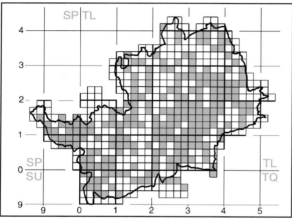

**Although brown long-eared bats** *Plecotus auritus* **are recorded throughout the county they are not as numerous as pipistrelles.**

I have come to think of our two most common bats, the pipistrelle and the brown long-eared as the house martin and swallow of the flying mammal world. Martins prefer the brick eaves of human habitations and extend them outwards by the construction of their own cavity wall nests and pipistrelles eagerly seek out any gap between wood and bricks to get inside cavity walls at the warm apex of a roof. Swallows usually only breed inside buildings, up in the eaves along wooden beams, and brown long-eared bats also like to cluster and have their young amongst the warm roof beams.

All 4 species benefit from human structures and the risk of such close proximity to a large territorial primate has reaped dividends due to a mixture of ignorance, tolerance and pleasure in their company on the part of the hosts. Timber treatments used to be lethal to them, but the introduction of non-toxic alternatives has saved thousands, if not millions, of bats in modern Britain.

Although bats do not make nests, clearly the protection and warmth is appreciated by all the species which share our houses. We should not underestimate the extra safety from predators afforded by a building when compared with tree hollows, for example, and although we more often see swallows courageously mobbing a cat or a magpie outside their nest site than we see bats evading cats or owls at night, both events are common. The high cluster position of brown long-eared bats when in torpor must also reduce the risk of attack by rats or mice in the same roof space. Tawny owls and squirrels are typical dangers for bats roosting in hollow trees.

Brown long-eared bats have much appeal to humans because of their rather dormouse-like black tinged faces around the eyes and the spectacular ears. At rest the ears are folded under the wings to leave each tragus, or inner ear, showing clearly. Although they tend to leave their roosts late on clear, light nights, you can watch them feeding into the tree canopy where their highly sensitive echolocation allows them to capture spiders and other invertebrates from the foliage.

In Tewin Orchard, where I can watch them regularly in summer, they favour the old Bramley apple trees and large oaks when first hunting. As the stone crops ripen they, too become a focus of attention. I noticed a number of bats fussing round the top fruits some years ago and I climbed up a ladder to inspect the plums. Nearly all were being subjected to insect attack and as well as the usual earwigs and flies, both wasps and bees were feeding or resting overnight inside the damaged skins. It made me realise how great the loss of food is to all kinds of wildlife occurs when orchards are grubbed up.

Wild plums and wilding apples are relatively common in Hertfordshire hedgerows and clearly help concentrate insect prey for bats. Under their feeding perches in the barn at Tewin Orchard they leave the remains of moths and the yellow underwings of *Noctua pronuba* are particularly noticeable. Michael Thompson, writing in the June 1983 *Mamm Soc* newsletter found moths to make up over 40% of their diet, with beetles, caddis flies, flies, spiders, bugs and earwigs also taken to a feeding perch. At one such perch in 1980 he recorded 806 moths retrieved of 51 different species, one of which was a new Yorkshire record, and a rarity, the figure of eighty *Tethea ocularis*. Large yellow underwings made up 33% of the total, followed by silver Y *Autographa gamma*, although by September, when the large yellow underwings ceased to be present, silver Y made up 57.5%.

(It is remarkable that some species of bats may eat over half their weight in one night: between 1,500 and 3,000 prey items. In human terms that would mean consuming about 12.7 kilograms of food three times a day.)

Long-eared bats are struck down by vehicles at times and I found my first dead specimen (with a broken wing) in Hanyards Lane, Cuffley on 31st March 1973. It may well have been that after hibernation it was not as strong as usual and was slow on the wing, but their feeding habit of diving down to prey which may have been weakened from earlier contact with vehicles, can bring about their own downfall.

In the early bat survey work we regularly visited a roost in Stagenhoe Home Farm at St Paul's Walden, Hitchin. During measurement we found 4 banded by Dr.R.Stebbings on a previous visit to the roost in 1972, one of which was by then 9 years old. This old roof roost was shared by pipistrelles in one wall and a Leisler's (referred to earlier) was found by shining a torch behind the chimney breast.

A colony of 24 of these bats in Orchard Road, Tewin (10th August 1978) included one with a repaired wing tip. (We

Brown long-eared bat in flight.

A roost cluster of brown long-eared bats in Ashridge where they have been found in a relatively modern house roof as well as in the Monument Cottage (below).

Mike Reed at Tewin Orchard. Brown long-eared bats are one of the few species to be caught in mist nest by bird ringers.

A diary sketch of an ice house near Wormley where bats hibernate.

have also found successful natural wing membrane damage recovery like this in a serotine at Admiral's Walk and pipistrelles at Rye Meads. One had a severe scar which narrowed one wing, but apparently had little or no effect on its successful flight.) The left wing of a female brown long-eared bat in a colony of over 18 in a house roof at Ringshall, Ashridge had no pigment and another also lacked any in each wing tip. We found the species in Waterford Church (21st October 1977), but farms and private houses are more typical sites with up to 20 and 30 bats recorded.

The little Coldharbour Cottage at Ashridge Monument includes a roost of about 20 in the little loft and the stable at Astonbury has produced a few including two found dead (26th May 1977) by Daphne Coates under their roof exit.

Whether in old or new properties, clean roof space seems to be the ideal, although the very feeding activity of the occupants themselves may contribute to the lack of spiders.

Because of their highly sensitive echolocation it is difficult to capture this species as it emerges from a roost, but bird ringers sometimes find them in their standing mist nets at night. Tom Kittle reported one from his nets at Kimpton Mill (27th July 1978) plus an adult noctule at Fowlmere, Cambridgeshire (29th July 1978) and a juvenile noctule (19th August 1978). The reason for this apparent contradiction is not that the bats failed to detect the net, but were attracted to the moths on or in the nets. By landing on the fine mesh to catch the moth they can become entangled themselves. One was caught by ringers in their bat survey at Rye Meads (28th April 1963) near tall trees.

The *HMBG* records now number over 200 sites and the larger roosts include 9 which had between 20 and 25 bats present, with one of 30 and another of 40. There have so far been 21 nursery roosts identified.

A vagrant big brown bat *Eptesicus fuscus* from North America turned up in a timber yard at Bishop's Stortford and was kept, after quarantine, by Roger Harvard. The location suggests that it arrived in imported wood.

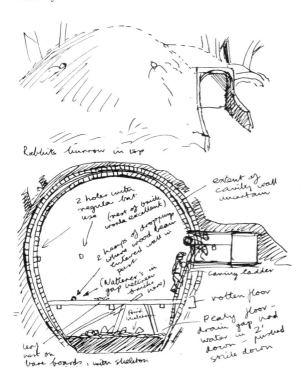

# Rabbit
## *Oryctolagus cuniculus*

*Lloyd (47) described rabbits as common but 'nowhere in such numbers as to constitute it a pest as in some parts of Britain'. A keeper told me how in pre-myxomatosis days fields around Welwyn seemed to move with so many rabbits that when his dog chased one to earth, he reached in and pulled 6 out from a blind tunnel, one at a time, pressed up against each other. He felt that anyone growing up since 1953, when the rabbit population was very low due to myxomatosis, would have no idea of the large numbers present or the damage to crops suffered prior to that date. (He had, of course been employed to spend much of his life killing the main predators of rabbits: foxes, stoats and weasels.) The 1990s have, however, seen a recovery to what must approach the pre-myxomatosis numbers.*

*W.H.Fordham (see p274) noted on 24th January 1943 how wartime control had reduced their numbers. He gave the figures for rabbits killed in the Odsey district:*

| | | | |
|---|---|---|---|
| **1937** | 38,493 | **1938** | 39,706 |
| **1939** | 40,727 | **1940** | 41,491 |
| **1941** | 42,300 | **1942** | 100 |

*The shortages of fresh meat in wartime obviously saw a rapid change to natural resources. 'The reduction in the area under grass is going to shorten the breeding season considerably and so help control', Fordham had also predicted earlier. H.A.Course later reported from nearby Royston: 'Though reduced in numbers by gassing and extra killing for food during the late war, (rabbits are) still common in the Royston district.'*

*Rabbits have been mentioned in early copies of the Trans, but more as a by-product, as it were, of the accounts: a jackdaw nest 'found 1 yard down a rabbit hole in 1912 at Baldock' (very unusual away from coastal areas in a well-wooded district); during exceptional floods in the county in 1894, when 'a few pigs and sheep escaped from the flooded meadows by swimming, but one sheep and a large number of rabbits belonging to Mr Blathwayt of Frogmore House, near Watford were drowned'. (This suggests enclosed farming of rabbits on a large scale: free ones would have swum to safety.)*

*Lord Ebury of Moor Park wrote on 11th February 1887 that two of his pet fox terriers had twice become trapped in hollow trees chasing rabbits up into the upper branches.*

**Rabbits are found in most habitats throughout the county.**

**Increasing**

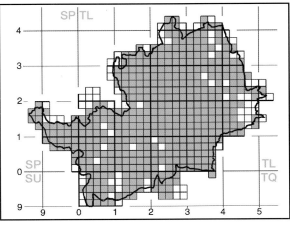

**Ken Leah entering his ferrets into rabbit burrows on farm land near Royston.**

*Sir Henry Chauncy, in 'The Historical Antiquities of Hertfordshire' (1700) wrote of Edward Wingate, owner of Lockleys, near Welwyn village:*
*'He made a fair Warren to this Seat, stocked it with a choice Breed of Rabbits, all silver haired, and planted it with great Store of excellent Walnut trees; and in the Front of his House, raised a pleasant Orchard, set with the best and rarest Fruit Trees, where several Cuts are made, through which the Mimeram passes in several Streams, stored with fair Trouts and other Fish, for the Provision of his Table.'*

*(Old jackdaw nest material had fallen to block the exit and an axe had to be used to extricate them.)*

One thinks of rabbits as very much restricted to ground level, but they have often been found high up inside hollow trees by ferreters and I have frequently watched them eating on top of quite tall coppiced stools and fallen trees. Droppings indicate that such vantage points are regularly visited. I despair of stopping the rabbits barking our 70 year old Bramley apple trees at Tewin Orchard where they climb up as much as 2m onto the old boughs and strip the bark, between January and April especially.

Despite the neglect of writers in the past, rabbits were clearly an integral part of the countryside economy: a destructive cause of reduced crop yields to the farmer, but a valuable source of food, finance and sport to other local people. Our county has many names which indicate the ancient farming of rabbits in warrens and Sheail (1971) illustrates the distribution of place names containing the word 'warren'. He marks 20 for Hertfordshire, most of them in the once much more populated eastern half.

Curiously, the same book shows neither wild rabbits or warrens in use by the 1790s on a map compiled from Board of Agriculture reports. Gregory King's 1690 animal population for Britain is shown which put rabbits second only to sheep in abundance. Sheail also quotes: 'Many hornbeams on Lord Lytton's estate in Knebworth, Hertfordshire, were ruined (by bark stripping by rabbits) in this way in heavy snows...'.

Rackham (1986) refers to Sheail and his reference to the first rabbits introduced here as being 'delicate and needed cherishing in this climate'. At first it could not dig its own burrow; Sheail records amongst the tools used in Henry VIII's warren a great auger 'to make and bore cony holes'. Earthworks were made to encourage burrowing'. This reference to 'delicate first stock' sounds more like talking up the price to me: rather like the hype over huge profits to be made from ostrich farming when the idea first became widely promoted.

It would be difficult to repeat the introduction of rabbits of Mediterranean stock to see if the transfer caused such a shock to the system, but our climate is much the same as the 12th century when the first large-scale introductions were made and it was one thing to prepare the new warrens for immediate use and quite another to need to do this because the newcomers were so 'feeble'. I have seen small portable augers used to trace subterranean tunnels and these would be useful when cropping the rabbits.

The Hexton book 'A Parish Survey' (1936) gives an insight into the abundance of rabbits at that time: 'They are so prolific that they have to be kept in check by an official rabbit catcher. Even then, hundreds may be seen during a short walk on a summer evening.'

*Looking back through my reports in the Trans I find I tended to commit the same crimes of omission as my forebears: whilst a rare bat receives a special mention and a separate paper, rabbits are so common that they hardly warrant a word in the reports. My daily diary has, however, kept a note of the rise and intermittent falls in their populations since the 1960s in Tewin and aspects of their behaviour are noted. They cause more loss of trees and damage to poultry practices than any other species. Tree protectors are pushed up and fences have holes forced under them which allow carnivores access to the birds. During wet, winter weather a run carefully re-sown the previous summer may overnight have its grass stripped off by rabbits, leaving a mud bath for the hens.*

*The Nat His Mus Coll. reflects the same disinterest with only 2 specimens for Hertfordshire, neither of which is like an average run-of-the-warren rabbit: a sandy-coloured specimen from Albury, Tring, (G.H.E.Hopkins) 27th July 1950, and a large cross between wild and domestic, 23rd November 1921. When I last went through the skins there was not one skin of a typical Hertfordshire rabbit, although there are in our local museums.*

*Laver (1898) wrote: 'This destructive creature is very common in all parts of Essex, and little need be said about it.' Dobson (1999) reflects our experience and describes them as 'abundant, increasing' in modern Essex. Anderson (1985) reported that they were the most common species recorded in Bedfordshire and had been found in 90% of tetrads. There are many LNHS records from the Hertfordshire part of their distribution circle: Gold (1974, 1975 and 1976), Hall (1978) and Cotton (1980). Burton (1974) had found them to be widespread in the outer suburbs, larger parks and commons in London.*

*Rabbits were certainly an inspiration for Beatrix Potter, who began her world-famous stories at Camfield Place, near Essendon, central Hertfordshire, with exceptional sketches of the species from life. Her grandfather, Edmund Potter MP, built the house (later the home of the authoress Barbara Cartland) and the door in the wall is shown in Leslie Linder's 'A History of Beatrix Potter', p94 (1971), and part of the door appears in 'The Tale of Peter Rabbit', p44, (1901).*

Top: **Adult rabbit.**

Centre: **Juvenile rabbits outside a burrow.**

Bottom: **Characteristic tracks in snow.**

**All at Tewin Orchard.**

Scientists employed to reduce losses to agriculture caused by rabbits preferred the control by myxomatosis to that of the (then legal) gin trap and stated that the suffering caused by the gin trap was unquestionable. Their use made their studies of trapped rabbits some of the most unpleasant investigations with which they had ever been concerned.

Tragically, the gin trap was one of the inventions of humans which went with colonists to the new world to develop the fur trade. The scale of the suffering to wild mammals that

Extensive damage to an oilseed rape crop by grazing rabbits at Dawley Warren at Ivor and Vaughan Williams' Tewin Bury Farm in 1999.

Conifers are being replaced by native deciduous trees in the woodland here and protectors are essential to prevent damage by rabbits and deer (Dawley Woods).

human trap devices have caused can only be guessed at. Amazingly, these traps are still legally used in trapping the wild fur-bearing mammals in many parts of the world.

In Britain, the rabbits which escaped from warrens led a precarious existence until the growth of the country estates, and pheasant rearing in particular allowed their survival to be ensured. The breach-loading shotgun transformed shooting and as landowners grew more and more enthusiastic to preserve game birds, including partridges, duck and hare, predators were trapped by gamekeepers.

At one time keepered estates in Hertfordshire would have bordered each other with little wilderness between (and keepers often went beyond estate boundaries to control predators which might visit their game coverts). Rabbits flourished as the foxes, badgers, polecats, pine martens, stoats, weasels, buzzards and other birds which also take rabbits were ruthlessly destroyed. Locally, a few foxes were spared for the hunt and some badgers for digging to be baited later, but they became much less numerous than at present.

Wild cats easily catch rabbits and Tomkies (1991) gives data on the prehistoric status and decline which suggests that they did not survive the 16th century in Hertfordshire. Any feral cats were also efficiently controlled when found on preserves.

Survival through winter was helped by farm crops and Sheail describes how fodder for sheep and cattle often replaced winter fallow so that fewer rabbits died of starvation. He gives figures for the early 20th century at about 50 million rabbits nationally (about 4 times the number of sheep) and nearly 100 million just prior to myxomotosis in the early 1950s. The pox virus myxomatosis, so deadly to rabbits, occurs naturally in certain South American species of rabbit with non-fatal, mild symptoms. It is passed between rabbits by their specific flea *Spilopsyllus cuniculis* in this country and since its introduction (in Kent in 1953), within a dramatic few years 99% of the rabbit population had died.

Resistance began to be detected as weaker myxoma virus strains followed the initial lethal one and soon 10% of rabbits which contracted these strains recovered. Twenty-seven years later it was estimated that rabbits had returned to 20% of their pre-myxomatosis population. The present day effects of the virus have diminished even more and rabbit numbers are much the same as 45 years ago in all suitable habitats around the county. On a shoot to reduce muntjac (before this type of deer drive was discontinued), only 4 rabbits in the Knebworth Estate and adjoining woods were shot (21st February 1968) compared with 20 hares, 4 grey squirrels, 9 jays and 27 muntjac (the main subject of the day).

Gamekeepers from several parts of Hertfordshire took part and other muntjac were netted, tagged and released. All the muntjac material was kept for research into breeding, age and other aspects of their biology.

The status of rabbits is very different now and although the myxomatosis outbreaks reappear each year around August, in 1999 the peak was around early December. Dozens died in this winter outbreak at Tewin Orchard and on one day alone I despatched 6 rabbits. There were still numerous healthy rabbits throughout the rest of the winter and just a few individual cases thereafter.

Clearly the peak of flea populations will also be the peak of the spread of the disease and mild winters allow the fleas, and therefore the infections, to continue. The rabbit resurgence has revived their extensive tunnel workings. Old warrens continue to be used, and Alan Keith recorded 100 holes in 100m of one bank at Ridge, south Hertfordshire.

**Newly excavated rabbit burrow in warren: oak/hornbeam woodland near Welwyn.**

Viral haemorrhagic disease was described as present in rabbits in Britain after 1992, but if it has appeared in the county it has not yet had any apparent effect on numbers. In his mammal report for the *HMG* survey in 1999, Brian Phillips recorded counting 60 rabbits at the A414 Hertford to Essendon roundabout (where he had also seen 3 polecat road casualties), and at *HMG* committee meetings at Stanborough Police HQ, it is possible to see 150 rabbits (a few sandy coloured) grazing on the sports field during the evening.

The lack of attention to the species in the past is being rectified now. Much valuable material has been published including the *Mammal Review* **16**, 3+4 (1986): Lagomorph symposium papers. A fascinating account of a rabbit warren near Chichester was described by A.M. & R.M.Tittensor (1986). Thompson & Warden's New Naturalist *The Rabbit* is a classic volume, as is the *The Private Life of the Rabbit* by R.M.Lockley. The county has rabbits in every suitable habitat and they penetrate urban areas along railway embankments.

# Brown hare

### Lepus europaeus

*Lloyd (47) considered hares to be thinly distributed across the countryside in suitable districts, but felt that the urban growth in south Hertfordshire had disturbed them from the Aldenham and Elstree Reservoir fields where, until 1935, he used to see them frequently. He noted declines from Tring and Aldbury, where in the 1920s as many as 6 could be seen in the same field, and also from Hitchin and Ashwell.*

*They were described as 'numerous' in Hexton in the Parish Survey (1936). Fordham blamed the arrival of tractors, and the over shooting of hares from these new farm vehicles by the drivers, for a reduction in numbers by World War II, but Course found them plentiful in Royston fields (1944) and there were encouraging records from Northchurch and Shootersway (1945).*

*Despite local persecution in places, Laver (1898) felt in Essex they were too familiar for much description and Dobson (1999) continues to give their status as 'common'. Beds Wildlife (1987) also gives 'widespread and common'*

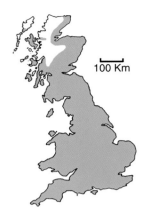

**Brown hares** *Lepus europaeus* **are widespread on open farmland.**

**Declining**

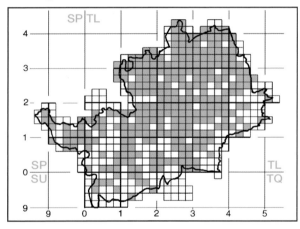

*Unlike rabbits, brown hares never resort to burrows and use their powerful long legs to evade predators. The places where they lie out, flat to the ground and hidden from view, are called forms.*

**The Hertfordshire photographer Jim Meads took this remarkable study of the moment hounds put up a hare from its form (it went on to elude the hounds). From** *They Still Meet at Eleven* **(1979) by kind permission.**

*status to them: 64% of tetrads had produced records.*

*Burton (1974) described hares as 'widespread in the countryside around London. Occurs in Richmond Park, but in few other areas within the suburbs'.*

Research by the Game Conservancy (Tapper & Parsons, *Mamm Rev* 1984 vol 14:2, 57-70) has shown that in our area, which has always been in the category of highest game totals on the estates (8+ shot per 100 hectares), there has been a significant decline measured over the last century.

In some parts of Britain during this time numbers went up, but overall in recent years the population has still diminished. A reduction of warm springs, the increase in fox predation, poaching, the incidence of a common disease of hares (pseudotuberculosis) and changes in agriculture practice have all been considered as reasons for the decline. Juveniles (leverets) survive best in cereal fields where they have cover at just the right time in early summer.

Historically, they were the most familiar mammal of field sports after deer because the species ran so fast and evaded harriers or long dogs with skill. They also show great stamina when followed by scent rather than vision by beagle and basset hounds.

Our distribution map is a fairly accurate reflection of the status. There are fields which seem ideal for them, but where they are never observed, within a few hundred metres of fields where they are always present. I have never recorded them, for example, from Tewin Orchard or the two fields either side, but in the more open Tewin Hill Farm fields, only 400m distant, they are easily watched courting and feeding. It may be that

they avoid rather enclosed, sheltered areas, yet I have seen many hares in woodland (especially Northaw Great Wood) so that where wide, open areas are fringed by trees they clearly do visit and lie up in cover.

Les Borg reported about 30 in a night survey with lamps around Dawley Woods in Tewin in 1999: an area where a few may be seen out in the fields in daytime when crops have been taken. (They also seek cover in the woods here.) In the large tracts of arable farmland in the north of the county they are still easily watched, especially in spring, but here, too, illegal use of dogs is common practice. The dogs, often worked with lamps and referred to as 'gaze hounds' because they sight prey rather than follow by scent (greyhounds, lurchers, whippets), are frequently taken onto land without permission at night.

Because they never burrow, if you startle one from young crops or stubble, as long as you keep staring at the spot where it ran off, you can walk up and locate the 'form' or depression in which they lie up. Ploughing is so quick and efficient now, often following straight behind the combine harvesters, that the days of long-standing mixed stubble and tilled ground are almost gone. I have known a well-grown leveret evade a border collie and hide in a field drain by leaping into a stream and then moving upstream to flatten in the dry tunnel. The dog lost the scent and the hare was left safe and sound in its temporary shelter.

Michael King of Walkern recently told me that he was training his spaniel in a field near his house and put up a hare as they left. It had remained motionless, flat to the grass, as they exercised for over thirty minutes with whistles and calls all around where it lay.

Regular paths and runs through the few remaining hedges are familiar in all arable districts, but the athletic courtship from late January to April is the activity we remember best about this lithesome mammal. 'Mad March' hares are rival males chasing females which turn and often 'box' the bucks

This form had been freshly vacated and I walked directly to the spot. In stubble, Northaw Great Wood 1962.

*17th August 1790*
ANNE HUGHES, *a farmer's wife in Hertfordshire, writes in her diary:*
*"Yester eve we did hav a right royal time att oure harveste partie.*
*John did take to top of the tabel, and did carve the hams and baked fowels, while Parson Jones did take the other end and cut up the beefe and bakon chine. And Farmer Welles did fill upp the glasses his side while we ladies did set the other side of the tabel. Johns mother cummen yerlie in the day did serve the bake hare, which everrie boddie did praise grately. Soon mouthes too full to talk till the beer and cyder did losen their tunges; then did they chatter right well. After all had fedd and satisfied inside, Sarah and carters wiffe did start to clere the tabels...Carter now did stand up and sing a hunten song, every boddie helping in the chorous at the top of their voices...Then to danceing. Old Granfer Tollu did ask me to trip a messure with him, which I did, and right well for all he be 80 cum next marche. Then more singing and so on, till at last everrie boddie did set them selfes downe with the pipes and glasses to tell tales.*
*Olde Granfer did tell us of a goste what did walk everie satterdaye night past the beech tree road who turned out to be a old gray goate. At this wee did laffe, and ole granfer was so excited he did set down with a bump on the floor; and I did give him a glass of primmy rose wine to take the hurt from his back-sete, and did tell him to set in Johns arm chair. So did we pleasure oure selves till nigh mid nighte."*

A brown hare shows up well in a young crop (north Hertfordshire).

Right: Gary Bolton's watercolour shows the black ear tips well; their ears are as long as their heads.

In 1969 an adult hare was caught in netting during a muntjac deer catch-up at Codicote. It was ear-tagged before release.

Stewart Bisserot's Thetford red squirrel *Sciurus vulgaris* shows the pale tail of the UK race.

with their forefeet. Their loping, energetic courtship is very attractive to watch and tracks in snow show that much activity continues through the night.

In 1969 an adult hare was caught near Codicote during a muntjac research catch-up and was ear-tagged. Six months later, in March 1970, it was amongst 200 shot on a drive, but was only a few hundred metres from where it had been tagged. This indicates how faithful they can be to one area. Road deaths take a serious toll and you become aware of how different they are from rabbits if you have to handle an injured one as I have had to do when it was hit by a car ahead of me. It is more like dealing with an injured young fox or dog and they have the most distressing scream.

The *HMG* has organised surveys for the national schemes and my return to fields east of Youngsbury, near Ware, failed to find any hares in January 2000. Previous visits by Steve Kourik produced sightings of 6 and my last visit in 1998 found 5. A similar walk on the Panshanger side of Welwyn Garden City by Peter Oakenfull also drew a blank in 2000. We cannot, it seems, be complacent about the future status of the species in the county.

# Red squirrel
## *Sciurus vulgaris*

*Lloyd (47) recorded the last few sightings of the native squirrel which, by the 1940s, had 'apparently almost disappeared from the county'. He noted H.G.Benson's comment that he 'used to see them at Ashridge until about 1918'.*

*A.H.Foster saw a pair in Highdown Wood (Tingley Wood on some maps) about 3 miles to the west of Hitchin on 11th June 1943, following information from a gamekeeper, and noted that these were the first he had seen in the district for some 10 years. He wrote a note in the 1944 Trans (22, 2:52) on the species in northwest Hertfordshire and despite many contacts with keepers, farmers, villagers and naturalists, only had 6 records for the 1939-44 period as the species* seemed to survive longest in the south of the county, with the last reports from my father who saw one in Northaw Great Wood in the early 1950s, and Bryan Sage, who reported one seen there on 6th April 1953 which was subsequently shot by the keeper. It is the last one recorded in the county: Sage (1954).

They survived for much longer in Essex and Dobson (1999) illustrates a similar direction of the decline (northward and eastward) across Essex, based on Harris (1973). In Essex the extinction was much later (1972) and is worthy of investigation: if an explanation can be found, perhaps a better understanding of how the grey species replaced the red can be given. Bedfordshire quickly lost their red squirrels, too: Beds Wildlife (1987) reported the last seen around 1945-1947. Burton (1974) points out that they were formerly widespread in London and last recorded from Epping Forest in 1957 and 1959.

Foster's final 6 Hertfordshire sightings were: a road casualty for St Paul's Walden, Whitwell (1939); a live one on the roadside between Whitwell and Kimpton at Cuckold's Cross (1941); a live one by the road between Preston and Kings Walden Park (1943); the Highdown Wood pair already given (1943); live by roadside at Preton Hill (1944); and Knebworth Park edge on a fence (1944).

Phyllis Hager made a particular study of the introduced grey squirrel around her home in Berkhamsted and kindly passed on her notes to me shortly before her death (1987). She noted from the Trans records that red squirrels were widespread in parts of Hertfordshire up to the 1920s. In 1876 and 1884 unusually large numbers were reported from the neighbourhood of Watford and both here and in St.Albans in 1925 it was described as common.

Dr.Shadbolt's anniversary address to the Herts Nat His Soc in 1932 reported on the 'invasion' of the grey squirrel. The introduced species over the previous 10 years he likened to the release of rabbits in Australia. In the 1920s people clearly saw the new species as a threat to the native red squirrel.

Sylvia Lloyd recorded, in her Amersham diaries (written 7 miles southwest of Berkhamsted), seeing a red squirrel leaping from tree to tree on the Latimer Road (14th January 1928), but 'a grey squirrel (alas) leapt over the fence into the wood just as I emerged, the first I have seen in the wood. This means the end of the red squirrel which had here its chief haunts.'

To the northwest of Foster's 'Hitchin area' records, the Hexton Parish Survey (1936) still reported a few sightings locally, but indicated control of grey squirrels was well under way, if futile: 'Of course, despite an enormous death toll, the grey squirrel is common, and often from the classroom windows may be seen disporting itself on neighbouring fences which bound the woods'.

Following the Mammal Society conference in Dublin in 1978, Patrick O'Sullivan and Patrick Warner took members to see the red squirrel research in progress in County Wicklow. After removal from baited traps the squirrel is measured, marked and then released.

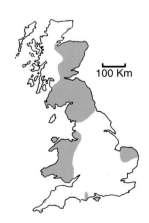

100 Km

Variations in the pelage of red squirrels *S. vulgaris* in the British Museum Natural History collection at South Kensington, by kind permission .

*Odd records since the 1940s must be viewed with caution because grey squirrels show a marked ginger-red colour to their flanks and sometimes a red tinge to the whole pelage in summer. They are heavier, lack the ear tufts and the tail differs in colour mixes and length, but a brief view amongst high branches can mislead. The Nat His Mus specimens reflect a past golden age with 5 specimens (plus many Roth mounted squirrels lacking data) as a selection able to run to three colour varieties. These include two rare albino and one strange grey-brown mix, which was thought at the time to be a hybrid (all from Tring); 1893 white male; 1893 grey/brown male; 1894 white male; 1895 red male ; and 1900 red male. The tail in the grey-brown specimen seems really odd because it is very long and mixed in colour. The ear tufts, colours and texture of the hair indicate the red species in̄ winter coat.*

*Lord Rothchild was one of many who introduced grey squirrels and the caption states: '9th May 1893 descendent of grey squirrels put out in Tring Park. Probably hybrid with English squirrel'. Interbreeding is not in fact known between the two species.*

*The story of the red species in Hertfordshire reflects the national picture. Andrew Tittensor (1980) considers that the large population between 1860 and 1900 was probably due to the habitat changes as vast areas of new plantations of foreign conifers became fashionable. The decline after 1900 appears to be linked with felling on a large scale of these plantations as they reached maturity. The World War I requirements increased this and the species suffered an epidemic disease soon afterwards. There was recovery up to the 1930s, but they would have found as they recolonised that many of the old sites had been taken over by the larger grey squirrels, introduced from 1876 onwards, but not really widely established until the 1920s.*

*The second decline this century saw the species become extinct in much of southern England. Monica Shorten (1954) always seemed anxious to show that the introduction of the grey squirrel did not simply drive out the red squirrel, but it is to be regretted that she, and all those employed to advise the governments of the day, omitted to raise alarm bells that might have led to the elimination of the new species before its dominance, through its heavier weight, forced out the red squirrel.*

*The grey species expanded and settled into what were once red squirrel strongholds, especially where very mixed shrub, garden and deciduous tree habitats survive, rather than those with conifers (preferred by red squirrels).*

*Shorten gives full details of the introductions of grey squirrels and includes Hertfordshire in the sites where specimens were found (in 1931) to have a chronic intestinal infection with a species of Eimeria which causes coccidiosis. A failure of the 1930 beechmast and acorn crops may have*

A case of mistaken identity: Chris Woodard (above) has received reports at Stevenage Borough Council of red squirrels seen in Shephalbury Park for over 20 years. In August 2001 two erythristic (sandy) grey squirrels were run over on a road near the Park and one was preserved. As well as the unusual red hair colour, the squirrel has a white patch at the base of the tail.

weakened the grey squirrel's resistance and thus could have led to the epidemic. This was, however, just a temporary set back and grey squirrels increased rapidly at the expense of the red squirrel.

It is, therefore, fair to say that despite the setbacks caused by disease and temporary loss of conifer habitats, if the grey squirrel was not present in Hertfordshire, we would have had the red squirrel present now and, with so many in fir plantations, they probably would have been on an upsurge in their population, possibly with calls for control, if not the reintroduction of 'squirrel clubs' to reduce their numbers. Because red squirrels are physically smaller and less able to utilise hazelnuts as food, the grey species will compete successfully wherever both types are found.

It is now also known that they carry, but do not die from, viral infections which are fatal to the red squirrels. This must have been realised by the ecologists who might have prevented the comprehensive takeover by grey squirrels by positive plans.

An engraving from 1909 of a pine marten chasing a red squirrel.
*(Die Säugetiere Deutchlands,* **Kurt Hennings, Leipzig).**

# Grey squirrel
## *Sciurus carolinensis*
Lloyd (47) quotes the 1939 annual shoot report for the National Trust Ashridge Estate of 700-800 grey squirrels, a figure typical of most years in the mid- and late-1930s, which 'seems to make little impression'. (I can further illustrate the density of grey squirrel numbers by quoting from a neighbour in Tewin who lost so much of her chicken food to a grey squirrel that she asked a gardener to shoot it. He sat by the wire enclosure with an airgun and shot the offending squirrel. However, this one was then followed by a further 14 as they each ran down the same central tree in turn before the gardener finally stopped for his lunch.)

The species is often used as an example of how the introductions of new species by man can cause enormous economic problems as well as disturbance to indigenous types. Nobody is certain why S.carolinensis should have been chosen out of the many species of North American squirrel to be released here. In fact records show that most species of mammal have been freely released into the parks and countryside in Britain and we are left with the ones which can survive in the conditions which prevail here.

Phyllis Hager has documented the spread from the Duke of Bedford's

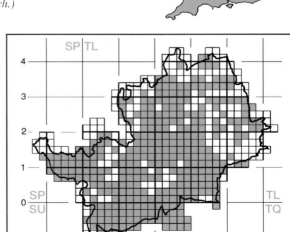

111

**Grey squirrel** *Sciurus carolinensis.*

**Increasing**

The black melanistic type of grey squirrel is a feature of north Hertfordshire, especially in Hitchin and Letchworth.

**Inspector Steve Kourik, Wildlife Officer for Hertfordshire Police, with a juvenile grey squirrel which attended a Mammal Society conference at Oaklands College, St.Albans.**

Woburn introduction of 10 squirrels in 1890. There were 30 other recorded introductions in other places. She plotted a colonisation southward into Berkhamsted via Heath & Reach, Leighton Buzzard, Whipsnade, Aldbury, Pendley, Tring Park (where they were already present via Lord Rothschild), Wiggington, Ashridge and, by 1923, Berkhamsted.

In just 25 years the species had expanded its range by 15 miles from Woburn and Tring to become firmly established in the Ashridge Estate by 1916. Hitchin, in the north of the county, had been colonised by 1910 and Tring by 1914. (Because they had been released in Tring Park independently, the Woburn and Tring colonies may represent a merger rather than an arrival.) The squirrels introduced by the Duke of Bedford were from eastern North America and their origins are discussed in detail by Shorten (1956). Although black variations are common throughout the original range, the subspecies, S.carolinensis leucotis is more prone to the melanic form. In England it survived in local populations, principally at Woburn, Letchworth and Ashwell. Brian Sawford at N Herts Mus has written of the variety (which will freely interbreed with the typical grey coloured types) and this colour form now has a public house named after it in Letchworth. As a result, we have this interesting pelage variation represented in the Nat Hist Mus and North Herts Mus collections, worthy of the further details below.

The earliest specimen was for Berkhamsted (Oldham, 1922) and there was a second (MacDonald, 1928) for Ashridge. Two normal-coloured Tring Park specimens (Roth, 1930 and Bishop, 1949) are also represented. A 1986 (pregnant female) specimen given by Daphne Hills, Letchworth is a striking black example and there is an Ashwell (Fordham) specimen. Daphne Hills also has specimens in preparation at the Nat Hist Mus and records have been received into Cambridgeshire: 2 pairs, in an unnamed public house gardens (D.A. 1st October 1993) and one at Camberton, Cambridge, P. Brackley, back garden (3rd February 1999).

She also has Baldock, 1997, Bragbury End (A 602 road) 1993 and a Markyate record, no name, behind house, mid-April 1994, as well as a male 13th December 1991 in the Hitchin/Willian section of the Baldock road, TL 219/306. I was given a black tail from the several that W.H.Fordham kept in his study when I visited him in the 1960s . He contributed notes to the Trans (**22**, 2:53, 1944 and **24**, 5:198, 1956) on 'Melanic Grey squirrels in Hertfordshire with observations of the arrival of two in the Bury Grounds at Ashwell 1943-1944 - an attempt to eradicate a small colony which had developed there by 1945'.

He wrote: 'In the winter of 1945-46, 5 black and 7 grey squirrels were shot at Ashwell, and squirrels left the village. Several were seen in the early mornings on roads leading *towards Odsey and a black one reached Therfield'. (It is amusing how he made it sound as if, due to the persecution, the squirrels were thumbing lifts by the roadside, and he goes on to record the examination of 8 black squirrels and of 18 subsequent sightings, only 1 of which was jet black.) Phyllis Hager (also 24, 5:198, 1956) noted that 3 of this colour were seen regularly in Hockeridge Woods near Berkhamsted in 1954 and one was jet black (1st January 1955).*

*As with the red squirrel, Dobson (1999) illustrates the change in status of the grey squirrel across Essex which is described as 'abundant, increasing'. Anderson (1985) had collated records from 52% of tetrads in Bedfordshire, where they were 'common' and Burton (1974) concluded that in London they were 'well established in almost every open space - only absent from the very heart of the built-up area'.*

**Summer breeding drey (above) from cut branches and (below) a typical winter drey against a tree trunk (Bramfield).**

Grey squirrels have been described to me by foresters, especially those trying to grow beech plantations in the Chilterns, as 'nasty tree rats', in addition to many other names which are not really appropriate in this kind of book. They are not a welcome addition to the woodland scene, although red squirrels damage trees, too, when their numbers are very high. I find it curious to have visited the red squirrel study areas in Ireland (coming from our county where it is now extinct) to be shown how bark damage can ruin timber in fir plantations and cause tops to break off in high winds so that control was thought necessary. Grey squirrels introduced to Ireland have so far had less impact and, despite their greater size, spread less than in England, Wales and parts of central Scotland.

Tree growers, farmers and anyone who stores fruit in the country approximately visible from the Ivinghoe Beacons rue the day edible dormice *Glis glis* arrived – p143 *et seq*. They have been found, like the grey squirrels, to seriously damage bark, and the regeneration of our native hardwoods appears to be seriously threatened at ground level by a combination of rabbits and deer, and at any level into the canopy by the two introduced rodents, grey squirrels and edible dormice.

It is worth noting here that Phyllis Hager pointed out some obvious differences between these squirrels and edible dormice in her talks and unpublished notes: the dormice are nocturnal, squirrels usually diurnal feeders; they lack the white fringe to the tail which tends to hang rather than be held up and over the back, as in squirrels; they hibernate between November and April whereas squirrels are active all winter; both are very vocal and both enter houses readily. At first they may be considered a charming addition to the garden fauna, but once a roof space is penetrated very expensive damage can be done, especially to electrical wiring and often in the most inaccessible of places.

Ingenious devices are now made to allow birds to feed at

**The destruction of unripe hazelnuts by grey squirrels commences as early as 22nd July. For the next few weeks, green shells and partly eaten white nuts rain down from the tree canopy wherever hazels grow.**

garden bird tables without loss of vast quantities of often expensive food to squirrels. The Forestry Commission has been engaged in research and advice over bark stripping in May, June and July, as well as horticultural, agricultural and garden damage. Competition for hollow tree nest sites and robbery of existing eggs or nestlings are also a concern. After the results of shooting and cage trapping were found to be ineffective, warfarin (the poison commonly used against brown rats and house mice) was made legal for certain parts of Britain in 1973. Poison hoppers have been widely used in Hertfordshire's woodlands (about 1 per 3 hectares is the recommended spacing).

Counties not allowed to use warfarin included those with red squirrels, but we should show the same concern for the indigenous dormice which may enter hoppers containing poison just as readily as squirrels. In trials it was found that although wood mice and bank voles succumbed to the poison in the vicinity of hoppers, breeding was unaffected in the populations between these sites. Anxiety, however, is also felt for predators of the poisoned small mammals, such as weasels, stoats, foxes, the recently re-established polecats, and badgers. Dormice are very local, yet, as John Tomkins has shown in Box Wood, Stevenage, they may travel long distances around their woodland nests to look for food. If the control of the introduced squirrel also affects such rare species, it should not be used.

We must question whether tree-living animals, especially the hole or cavity nesting or roosting species like the bats, dormice, hawfinches and tree sparrows, have also been affected by the aggressive colonisation of these squirrels. The best recent accounts of the introduction and its effect on the red squirrels is in Gurnell and in Holm (both 1987).

Although the two species can survive together in a large conifer area such as Thetford Forest for a few decades, the red squirrels are now very localised and barely continue there. Holm is right to point out that when red squirrels mysteriously disappeared from Ireland in the 15th century and from Scotland in the 18th century, if these events recurred today simultaneously in both of these last strongholds, it would be the end of the species in Britain, with no chance of our own native stock ever being reintroduced to such places as Hertfordshire. I can only contribute a regret for the long lost pine marten which is pictured in an early German illustration (see p111); this shows how useful such a natural predator would have been when the grey species was released here, if only the gamekeepers of the day had not trapped or shot them to extinction.

# Bank vole
## *Clethrionomys glareolus*

*Although albino bank voles are commonly sold as pets there are no colour variations in the large range at the Nat His Mus. There is a large Welwyn specimen (21st April 1901) collected by W.R.O.Grant. Lloyd (47) described the species as common and noted that a number of bank voles which had been 'trapped by Wilson at Batchwoood, St.Albans, were never caught where there was no overhead cover'.*

*They are well recorded in Bedfordshire (29% of tetrads); Laver (1898) noted that the first British specimen was described by Yarrell from Essex in 1832. Dobson (1999) confirms their modern Essex status to be 'abundant' and Burton (1974) reported them widespread in hedgerows and woods in the outer suburbs of London.*

Bank vole *Clethrionomys glareolus* showing contrast between main coat cover visible above ground and its underfur.

Bank voles are found whenever surveys have been made.

Joyce Eldridge made a study of bank voles and wood mice in Panshanger Park, near Hertford between 1964 and 1966, some of which she brought to show me for comparison. Her paper with diagrams was published in *Proc Zoo Soc Lon*, **155**, 2:231 (1968). The area of parkland, owned by Lefage Redland Aggregates, was TL 280/121. She illustrated how 103 wood mice and 56 bank voles were partly recaptured and showed how they were distributed in relation to vegetation.

The mice were evenly distributed in the woodland. The bank voles were at their greatest in the bracken areas and when present amongst the trees, it was in the areas of denser ground cover. That the voles were in thicker cover and the mice in more open woodland indicated their more diurnal activity: wood mice are much more nocturnal.

Curiously, no field voles were caught in grassland during the work, although when she brought examples of the live voles to show me, they exhibited variations in tail length. Despite this and the range of colours in the hair, the voles certainly were bank voles. She recorded their movements during an abundance of food when the bank voles may have moved into the woodland for acorns and other food.

Weights measured indicated a slight late winter loss. 15g was taken as representing a mature vole and mouse, but bank voles may weigh up to 36g and wood mice up to 28g. Few bank

**Widespread, probably stable**

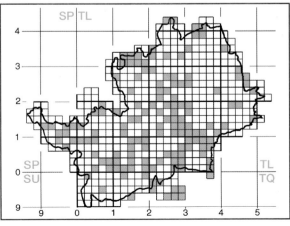

Susie Clark frequently tamed wild bank voles as a child.

Bank vole.

voles are smaller than this until the influx of young in December (November for mice). With the onset of reproduction in April there was a period of growth and a rapid disappearance of over-wintered voles and mice in July and August. She found the same loss occurred with the summer generation in September and October, with the late-born young growing to a steady over-wintering weight of 15-16g. She found no winter breeding. Her study is one of the most interesting and thoroughly worked surveys of small mammals in the county.

Bank voles tame quickly and some become surprisingly reluctant to bite. They overlap the woodland habitats of the wood mice as long as there is undergrowth and will live in the grassland habitats of the field voles, again, as long as there is cover in the form of tussocks and borders of hedges, briars and bracken nearby.

During one of my own live-trapping sessions I caught 10 in Balls Wood during the low point of the year in their population (March 1976) over 68 trap nights. They are found in all parts of the county where surveyed. The ability to climb well sometimes results in nests high up in shrubs, often in the base of old bird's nests. With an annual production of 5 litters possible and about 4 young in each, they can damage vegetation, but have rarely been known to reach the 'plague' numbers of field voles. They may occasionally take seedlings and fruits, and can bark young trees to a significant degree in places (including young apple trees, even under the guards). However, they are a valuable food source for birds such as owls and kestrels as well as the predatory mammals.

# Field vole

## *Microtus agrestis*

*Lloyd (47) devotes just one line to the species: 'Common and widely distributed'. They reach very high populations at times and cause great forestry damage to young plantations. Predators are attracted to such areas and respond to these vole 'plague' years by breeding in greater numbers.*

*There is a well prepared range of albino skins from Tring in the Nat His Mus Coll. with specimens also representing Tring, Tring Reservoirs, Northchurch and Kings Langley.*

*Widespread in Bedfordshire (42% of tetrads), Laver (1898) notes for Essex: 'This vole abounds sometimes to such an extent as to entirely destroy the herbage'. He kept one and was amazed at how much clover it consumed in 'four-and-twenty hours'. Dobson (1999), whilst noting its abundance in modern Essex, reports a decline in recent years as rabbit numbers have increased and marginal vegetation has decreased. Burton (1974) described the vole as 'found on unmown commons and parks throughout the suburbs' in London.*

Bumble bees start colonies in abandoned field vole nests.

116

Active night and day in grassland runs where they make nests of chewed grass, the field voles reproduce with litter after litter of 5 young on each occasion between April and September. Nearly all over-wintering field voles were born the previous summer, but those from spring litters are able to breed themselves by the end of the summer.

The species is a very important, if cyclical, part of the food chain for both predatory birds and mammals. It was considered by Brambell (1970) to be our most abundant vertebrate, based on the extent of its habitats, which exceed those favoured by bank voles and wood mice. Changing practices in agriculture may have altered this situation and wood mice are so numerous in such a variety of habitats, including urban developments, that field voles are more likely to be the second most abundant now.

From painful personal experience I would liken their bite and aggression in the hand, when compared with their more amiable relative the bank vole, to the disposition of the edible dormouse compared with our native dormouse.

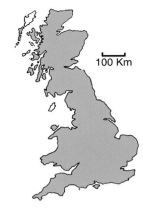

**Field vole** *Mycrotus agrestis* **is recorded across the county with concentrations wherever farm set-aside policy now leaves fields of long grass.**

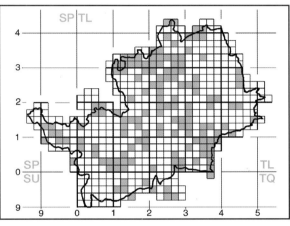

# Northern water vole

### *Arvicola terrestris*

*In 1891 Roberts wrote in the Trans 7, 3:41: 'Of the voles, the one most commonly seen is the water vole, which we meet so frequently on the banks of our streams and ditches'.*

*A palaeolithic tooth from Hitchin listed in Trans 11, 2:64 (1901) is probably our earliest record of the species in Hertfordshire. There are 5 normal coloured specimens in the Nat His Mus Coll from Tring and a striking black one from 'Waters Place, within 80 yards of the River Ash, Easneye, Ware, Herts: H.T.Buxton'.*

*Lloyd (47) reported it 'widespread in suitable situations, but far from abundant. I have never seen one in the vicinity of the reservoirs or the Tykewater at Elstree, during many years of watching'.*

*There is an albino example from Saffron Walden in the Nat His Mus Coll. and Laver (1898) found the species common*

**Water vole** *Arvicola terrestris* **photographed in the Lea Valley.**

Les Borg

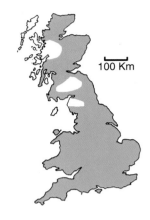

100 Km

*in all parts of Essex. Dobson gives very full data on the status in modern Essex and whilst still 'common', he considers it to be declining. It was 'well distributed along the river systems' in Beds Wildlife (1987), but Anderson (1985) considered it scarce with records from 22% of tetrads. Burton (1974) described them as fairly widespread on suitable rivers and noted that they were 'most abundant in Middlesex on the River Colne and its tributaries'.*

Water voles were one of the wild mammals I regularly watched from my early schooldays in the 1950s on the walk from Hertford North Station to school through the Lea water meadows where the river meanders through the castle grounds. They were readily visible on the banks and swimming there. The road constructed through the area has altered the habitats and the voles are far less common generally, with a marked decline also around Hitchin noted by T. James since 1980. This has taken place in a county with slow colonisation by the introduced American mink *M. vison*.

The national decline has been well publicised and in our county Jenny Jones in particular has continued to monitor sites in association with the *Trust, HMBG* members and other field workers. Rivers and water areas in the survey include: Hiz, Purwell, Oughton, Ivel, Rhee, Lea, Lea Ditch, Lea Navigation, New River, Essendon Brook, Stort, Stort Ditches, Moat at Furneux Pelham, Ash, Rib, Pond at Weston Park, Stevenage Brook, Beane, Beane Back Ditch, Mimram, Mimram Ditch, Ver, Colne, Gade, Grand Union Canal by the Gade, Pond at Boarscroft Farm, Bulbourne, Tring Reservoirs, Chess, Pond at Fir and Ponds Wood, Pond at Cuffley Camp, Northaw Brook and Mimmshall Brook. Of 85 positive historic sites, only 46 were reported positive after 1996. Of these, 32 were negative after survey work had been carried out.

The Hertfordshire Monitoring Survey of water voles described in Jones & Molloy (1997) has highlighted the decline of the species along many stretches of river where they had previously been recorded. The losses may be due to a range of factors including habitat degradation,

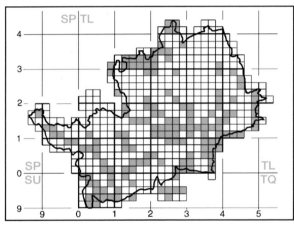

**Water vole distribution pre 1990 (above) and post 1990 records (below).**

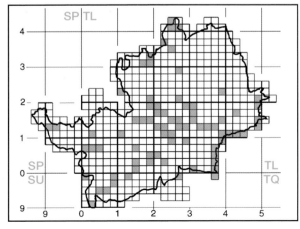

118

Left: habitats in the wetland in Cassiobury Park were little changed between F.L.Griggs' 1904 drawing and my 1970 photograph, but the water voles are now much reduced in number throughout the county.

A water vole swimming at dusk and (below) a latrine platform.

reduction of river water quality, fluctuations in water level, an increase in the fragmentation of populations which leads to unsuccessful breeding or an increase in predation, frequently by mink.

Where sites have been listed as negative, observations include: polluted; canalised, banks mown; virtually dry; urban area, disturbed; mink; heavily disturbed; in some places virtually no bank. Nine sites had dried out or become just swampy and mink are featured in 6 of the comment columns.

The general view now is that where otters are present you will find water voles, but where mink are active the water voles disappear. The exception, perhaps, is in urban areas where mink are present, but scarce due to disturbance by domestic animals such as dogs. When mink first arrived on the coast of Essex in the 1970s I watched water voles swim rapidly from the banks of saltings behind the sea wall at Walton-on-the-Naze as a mink hunted along the bank. Stoats and pike are other predators and I have found water vole remains in heron pellets near Tring.

Our distribution map is incomplete, but my early tetrad markings produced a cubist illustration of the rivers and streams where the water vole was found. The *HMWT* surveyed the River Mimram in 1999 and the report in H.Pearce, M.Baker & G.White (2000) includes examples of the water vole survey form and vole activity sheet used. Locations where voles were found are given, but the overall impression is of a low population compared with former records and considerable concern is expressed over the presence of mink in both the upper sections of the river and lower, in Panshanger Park. As well as management recommendations for the river habitat, the report feels that the control of mink is essential.

Now protected under the *Wildlife & Countryside Act, (1981)*, these distinctive large voles give a familiar 'plop' sound as they dive, either when disturbed from the bank or if

Water vole and a bank vole flat skin compared.

*Considerable research by HMWT and the Mammal Group has been concentrated in the Mimram Valley in central Hertfordshire*

swimming, in which case they duck down from the surface suddenly.

Ann Trotman had one caught by accident in a hand net during a fresh water ecology course along the banks of the Chess at the Chorleywood Field Studies Centre in 1970 and I have found one drowned in an eel trap. If you approach a stream bank the high water table in the surrounding soil can cause your footfall to drive water voles out from a subterranean tunnel. They leave a stream of bubbles as they cross to safety underwater and vanish into another hidden tunnel entrance. Droppings and food debris can be seen at little platform sites under banks.

It is the 'water rat' of *Wind in the Willows* but is, of course, a true vole, although brown rats will frequently run along

**The River Mimram at Tewin and Robin Cole's aerial view of Tewin Bury Farm with marsh (left) and woodside vegetation along the course of the river and ditch (centre).**

river or stream banks as well. Our indigenous otters have lived in harmony with water voles historically and it is not surprising that the smaller, alien mink has had such a devastating effect on the native water voles; they can enter runs and locate voles more easily.

The surviving colonies of water voles have to live with the consequences of escapes (and deliberate releases) of mink from fur farms. Once again we have permanently damaged our native ecology in much the same way as we did by releasing grey squirrels.

As well as Dr.Jenny Jones' surveys across the county, the *HMWT* has reported on the status of water voles (including crayfish and otters) along the River Mimram (see p117 *et seq)*. Four typical sections of the river are illustrated below.

*Management of the nature reserves and the farms in the Mimram Valley is compatible and there are well maintained public rights of way.*

**Robin Cole's view of the river winding past Tewin Water House (centre) and its widened section in Panshanger Park (below, centre).**

# Wood mouse
## *Apodemus sylvaticus*

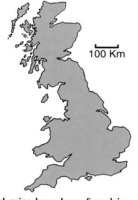

**Wood mouse** *Apodemus sylvaticus* **at base of hornbeam (Hopkyns' Wood, Tewin).**

100 Km

**Wood mice have been found in almost all habitats surveyed.**

*Lloyd (47) reported them as common and the Nat His Mus Coll. has easily the most comprehensive and well cared for collection of any Hertfordshire (possibly British) mammal. Most are from Tring, with older, round skins and many flat skins of the 1970s. The Roth Coll goes back to 1897, with samples from 1904 and 1912. There are separate boxes for Berkhamsted Common and Ivinghoe specimens.*

*Joyce Eldridge's 1968 Panshanger study of wood mice and bank voles has already been described in the bank vole section. Other studies included one by Matthew Gaved at Lemsford springs, using Longworth live traps on a mapped grid (1971). More recent surveys have provided records from students' projects at the University of Hertfordshire. Records from houses are frequent.*

*A late nest of 5 juveniles came up with potatoes on a main crop plant I pulled up (7th October 1979) at Tewin Orchard and I have found them under vegetables several times since then. Other vegetable gardeners have complained of them to me and Laver (1898), who found them widespread in Essex, noted that newly sown peas or corn are 'especial objects of its attention'. Dobson (1999) describes barn owl prey information for Essex, where they are still 'abundant'. They are recorded across Bedfordshire (46% of tetrads) and the LNHS area, where Burton (1974) mentioned that they often enter houses in winter.*

The wood mouse, most numerous mammal of Hertfordshire, was the first animal I watched at length in my teens. I built a series of boxes (described in *Mammal Watching*, 1981) and kept the wild mice from the garden in as natural a world as I could make. I had already kept newts in aquaria years before and later found yellow-necked mice in the garden, but wood mice soon occupied a series of linked boxes and tunnels which dominated the room.

Wood mice can be found in almost every type of habitat, including houses, gardens, factories, fields, woods, banks, scrub and marshland. They prefer the security of a canopy over their heads, but at night will feed in more open areas. They climb into roof spaces, especially from open

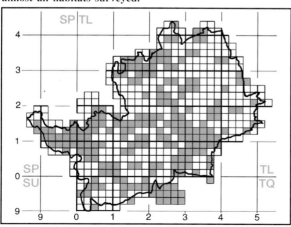

barns. The delight of these bright eyed, large-eared and long-tailed mice is their great speed and agility. They tend to appear to naturalists when they are watching something else: most badger watchers have seen them at dusk as a sideline to events around sett entrances, where they seem to slip into the holes as freely as the badgers themselves, from smaller runs close-by. It is rare to see healthy ones in daylight, but they will climb through shrubs and may appear collecting rose hips or hazels close to your head as you wait, binoculars raised, watching birds, for example.

The species is often found in association with yellow-necked mice (see next entry) and the attraction both species have for hazelnuts will find them climbing, removing, gnawing, eating and storing this sweet, nutritious food from August onwards whilst stocks last. Grey squirrels may now dominate the tree canopy at such sites, but the mice are equally enthusiastic and despite the need to gnaw into the shell (unlike the quick split achieved by the squirrels) they locate a surprising number of nuts.

**Wood mouse adult and juvenile (Welwyn Garden City).**

Before Eldridge's live trapping work in 1968 I had caught 73 during a survey in Northaw Great Wood, described in Sage, Ed (1966), which also has an extended account of my captive population observation.They were the most common small mammal in the more open areas under trees, but also turned up in all the other woodland habitats there.

Gurnell (1979) gives a very good account of the mice, with photographs illustrating some of the behavioural interactions between them. If you keep a colony in artificial light (to overcome their nocturnal activity cycles) you can watch these relationships and Gurnell gives a single peak during the short summer nights which develops into two peaks, one

**Wood mouse in bee hive where it had constructed this nest.**

at dusk and one at dawn, during the long winter nights. They are prepared to move out into open woodland, whereas bank voles prefer to keep some cover over their heads under the mature trees even at night.

Although I have partly uncovered wood mouse tunnel systems, especially on my vegetable plots, Gurnell gives a clear diagram of burrow systems which can be 6-30cms below the ground. They can throw out little heaps of soil like miniature badger setts and favour potatoes, especially those late crops left into the autumn. The loose trench structure allows them easy digging and nesting, with subterranean food storage laid on.

Idle gardeners are thus a friend, but when a litter of young is disturbed I found that they are retrieved later by their mother and taken to another nest or, in one case where they were old enough, to scatter and escape in all directions.

Wood mouse from above to show dorsal colour and long tail.

A wood mouse nest in the top of one of my beehives (5th May 1989) was 130mm x 45mm deep, giving an inside cavity of 50mm across. It was made up of straw from the fruit tree mulch next to the hive, with a small amount of fresh green grass around the base, some intact, some gnawed. Although disturbed from the nest on 4th May, the wood mouse was in occupation again on 5th May when I removed the structure. Mice can destroy weak colonies of bees. Pygmy shrews, bank voles and brown rats have also turned up in hives. Mouse guards are little protection in long orchard grass: small mammals will even chew through the base wood from underneath. It is better to keep hives on short grass, concrete slabs or old milk crates.

Flowerdew (1984) has shown how few, if any, wood mice live to see a second winter (most have died by September of the year following their birth) and their numbers fluctuate in woodland as owls and nocturnal mammal predators reduce their numbers. Dispersal of young also maintains fairly constant populations from year to year as adult males and possibly the adult females show aggression towards the young.

# Yellow-necked mouse
## *Apodemus flavicollis*

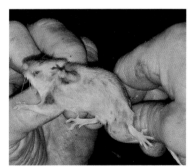

Yellow-necked mouse *Apodemus flavicollis* **showing yellow throat patch (Hertford Heath).**

*Lloyd (47) reported that 'little is known of this species in Hertfordshire ...' and gives a typical record from a house found by G.Tite of Tring Museum, in his home in the town, March 1938. (It was a pregnant female and was preserved, but not in the Mus Coll.)*

*Sage (1955) and both Fordham and Hager (1956) added records from Hitchin, Odsey (in a fruit store), St.Ippollitts, Northaw Great Wood (several records after 1954), Cuffley, Welwyn and Tewin. In Sandon, Colonel and Mrs Faure-Walker had their pantry raided at their farm for walnuts, cherries and a quantity of chutney (1972). Lord Cranbrook noted their liking for fruit stores indoors, measured a specimen he caught at St Ippollitts and gave Phyllis Hager the details which she listed in her Mammal Notes (1956).*

*Matthew Gaved found them in his garden in Tewin Wood and we regularly had the mice in our loft at Tewin Orchard in the 1970s. In July 1980 and 1981 they also bred in empty beehives at the Orchard. They are taken by owls as I found in the late 1950s in the Home Wood, Cuffley where 2 were amongst a larder of small mammals in a beech tree. A tawny owl had stored them in her nest just prior to the hatching of the eggs.*

Fordham added a further note to his Odsey information in 1956, contributing Hertford Heath, Bishop's Stortford and Barley to recorded sites. He commented that several had been caught in his house, near the apple store and cats occasionally took them outdoors.

My late neighbour, Eileen Soper, who lived at Harmer Green, asked me to catch small mammals in her bedroom whilst she was in hospital and I secured two yellow-necked mice. (The medical staff had insisted on this before Eileen could entertain thoughts of going home. I had released the mice at Tewin and said to the hospital staff: 'Trust Eileen to have an exclusive species, not merely house mice'.)

Later, I happened to re-read Eileen's 'Wild Encounters' book which gives delightful accounts of their garden wilderness in the 1950s. Yellow-necked mice had made regular visits indoors then, at one stage gnawing through their telephone cable. The release I made in 1992 also had a rather strange twist to it because I carried the mice in two plastic bags, suspended from my hand as I steered the car home. They must have chewed through the plastic enough for one to make a sudden departure as a kestrel flew across the field above the Orchard and banked over the windscreen, hovering for a moment as I drove slowly past on the narrow bend. I am convinced it spotted the mice. One mouse landed on my left foot and the other did not extricate itself from its bag until I was round the next corner. After parking, both jumped out of the car when I left the doors open by our house. (The species was already present in the garden here and would visit our loft from the barn.)

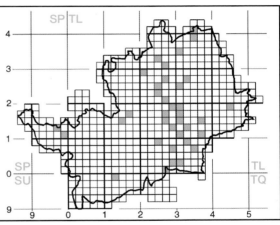

Mostly in woodland.

Local, but under-recorded

Laver (1898) did not distinguish the species in Essex, but David Corke made a particular study of them there and Dobson (1999) describes them as 'fairly common'. In Bedfordshire, Anderson (1985) had records for just 3 tetrads and considered them 'vulnerable'. Burton (1974) only knew of records from Kent and Surrey in the LNHS area at that time, although Hertfordshire records from Northaw Great Wood and Cuffley, within the LNHS circle, had been made in the 1950s and 1960s.

Corke & Harris have given 1894 for de Winton's first description of the species in the UK and 1905 for Laver's first published observation in Essex (via Cole). Laver noted (1915) that if a 'field' mouse was caught indoors it generally turned out to be this species. This has also been my experience. Records are shown for most of Essex where research has been carried out and Corke observes that the

A survey of 9 year old boxes put up for dormice in woodland near Haileybury College revealed use by yellow-necked mice and birds. A mouse tries to hide as the lid is raised.

A painful moment: Peter Oakenfull was bitten as he removed one of the mice for identification.

*species is found mainly in woodlands adjacent to arable farmland.*

*Our Hertfordshire records bear this out. Dobson (1999) describes them as fairly common and follows his reference to Laver with figures of 50% of national records in the recent Mamm Soc survey from houses compared with 2% for wood mice. He also reports the species to use dormouse boxes and I found a pair in one in Hopkyns' Wood, Tewin. They, too, were clearly spending the daylight hours up in a tree and were still there when I twice returned to photograph them over the following weeks (see next section).*

*Dobson makes the very significant observations about them being much more arboreal than wood mice and unlikely to be caught on the ground as easily. He indicates that old pollards are ideal retreats where hollows abound and the link with ancient woodland sites is obvious. Houses probably appear to be just another version of an old pollarded hornbeam to yellow-necked mice.*

*It is not included in the Bedfordshire Wildlife book (1987), but records had already been made in 3 tetrads in the 1985 Beds Nat survey in the central east of the county.*

Yellow-necked mice might be described as the 'turbo' version of the standard wood mouse, as I found to my cost in the garden of my childhood home in Cuffley. I had got to know wood mice and kept them, but yellow-necked mice were also living in the old field oak after which the house was named: Oak Cottage. They are larger, squeak loudly, bite and will jump very high, suddenly.

During the recent *Mamm Soc* survey for yellow-necked mice I helped Steve Kourik live trap with Longworth live mammal traps in Datchworth and one was found which behaved exactly in this way. In 1997 he had recorded the species caught by a cat at Watton-at-Stone and 2 caught in the same rat trap at Ware (Guy Philipson). A further record (also 1998) came from one caught in Little Berkhamsted, found inside a poultry shed at Buck's Alley.

The national distribution indicates a rather local, southern species and Flowerdew (1984) gives interesting information on recent work which shows that the species has a preference for drier areas with mature woodland. Wood mice tend to avoid these larger mice in captivity and, apparently, in the wild, although in Europe they have been found to interbreed. Their weight is half as much again as the average wood mouse and they usually have an attractive yellow band across the whole chest. Hours of pleasure can be had in unsuccessfully coaxing one to climb up a stem or to sit up so that the yellow neck pattern can be photographed.

Corke's observation (1972) that the species does not live in built-up or marginal areas like the wood mouse, despite its liking for human habitation in rural areas, sums up its curious status which has emerged from our records. Much more needs to be found out about its distribution and the factors which regulate its populations. The results of the *Mamm Soc* surveys have already shed some light on these questions and they may be residents of the tree canopy in daylight, with movement on ground to feeding areas strictly after dark. If live traps are set through woodland, it may be that they only climb down to venture into fields to feed beyond the average trap line, thus missing the traps.

The pair I recently found in a nest inside a nest box put up for dormice was on 11th January 2000 and they were still present on 18th January 2000 and 13th February 2000. An old partly-fallen ash tree forced down a hornbeam with the box so that it hung 2m above the ground in Hopkyns' Wood. The tree had partially fallen several years earlier, but is held up by the hornbeam. This area of the wood has dense ivy growth on an old oak and other fallen trees left above a swallow hole. Records of yellow-necked mice here, in outhouses in the adjoining Tewin Wood and in our own cottage roof (250m away) go back over 25 years.

I have already described the removal of yellow-necked mice from the upstairs rooms at Eileen Soper's house in nearby Harmer Green, which again points to them enjoying the high life rather than seeking shelter in tree roots or tunnels on the ground where wood mice are so easily live-trapped during surveys. It may seem unfortunate to compare them with the two species of rats present in Britain, but the preference for climbing and living above ground reminds me of the black rat compared with the more terrestrial brown rat.

Huma Pearce, *HMWT* Species Project Officer, stencils numbers onto boxes put in groups in trees to survey dormice at Haileybury College in June 2001. It is expected to find yellow-necked mice also using the new boxes as well as the existing ones there.

# Harvest mouse

### *Micromys minutus*

*Lloyd (47) devoted a good deal of space to our smallest rodent, which he considered 'now a doubtful denizen, though formerly (as elsewhere) apparently not uncommon'. He listed Bond's first record for the county, near Berkhamsted (1895), Crossman's nest with adult and young, also near Berkhamsted (1900), and Cranfurd's Bishop's Stortford record in a cornfield (1930). Despite the residence in Hertfordshire earlier this century of three very eminent writers on mammals (Lydekker, Oldham and Foster) none noticed the presence of the mouse in the county. Foster (1934) reported several people with local knowledge of the Hitchin area to have seen the mice in the past, but 'not recently'.*

*We now know that harvest mice live in marginal wetland habitats, but it does seem amazing that nobody recorded that they had come across them in the hayricks or corn stacks earlier this century, especially because Oldham once made the observation (reported in Foster, 1934) that 'wood mice were rarely, if ever, seen escaping from stored corn when*

Harvest mice *Micromys minutus* earned their English name from readily colonising cereal crops as they grew in summer.

**Harvest mice construct nests in living stems by stripping leaves and weaving them into a tight ball.**

In Welwyn Garden City in 1998, Keith Seaman and Peter Oakenfull caught 49 harvest mice in mixed cereal crops next to a marsh. When they started to survey in 1997 they used tennis balls with 12mm holes cut in them as part of the Mammal Society national survey. These were fixed to canes in foliage and although the technique was later considered a failure due to the inconsistency of the results elsewhere, six out of 40 used in early summer had complete or partly built nests by September. A tennis ball survey has been revived by the Mammal Society in 2001.

hundreds of house mice were disturbed during threshing'. Not a mention of harvest mice.

Darling (1970) found large numbers of harvest mice in one of his clover fields next to Therfield Heath and Newton (1972) recorded nests in a standing wheat crop where the mice had spread out from a hedgerow, near Hoddesdon, but since the modern mammal survey, most information has come from wetlands and ditches. John Tomkins showed me the first example of a harvest mouse population explosion I had ever seen at a Stevenage building site where grass near the stream towards Fishers Green had been left whilst plans were finalised. (The site was only partly destroyed.)

I first saw these mice as a child when my brother and a friend, Martin Hale, discovered a nest on the railway embankment at Cuffley, either in 1949 or 1950. At John Tomkins' site, the ginger-rumped little mice could be seen in large numbers and many would drop from the grass as you walked across the field. Nests were easy to find in all parts of the long grass. Dispersal encourages juveniles to seek standing crops in any nearby farm field, however temporary that cereal crop may be, to breed and make their own nests. They will reproduce rapidly into the autumn and non-breeding shelter nests in winter tend to be tucked away at ground level in thick cover.

Tomkins also found the species at Watton-at-Stone in a stream bed (1969) and he counted 6 juveniles in one of the Stevenage nests (30th August 1971); Gladwin reported Reeve to have found several nests in reeds when clearing part of the Stanborough Reed Marsh Nature Reserve (1971); Newton recorded 11 nests (1974) and then 12 nests (1975) at Brickendon Liberty; and when Harris led a meeting with me at Rye Meads (29th September 1974) to promote the survey work on the mice, we found 35 breeding nests. A winter grain store record (24th February 1979) was made by Darling and I have on file 64 Hertfordshire record sheets made for the first Mamm Soc national survey which give details on habitats, numbers, status of site and plants present. In recent years both Keith Seaman and Peter Oakenfull have developed live trapping methods in marsh areas. Further Mamm Soc surveys have shown a reduction, but it is difficult to return to any site and expect to find (a) the same conditions which made it ideal for the mice up to 25 years ago and (b) evidence of the mice where you found them before, possibly when their numbers were very high. My most recent specimen was one dead in a long-term set-aside pasture next to winter wheat, Tewin Hill Farm, 13th February 2000.

Laver, (1898) gives a very different account of the mouse from those early ones which mistakenly suggested rarity, even extinction, in Hertfordshire. He wrote: 'This very beautiful and active little creature occurs in all parts of Essex. In the wintertime it is found in cornstacks, especially those placed in the fields, and most frequently, I think, in oatricks. I never *discovered more than a dozen in one rick, although others have informed me that they have been found more abundantly in such situations ...'.*

*He goes on to describe studies of captive mice and was clearly as enchanted by them as the great naturalist Gilbert White had been a century earlier (and as the many modern naturalists who have kept colonies continue to be). Corke & Harris (1972) devote considerable space to the species in Essex and describe in detail the nature of harvest mouse records there since Laver's Victorian observations. Of particular interest was the reference to swarms of the mice (like those observed by Tomkins in Stevenage) and their presence in coarse herbage (Thompson, Coggeshall 1931). Dobson (1999) describes them as 'fairly common, declining' and reports that nests have been found in Essex in protective tubes for trees, as Alan Guilford has found at the '100 year Wood' plantation in Tewin.*

*A concentrated effort was made in the Beds Nat Hist Soc surveys of the 1970s and 1980s to locate the mice and they,*

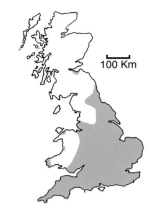

**Harvest mice are found locally throughout the county in suitable habitats.**

*too, show that early accounts, such as those of Elliott (1916) and Palmer (1946) which suggested that the mice had become rare or absent, were as equally inaccurate as the early Hertfordshire observations had been. By 1985 the map for Bedfordshire showed almost total tetrad coverage for the county, thanks to hours of field work by the Society members. Burton (1974) gives their London distribution: 'found in many rural areas around London including Bookham Common and Rye Meads, Hertfordshire'.*

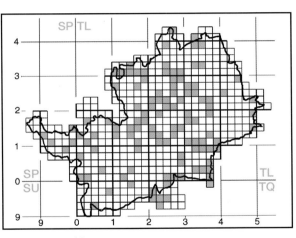

Hertfordshire was one of the counties associated with revival of interest in this species in the late 1960s. I took part in a *Living World* (radio 4) programme devoted to harvest mice, which was produced by Dilys Breese and recorded on the River Mimram at Tewin (where the koi fish farm now flourishes). Robert McCready, who lived at Wormley West End at the time, contributed much to the study by translating for me the 1955 German paper by Piechocki which gives valuable European information and observations on behaviour. I circulated this to many colleagues interested in the species.

These attractive little mice favour wetland and marginal habitats where they can spend the summer above ground, climbing and nesting in various types of grasses. Progress on their study in Hertfordshire was published in *The Grebe*, Journal of the *HMWT*, Vol 1:3, 1973.

They may live entirely over water: the harvest field (from which Gilbert White was the first person to describe them in

**Insects form an important part of the diet of harvest mice, and the tail is prehensile.**

**At the *HMWT* Sawbridgeworth Marsh Nature Reserve, Stephen Harris shows a nest high in cover.**

**Christine and Dr.John Dony (1899-1991) listed the flora at a Stevenage site in 1971, with Trevor Lording in attendance (right).**

1767) is a secondary habitat, to which an expanding summer population can spread as the tall stems appear next to their ditches or stream bank homes. Overgrown river banks will include tall grasses and shrubs which contain the woven nests which we can locate in late winter as cover dies back.

They construct their nests from the living plants so that the grass leaves are stripped into round structures the size and shape of cricket balls without killing the plants. The foliage will yellow and dry out from the damage, but remains attached and in less than a month the young have been born, mature and then, finding themselves deserted, eat their way out and make their way in the world.

Gamekeepers often notice them from long grass in their rearing fields and, like some farmers, call them 'those little red mice' from the bright ginger rump seen as they fall to safety when disturbed in long grass.

Following the first *Mamm Soc* national survey map, published in 1977, Harris, who collated the first sheets, circulated an up-dated 1987 distribution with the Society's October newsletter. Trout (1978) published reviews of wild and captive studies on the species.

Our Hertfordshire record sheets include nests associated with hawthorn, blackthorn, silver birch, elm, young conifers, willow, dogwood, sallow, bramble, greater willow herb, hogweed, wheat, rough grass, water grasses (*Glyceria maxima, Phalaris arundinacea, Phragmites communis, Carex sp., Calamagrostis epigejos*) nettle, cocksfoot, couch, brome, cowslips, violets, orchids, meadowsweet, docks and bracken.

Captive-bred females will construct nests in large, high containers with ample standing grass stems and establish large colonies. In captivity you quickly become aware of their need for insect food as well as seeds and Clive Banks introduced me to flake fish food as a very useful subsitute for live items. Poultry chick crumbs, growers pellets and quail pellets also have a high protein content. My colonies were returned to the wild in Tewin.

As Laver noticed in the last century, if young are not dispersed to establish other colonies or released into suitable wild wetland sites, they can become cannibalistic and badly bitten tails should be noted as indications of worse treatment to come.

Much the same can be said of all small mammals kept in confined spaces when individuals start to turn on each other from over population. (It would, of course, be unfortunate to see any connection between the aggressive behaviour of such small mammals due to over population and our own vastly superior species.)

130

# House mouse
## Mus domesticus

Peter Oakenfull

*Lloyd (47) is brief and to the point: 'very common in all suitable situations, not only as a direct parasite on Man's dwelling places'. A musical mouse was exhibited to members of the Herts Nat Hist Soc in 1884: it sang. (Modern studies have found that such mice have inflamed lungs and then squeak in this way.)*

*Householders are reluctant to say that they have house mice except when contacting their Environmental Health Department and the contrast in some counties between the distribution maps of harvest mice and this species reflects the understandable eagerness of people to record the presence of the more attractive native mammals.*

*When East Hertfordshire District Council, through the good offices of Susan Summers, released their mouse and rat call information for the mammal survey (Trans 28 (3) 17, 1982), we were able to publish information over a significant area.*

*The map should, however, be coloured for the whole county; the mouse occurs throughout. It would be a useful exercise for all the council districts to be written up from the different departments: this would eventually fill every tetrad.*

*There are 5 Tring specimens in the Brit Mus Roth Coll with 1 light phase. Laver (1898) recorded nearly a score of white specimens in Essex with pink eyes, caught when threshing a stack of wheat on Stebbing Ford Farm, Felstead (1897) and commented: 'Who does not know this foul-smelling, but nevertheless pretty, little beast?'*

*Anderson (1985) shows them in about 25% of the Bedfordshire survey tetrads. Dobson (1999) describes them as 'common, declining' in modern Essex, but points out that Yalden (1977) has shown them to have been present since the Iron Age.*

*Their numbers were probably at their greatest when cereals were stored and threshed: Dobson quotes Fitch (1890) who described a Finchingfield farmer who hired 4 boys to kill mice which had infested a wheat rick. With the help of men on top of the stack, over 3,000 were accounted for. Burton (1974) reported house mice as 'an urban animal, abundant in the centre of London, but often rare in the outer suburbs'. Since that time they have come to feature in the tunnels beside the tracks in underground stations and mainline stations such as*

**House mice can grow big and strong on porridge oats.**

100 Km

**When a sample of calls to the environmental health department was made in East Hertfordshire, an idea of house mouse presence was obtained.**

**Widespread, stable, possibly increasing**

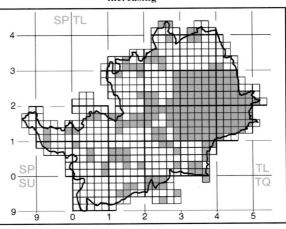

**House mice** *Mus domesticus* **climb easily and breed rapidly.**

*Euston as a diversion for passengers awaiting trains.*

*Foster (1934) listed black, pied and white varieties from the Hitchin region and makes reference to William Ransom's old diary note for 2nd February 1811: 'One of my men caught a mouse nearly white at the farm; it is rather remarkable that several at different times have been caught there of nearly the same colour' and William Lucas recorded, 13th March 1829: 'I found a brood of white mice on moving corn at the Highlander barn'.*

After many years of keeping and handling mice I was once roused from my sleep by a rustling sound next to the bed. It was light enough to distinguish a mouse sitting on floor beside me. Half asleep, I reached down to pluck it up by the scruff of the neck, but suddenly it leaped over my arm and disappeared into a cupboard. Its action made me jump so much that for the first time I felt sympathy for people who react to mice and even jump on chairs to avoid them. With such an excellent escape strategy, using sudden movement like this, plus a diet which adapts to almost any type of food (including the remains of sandwiches at the bottom of coal mines), they have successfully adapted to human shelter in all its forms.

They do like grain and products based on wheat and their distinct stale smell is often present in old corn sacks. I have had them in sacks from farms, but the mice which get into our corn bins at the orchard are usually wood or sometimes yellow-necked mice, which lack the characteristic scent. Like these, house mice love stored papers and construct nests which, when found, fall apart into a shredded heap at your feet. The nests give off the same odour as stored grain. People often confuse their small black droppings with those of bats, but the pungent smell is a quick guide to which mammal was responsible.

Although generally nocturnal, I found that individuals occasionally came to an enclosed small mammal table in daylight. Modern houses are just as prone to attack as old ones and the ducting systems for ventilation may be the perfect means of colonisation with a pair (if undisturbed) capable of producing about 5 litters per year in the urban setting. On farmland the rate increases up to 10 litters of young per year.

Young house mice are able to reproduce after 2-3 months, sometimes earlier, and gestation is 20-21 days. In a year, just two mice could thus progress to several thousand if there were no human controls on their numbers or forms of natural predation.

As has been shown with other species such as foxes and badgers, they are able to regulate their breeding. Over population appears to induce anxiety from hormonal changes in the females.

# Brown rat

## *Rattus norvegicus*

*Brett (Trans **2**: liv, 1883) reported that it was known for 1,000 rats to be killed in 1 day in Watford in Victorian times. They used to be sold to public houses at 3 shillings (15p) a dozen for sport with dogs, but by 1891 this was prohibited.*

*Lloyd (47) noted that the species was a very common resident which often does a vast amount of damage. In 1892 a dark specimen from Wheathampstead was preserved by the taxidermist, Cane of Luton. There are 3 Tring specimens*

**Brown rat** *Rattus norvegicus* **feeding.**

*preserved in the Nat His Mus Coll : 30th August 1895, 4th October 1906 (which has white on top of its head) and 8th January 1913.*

*Their seasonal movements were published with those for house mice (p131 et seq.) for east Hertfordshire by Clark & Summers (Trans **28**, 3: 17, 1982). Laver (1898) gives a good account, especially for the Essex Marshes where I have also watched many along the saltings. He reported two hairless rats from here (except for their whiskers) caught at Thorpe-le-Soken and forwarded to the Royal College of Surgeons (Bree, The Field, 5th October 1872).*

*Dobson (1999) confirms that it is 'common' and quotes Victorian kills on farms of 'plague' numbers in 1890: 318 rats killed in 2 stacks and 594 (with about 1,000 mice) killed during threshing in Laindon Parish. In Bedfordshire it is described as widespread and common, with records from 55% tetrads shown by 1985. Burton (1974) reported them to be abundant throughout the urban, suburban and rural areas of London.*

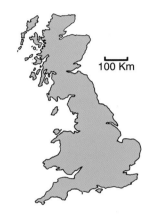

**Brown rat records indicate presence everywhere.**

A report (25th August 1989) by the Institution of Environmental Health Officers described Hertfordshire, along with Essex and Bedfordshire, as the area of Britain showing the biggest increase in rat population (41%). Factors cited were the mild winters, wet summers, an increase in litter (which provides food) and habitat, and a cut back in control in sewers by councils, British Rail and farmers.

This news came during one of the hottest summers this century, when the rat population where I was observing their numbers at Tewin Orchard had, apparently, nearly disappeared locally. Over the last 20 years I have kept diary

**Increasing**

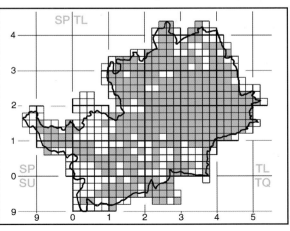

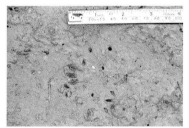

records of the general fluctuations in rat numbers and included trapping results in the *Trans* (1982) report. Rats are fascinating to watch and amazingly resilient, but despite the mild 1988/89 winter, the dry summer really did appear to reduce breeding success dramatically.

Because they are important vectors of infection, including Weil's disease that has killed several farm workers in Hertfordshire and also at least one person who was participating in water sports, it is wrong to allow their numbers to increase in premises where they may spread to neighbours and contaminate ponds or food stores.

Whenever wildlife is fed in captivity or in the open, rats are likely to be attracted. I have known juvenile rats to leave their nest in favour of sleeping in the cosy covered food platform of a mammal table constructed against a house rear window. Others were the first family to feature over a video surveillance link of the inside of the artificial badger sett at Tewin Orchard in December 1989. I described my personal interest in the species in *Mammal Watching* (1981) and because females can breed after less than 3 months, producing 5 litters of 7-8 juveniles each year, they can quickly exploit a favourable niche.

First recorded in England in 1730, the species has now spread worldwide and replaces the smaller black rat in many temperate regions, probably by its greater ability to withstand cold and to hunt for food under adverse conditions. In the tropics, however, the black rat is able to maintain its position (Taylor 1977).

From the top:

**Rat burrow and spoil heap, reminiscent of a badger sett, but in miniature.**

**A litter of 13 brown rats under shed floorboard.**

**Footprints showing how hind toes splay out sideways.**

**Siblings sleeping together.**

Above: **Staddle on a farm grain store near Kelshall. Staddles were used to prevent brown rats climbing into barns where crops were stored.**

Above right: **An excavated staddle (Warrengate Farm, Tewin) showing the depth to which they were sunk.**

(All pictures on this page from east Hertfordshire.)

# (Black rat)

## *Rattus rattus*

*Also known as the ship rat.*

*Nobody, to my knowledge, has commented upon the similarities between the extinction of the black rat by the heavier brown or 'common' rat and the replacement of our native red squirrel by the heavier, introduced, grey squirrel. The two encounters did, however, have the same effect on the species with the smaller physical size. Admittedly both rats were introduced, whereas red squirrels are indigenous, but where two closely related species compete, size does appear to matter. Black rats were once a feature of Hertfordshire's mammal fauna. Colour is little help in its identification.*

**One of Douglas English's classic plate camera studies of black rats** *Rattus rattus* **from 1915.**

*One of the most thorough papers written on a mammal species in the Trans is by Davis & Lloyd-Evans (**25**:1, 4-6, 1958): the 'Occurrence of the Ship Rat (Rattus rattus L.) in Hertfordshire' which described Davis' records at the Ware maltings in warehouses, barges and riverside premises in 1951.*

*Lloyd-Evans made records there in 1955, sent a specimen drowned in a water bath (2nd April 1955) to Tring where it was prepared as a cabinet skin by A.H.Bishop and saw 2 of the brown colour forms, referred to as 'R. r. frugivorous'. Contemporary cuttings show the interest in 1951 and Alan Ward kindly researched this from borough council records for me. The sanitary inspector mentioned, Mr.C.J.Lucas, was still living in Cromwell Road, Ware, in the 1980s.*

*Although skull evidence from a Roman well in York (Rackham 1979) indicates earlier colonisation, Davis & Lloyd-Evans' paper is worthy of edited extracts here because the species is of special interest since it has been lost from the county list only in the last 40 years:*

*'The ship rat (R. rattus) was first brought to Britain on ships; it spread and flourished until the arrival of the brown rat (R. norvegicus) in the early eighteenth century, and then was rapidly replaced by the new invader, hanging on precariously only in the seaports where it could be reinforced from overseas.*

*'Oliver Goldsmith, in his "History of the Earth and Animated Nature" (1774) states: "This animal was formerly as mischievous as it was common; but at present it is almost utterly extirpated by the great rat, one malady often expelling another. It is become so scarce that I do not remember ever to have seen one."*

*'While ship rats are now found in Britain mainly in port areas, they also occur in some inland towns, particularly those linked to ports by inland waterways. The occurrence of ship rats in Ware provides an interesting illustration. At the end of 1944, the County Agricultural Committee started rat control measures at a canal-side warehouse in Ware; the premises were then infested by brown rats; good clearances*

*The brown rat has replaced the black rat much as the grey squirrel has taken the place of the red squirrel. Wood mice and yellow-necked mice seem able to coexist because they exploit different foods and habitats. Much the same relationship applies to the common dormouse and the edible dormouse.*

*Both species of rat are particularly destructive to ground-nesting sea bird populations when introduced to islands due to activities of humans.*

Archibald Thorburn's line drawing of a black rat from *British Mammals* 1920. The tail length is exceptional, especially when compared with the brown rat *Rattus norvegicus.*

100 Km

were claimed, and the buildings remained free from rats for a considerable time. But in 1947 it was reported that reinfestation, mainly by ship rats, was taking place rapidly after treatments; in earlier years ship rats were seldom found on this site. In 1946 barges loaded with foreign wheat and other imported commodities had begun to arrive at this warehouse after a lapse of many years, so it was inferred that this accounted for the change in species of rat.

'One of the Ministry of Agriculture's scientific staff, Miss B.Jones, inspected a wheat barge on this canal side at the end of 1947 and found ship rats living and breeding on it.

'Early in 1951 R.A.Davis inspected four barges at Ware and found evidence that ship rats were travelling regularly on these vessels. The design of the barges favours the carriage, and even the breeding, of ship rats; one type has cutaway corners to the bulkheads between cabin and hold, and thick rat smears lead up to the corner hole and down the other side; there were holes with smears in the "ceiling" (floor to the landsman) of the cabin, under which nesting material had been dragged. In the space behind the cabin locker there were condensation and bilgewater to which the rats had access. There were plenty of old grain residues in parts of the barges, even in one carrying Vermiculite at the time of inspection. Fresh faeces of both species of rat were found in bags of wheat pollards from the River Plate, sometimes in juxtaposition in the same bag.

'On his visit to Ware in 1951 R.A.Davis inspected a very large maltings and found it heavily infested by ship rats; up to nine months before his visit only a few common rats had been seen there; he was satisfied that the maltings staff were well aware of the difference in general appearance of the two species. This maltings was built in 1906 and rebuilt after being completely destroyed by fire in 1907; during the last war (1939-1945) a large timber yard was established beside it, and local opinion puts the blame for the infestation on the timber barges, which did make occasional trips loaded with grain instead of timber; ship rats could subsist on grain residues in these barges for a time. Four other maltings in Ware were said to be infested by ship rats according to the sanitary authorities, and ship rats were subsequently reported also from Bengeo and Wareside.

'The older maltings in Ware were very difficult to proof, and ship rats use air-conditioning trunking as runways; there are numerous other runways on all floors of the buildings, holes gnawed, smears and ship rats' droppings. Ship rats drink the condensation on pipes and walls associated with the cisterns; they inhabit the roof-space and use the rafters as runways. Indeed most of the population seems to be in the upper stories; they spread from building to

136

*building along wires and cables, and travel from house to house under the intercommunicating roof spaces along the High Street. At one maltings in Ware an ingenious method of destruction was to attach a string to a wire cable running between two buildings and to jerk it when ship rats ran across, dislodging the rats which fell into the space between the buildings, where they could sometimes be killed.*

'*A second inspection by R.A.Davis in August 1951, showed ship rats still present in barges and riverside premises at Ware, though some degree of control had been achieved. Until they died out, as the maltings were redeveloped for housing and offices from the 1960s, more than 20 black rats would be picked up after poisoning campaigns. Away from Ware, Palmer, a pest contol officer, recorded 14 killed from a threshed stack at Allen's Green, near Sawbridgeworth, in 1928.*'

**Ware docks about 1920. The black rats were established in the maltings (see text) and received regular recruitments to their number from the barge traffic between the Port of London and the Lea Valley. Photograph reproduced by kind permission of D.Gray,** *Hertfordshire Mercury.*

*As well as good specimens in North Herts Mus, there are 3 striking Watford skins in the Nat Hist Mus all of which illustrate the long, thin, dark, tapering tail which is always longer than the body length. Their large, oval, almost hairless ears and eyes (much bigger in proportion to the head than those of brown rats) further confirm their identification from the latter species. Due to the absence of this rat in Hertfordshire now, I will give full measurements of the 3 Watford specimens:*

1 (dark)     31/7/1913:     HB 161, T 219, HF 33, E 24
2 (normal)   31/7/1913:     HB 176, T 220, HF 34, E 22
3 (normal)   31/7/1913:     HB 163, T 202, HF 36, E 22
(Key: HB=Head and Body, T=tail, HF=hind foot, E=ear)

*One was identified by The Field in the autumn of 1899 after a dog killed a rat in Bancroft at Hitchin, and the following spring 8 were trapped in the same garden. Lloyd (47) curiously makes no mention of the species, but Davis & Lloyd-Evans summed up:*

'*In conclusion, the ship rat is well established at Ware, and is found regularly on barge and lighter traffic on the Lee Conservancy canal system, together with the brown rat, sometimes in the same barge. It seems likely that similar conditions may apply to other inland towns in which ship rats are known to occur, and the importance of inland waterways traffic in the spread of rats should not be underestimated*'.

*The Ware account is particularly fascinating and a very valuable piece of local Hertfordshire history. Foster (1954) noted that although Letchworth Mus had no record of black rats, Buller killed 2 in 1864 when the old Hermitage was being altered, and Barnard, the official rat-catcher to Hertfordshire County Council from 1915-1925, said that although he had hardly ever met with the species, in or about 1918 whilst clearing rats from Wallington near Baldock he found several. He also found some whilst working the timber* premises in Bancroft, Hitchin, 1920-21.

There are historic mummified specimens from Baldock houses which show their former abundance and there are Roman sites in London, York and Wroxeter where their remains were found, dated from the 3rd-5th centuries. If they were the first mammal to associate with humans, as seems likely, they were also the cause of transmitting lethal viruses to humans. Their role in the Black Death is the subject of modern controversy, but whether the disease which killed a third of Britain's population (and about 25 million people in Europe) was plague, or possibly anthrax, the rat flea was certainly significant in human deaths in the 11th and 14th centuries.

Laver (1898) considered the species almost extinct in Essex although in that era (and to recent time) it still arrived about the docks in the East End of London as a result of vessels lying in the river in the neighbourhood. A very helpful account is given in Dobson (1999), who shows that a colony still survives in grain silos at Tilbury at the southern-most tip of Essex. Burton (1974) had described it as found in the West End of London (Oxford Street), the Port of London and a few other areas. Although he thought it was one of Britain's rarest animals, he considered it was unlikely that anyone would legislate to protect the species. In Bedfordshire the last report was from Whipsnade (1949) given in Beds Wildlife (1987).

# Common dormouse
## Muscardinus avellanarius

Roberts (1893) exhibited a dormouse to the Society which had been taken from Aldenham and said 'I fancy that the species is not very abundant in the county'. The 'Zoologist' (1887) had, however, described them as very common in the nut groves on Buckland Common, on the borders with Buckinghamshire, and a nest had been found at Haresfoot 'many years ago, but none had been noticed since'.

Apart from one male specimen caught on 29th July 1902, the 11 Nat Hist Mus Roths Hertfordshire specimens (see picture on p141) all appear to have been found during hibernation or in autumn nests:

23rd October 1902, female, Tring;
24th October 1902, female Tring;
4th November 1902, 1 male and 1 female, Tring;
5th November 1902, female, Tring;
14th November 1902, sex?, Champneys, Wigginton;
15th November 1902, female, Tring;
8th December 1902, male, Tring;
24th October 1904, 1 male and 1 female, Tring.

Of these 11, only 3 were recorded as male although in two the sex was not recorded. Lloyd (47) reported the species rather rare and unknown in many districts 'partly no doubt

**Common dormouse** *Muscardinus avellanarius* **pictured in captivity, found in hibernation in Broxbourne Woods, described on page 139.**

owing to the fact that it is unprotected and may therefore be taken by dealers to be sold as a pet'.

He gives a number of records for the Boxmoor and Berkhamsted districts and mentions that Lydekker described the county border country between Aylesbury and Hemel Hempstead as a district where they were found in good numbers. 'Now even there it has greatly declined', he added.

He gives Aldenham (1893) and St.Albans (1903) records and quotes Foster's Hitchin data which concluded that 'whilst 30 or more years ago one used to see dormice in our district rather frequently, now they are few and far between.' He gives Buller's comment that they were 'very common in his boyhood, south of Hitchin'; a report by Passingham of 'many, often found by my dog' and Warren's similar view for the turn of the century, in contrast to an almost total absence of records for the 1930s. (This was at the time of grey squirrel expansion in the county.)

Westell described them as local in the Letchworth district and in Foster's summary he could only mention that one had been found in 1927 in the neighbourhood of Baldock. This seemed to reflect a national picture of decline from what was once a popular Edwardian pet mouse to being a very scarce species, local to old woodland. Whiteman (1936) gives a single Hexton record for 1934 'when a boy discovered one in its nest which he mistook for that of a wren. Feeling inside for eggs, he discovered the mouse, which he kept as a pet for some time'.

Laver (1898) gives a good account of the species in Essex. Corke & Harris (1972) comment that it seems certain that dormice are less common in Essex since Laver's time. All their recent records were from coppiced woodland and they noted that live traps on the ground were not appropriate in locating the presence of the species. They concluded that whilst the records suggested dormice were very rare in Essex, if a better way was discovered of surveying for them, they may be found to be a normal inhabitant of most of the coppiced woodlands.

Dobson (1999) illustrates their 'scarce, declining' status in modern Essex with a distribution map which shows how little they are known away from nature reserves there. He reports cat predation (up to 25 by one cat at Mill Green). Beds Wildlife (1987) records just 3 sites, from southwest Bedfordshire (even fewer than for the edible dormouse) and Anderson (1985) considers the species 'vulnerable'. Burton (1974) gives no Hertfordshire information for the London area, although he reported that 'overlooked for many years,

Common dormouse records are mostly from ancient woodland sites where coppice management has regretfully ceased.

**Serious decline**

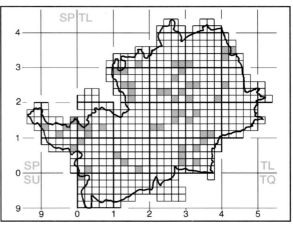

John Tomkins with one of his dormouse nest boxes made with a plastic drain pipe.

John Tomkins showing Ralph Newton, John Gurnell and Martin Hicks a dormouse in a stand of fir trees at Box Wood, Stevenage.

Before the dormouse was released, Martin Hicks demonstrated his relaxation techniques

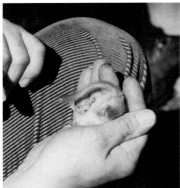

*this species has recently been recorded in rural areas bordering the outer suburbs in Kent and Surrey'.*

Just as the Edwardian records from Tring in the *Nat His Mus* show how vulnerable the species is during its occupation of winter nests, our modern information reflects the same story. Between the late 1960s and early 1980s they have been found in hibernation in London Colney, Northaw Great Wood, Tewin Wood (1 in a hollow hornbeam), Tewin village (2 killed by a cat from a hollow yew), Goffs Oak (1 in a compost heap, replaced asleep), Walkern, Astonbury Woods, Broxbourne Woods (during coppice work, kept until spring and then returned there) and Hudnall Common. One seen in January 1975 must have broken hibernation: it was climbing in a willow at Wilstone Reservoir. It showed no signs of lethargy and ran onto the ground and under a log. Watery Grove on the Knebworth Estate near Stevenage, produced a very late breeding nest on 24th October 1970 (Tomkins) and 2 nests were located there by the writer in 1974, 300mm off the ground, one woven into sedges with soft leaves and old man's beard *Clematis vitalba* inside, hidden amongst low branches and brambles. The other was on a fallen tree, overgrown by shrubs, woven in grass and well concealed with a clear entrance hole. Martin Hicks made a survey of hazelnuts opened by the mice in 1991, but found no evidence of the species where the A1(M) widening scheme may remove a further section of ancient oak/hornbeam woodland.

Tomkins has been bird ringing regularly in Box Wood on the northwestern edge of Stevenage and has found use of his boxes by dormice, two of which he was able to show to a group of us who visited the site in 1986. Tomkins had made boxes very quickly from plastic drainage tubes cut to size, with blocks of wood inside the base and wooden covers to keep the occupants dry. It does seem that when someone makes a special effort to study the species with nest boxes in suitable woodland sites, summer nests and individual dormice can be located.

When Banks and Barton made searches for old summer nests as cover died back in winter at ancient woodland sites they found examples in Wigginton, Ashridge, and towards Whipsnade (examples were 3 nests in brambles and 4 in honeysuckle mixed with maple in a single area). These, and Tomkins' records, suggest that in established old coppiced woodland areas of the county (as in Essex) the species survives well enough to be located, but so little of this habitat is left that all should be treated as inviolate. The replacement of our ancient woods with conifer plantations this century also appears to be an important factor in the loss of this species to so many districts.

Whether or not grey squirrels cream off the hazel crops in years when the nuts are few, their presence could be vital to the weight gain of dormice to ensure that they survive in hibernation. Their numbers in these areas seem to be much reduced. The paucity of records from new areas is a great cause for concern.

We had 23 dormouse habitat record sheets from the surveys before the 1990s, but the impression I have formed (without extensive data, it is true) is that dormice are becoming increasingly isolated and reduced in numbers and may go the way of red squirrels in the county unless:

- every site which has ever produced records is given maximum protection from development or the type of management which might further adversely affect them;
- positive work in woodland is carried out to encourage the appropriate food plants, ground cover and tree canopy;
- boxes are provided to monitor populations and provide added protection to individuals;
- where possible, corridor habitats should be constructed to link areas where dormice live to reduce the isolation of populations;
- conifer plantations continue to be replaced by native oak-with-hornbeam woodlands.

When dormice open hazelnut shells to eat the kernel they leave a distinctly smooth inner rim with a pattern of tooth marks at an angle to the opening.

The loss of hedgerows may be another vital factor which explains why the species is in retreat: the cover and above-ground circulation from wood to wood has been taken away over such vast areas. It is not difficult, for example, to link two known dormouse woods without expensive tree planting if coppiced scrub or bushes are heaped in a line between the sites. Nettles, brambles and grasses quickly colonise between the branches and by the time the original cuttings have rotted a high shrub layer is established. Even in places with high rabbit numbers, young trees grow up from the protection of the shrubs so that dormice are able to move along briars and branches after as little as 3-5 years, depending upon local conditions.

Better still, new hedgerows should be planted with oak, hornbeam, bullace, beech, hazel, cherry and crab apple as typical dominant species. Before it is too late to save the dormouse a massive hedgerow and woodland programme of regeneration should be put into effect in the county.

The Northaw Great Wood dormouse records indicate this to be the central population for the area; a site where successful public access and daily activities have been managed without detriment to the wildlife. Perhaps a link continues along the Cuffley Brook, Scout Camp, Newgate Street bridge railway route into the Broxbourne Woods complex via Ponsbourne Park.

Local work on dormice is to be encouraged and valuable information is being gathered on a national level by Martin Hicks (who also works in Hertfordshire), Keith Seaman, Sarah Bryer, Peter Oakenfull, Stephen Whitbread, Dr.Pat Morris and Paul Bright. It has emerged from their research

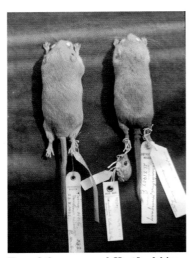

Two of the preserved Hertfordshire dormouse specimens from Tring (see p138).

work that dormice spend much more time in trees and above ground than was previously thought. They prefer a continuous well developed shrub layer in open woodland, woodland edge, coppice, scrub and hedgerow along which they move and feed on insect foods as well as fruits.

Although they are found in places which lack hazels, in general their numbers, which are always at a much lower density than other small mammals, may be significantly linked to hazel crops because of the need to put on weight to survive hibernation. As already mentioned, grey squirrels have almost certainly contributed to the decline of the dormouse due to vigorous competition for food in years when the nut crop has failed. Bright suggests climate as another possible cause for decline and has shown that by providing boxes in a wood, about twice as many dormice are present as there are in a wood without boxes, which is exactly what occurs when nest boxes are put up for small birds.

In midsummer he found low body weights between the spring peak of food from flowers or insects and the autumn fruits, nuts and berries. Dense, early fruiting blackberry bushes (*Rubus fruticosus*) are clearly an advantage in the woodland shrub layer. As dormice are a special feature of southern woods such as those in Hertfordshire and are a red data species (the list of seriously threatened plants and animals), a special conservation effort is needed for them in the county. Dot Eaton held a Mammal Society meeting over a decade ago where she demonstrated captive breeding at Windsor. She later investigated Tewin Orchard and Haileybury College for controlled release sites: both had historic records for dormice and could be supervised. Later, an enclosure was constructed at woodland near the College and dormouse boxes fixed to surrounding trees. I was able to visit the wood with two of the College tutors (Roger Humphreys and Dr.Fiona Hughes) in April 2000 and found just one box with a possible domed and lined dormouse nest inside; most were in use by other small mammals or nesting birds. Likewise, at Tewin, my survey of boxes only found a pair of yellow-necked mice (on 3 occasions), a nest of hornets (at which I closed the box lid and decended the ladder at unusually high speed), several nests of small mammals, blue tits and great tits.

It is proposed that the *HMG* take on the restoration of the Haileybury habitat and provide new boxes for a joint College venture to manage the woodland for the dormice in particular. Restoration of the release pen would be easily achieved. Haileybury College already carries out conservation projects at Tewin Orchard Nature Reserve and work parties achieve much in their community projects generally in the county.

# Edible dormouse
## *Glis glis*

*Also known as the fat dormouse. Lloyd (47) gives an informative account of the species, introduced by Lord Walter Rothschild at Tring on or about 4th February 1902, which quickly became a part of local folklore. Lloyd was told of a Hastoe man who was convinced these dormice could only be killed by an iron bar or implement, not by wood, and at Wigginton that they were a hybrid between rabbits and rats. At Aston Clinton they became known as 'chinchillas'.*

**Edible dormouse** *glis glis* **in captivity at Tewin Orchard in 1971.**

This large European species of dormouse is represented by 6 Tring specimens in the Nat His Mus Coll. (for 1902, 1905, 1950, 1952 [2] and 1987). The distinction of being the only species of mammal successfully introduced into Britain solely from Hertfordshire may be viewed with some reserve by those who manage woodland or store apples in their lofts. Lloyd gave details of the spread into Buckinghamshire and whilst the stronghold is still around the Chilterns, there is evidence of a gradual dispersal, with records from more central Hertfordshire, often as a result of human agencies. Anderson (1985) shows only 4 tetrads for Bedfordshire.

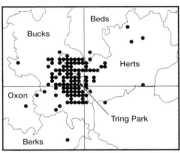

**The total known distribution of edible dormice from Pat Morris' survey 1997/98.**

The colonisation by the species has often been described as very limited, but comparisons seem to be based on the dispersal of the grey squirrel or muntjac. Both of these species are very mobile and explore readily as their numbers build up in an area. Edible dormice show similar traits to the common dormouse (p138 *et seq.*) with strong loyalty to a particular area. When 3 of them escaped in Tewin Orchard in 1976 we heard nothing of them and presumed they had died out.

They had been removed from an apple store in a Berkhamsted roof space following a complaint to Clive Banks and I had brought them home to study them. (It is now illegal to keep them or move them without a licence.) Ten years later on 21st June 1986 I heard one calling in the dark from the top branches of a Bramley apple tree in the orchard. This shows how they can stay in an area undetected for a long time and, if there is suitable food and cover, remain in the vicinity.

They seem to tolerate large numbers

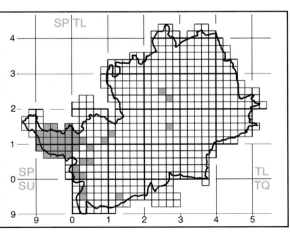

Brian Barton checks for occupancy of a box during the edible dormouse survey near Tring.

of other edible dormice around food at sites: Clive Banks and Michael Ferrero caught 36 in a Tring roof (1970), 11 in another (August 1971) and 5 at Redbourn (September 1971). Terry Holder recorded 8 together at Wigginton (1974). Unless I had kept them I would not have recognised their call and not everyone regularly walks around orchards closing poultry sheds at night. I would like to think that their Latin name *glis* comes from the unforgettable sound which can be immitated by repeatedly saying 'glis, glis, glis' in a deep voice with a fixed grin and heavy lisp. They are not very friendly mammals and the call can intensify, like the deep roar from a healthy beehive, if you disturb them, just prior to their biting you.

Gotch (1979) gives *glis* as from the Latin word *glinis*, a dormouse, and the English name *dormis*, from the Latin for 'I sleep' in reference to their long hibernation period.

Despite the autumn lethargy induced by hibernation, one of the specimens we were given in October 1970 promptly gave birth to what seemed to have been a very late litter of 3 young on 9th October 1970.

Holes in old trees may be the preferred summer nest site and 3 were found in a felled beech tree at Rossways, Berkhamsted (June 1970). Two called from a beech tree in Ashridge as Banks and Barton watched badgers on 9th July 1970.

Lever (1977) gives much information on Hertfordshire and the surrounding countryside in *The Naturalized Animals of the British Isles* and I can only conclude that there will be a slow expansion of their range. The species is firmly established in suitable well-wooded habitats and gardens.

They are not popular in the Chiltern forestry areas, gnaw quickly through wooden enclosures to escape if kept in captivity and are certainly able to run over house roofs to locate apple stores with skill. They easily gain access to lofts through gaps in the facia boards. Two specimens in Stevenage caught by Christopher Woodard (1997) may have been released there and I recall seeing them on sale in a pet shop in the town in the 1970s.

Amongst his many projects on mammals, Dr.Pat Morris has led the research on dormice and has spoken to *HNHS* on several occasions. He is shown at a Mammal Society meeting following presentations to some of his students.
From left to right: **Leigh Barrett, Heather Devany, Pat Morris and Christine Trimmer.**

Pat Morris points out that many people who trap them in their roof spaces do not want to kill them and release them at considerable distance from their homes, thus spreading the dormice beyond natural barriers that had hitherto constrained their distribution. He describes their ambiguous legal status, population size, economic significance and field work in 3 papers (2 in 1997, 1 in 1998) and concludes that there is a population of about 10,000 in the survey area of 6 counties. These surround the original introduction site of Tring Park, illustrated in his 1997 review.

Past President of *HNHS*, Brian Barton, is pictured in one of the two *Journal of Forestry* papers (1997) examining a nest box. Sian and Brian Barton helped considerably with the survey and it is interesting that 3 dormice were found in July 1996 in a cold and lethargic state. Our native dormice and bats also practice daytime torpor where they can allow their body temperatures to drop to conserve their energy, even in the summer months.

Morris finds that the tree damage in this country is 'probably controllable' and peculiarly British; 'tree damage occurs elsewhere, but is not a major issue in Continental European literature (although damage to fruits and nut crops is, Santini 1978)'. Questionnaires have produced one unsubstantiated record from as far east as Cheshunt, but I can confirm the validity of his Stevenage records which are nearly as far east.

Nest-tubes for capture, survey and control of the dormice are illustrated in the 1998 paper by Morris & Temple and proved to be a considerable success.

**When a hedgerow is partly removed for road safety (Churchfields, Tewin) the amount of cover such habitats provide for small mammals and other wildlife can be seen in cross section.**

**Live traps for surveys of small mammals include commercial squirrel cage traps for edible dormice and the Longworth trap shown here, painted dark green in camouflage, for the smaller species.**

145

**Coypu** *Myocastor coypus.*
**After a wood engraving from** *The Royal Natural History* **(1894), edited by the distinguished Hertfordshire wildlife author, Richard Lydekker.**

# (Coypu)
## *Myocastor coypus*

*Lloyd (47) did not refer to escapes of coypu from fur farms after 1932 and I only received 3 unconfirmed reports early in the 1970s before all news ceased. Lever (1977) reported their presence in southwest Hertfordshire by 1962 when the third eradication campaign began and any individuals which did colonise from the established wild populations in Buckinghamshire and East Anglia were soon trapped or died out. The last MAFF eradication campaign was successful by making payments to trappers guaranteed for 10 years so that there was no advantage in keeping a nucleus of the animals to maintain a steady income as in the case of squirrel bounties paid on tails: the quicker you trapped all the coypu, the quicker you could do other paid work whilst the income for the trapping still came in. This incentive scheme operated from 1981-1991 and a massive effort on the same lines against the grey squirrel would be ideal now for the conservation of the indigenous species.*

*Coypu are from South America and live in rivers and lakes. In 1973 it was estimated that they had reached a population of 10,000 in East Anglia, reduced to 7,000 by 1976. No Hertfordshire records have been received since the 1970s.*

# Red fox
## *Vulpes vulpes*

*Lloyd (47) is brief and to the point: 'widely distributed and unnaturally preserved for hunting in some districts. There is still room for a fair number of unpreserved foxes in the well wooded and hilly parts of the county.'*

*Before fox hunting became fashionable in the 18th and 19th centuries they were included in vermin payments by church wardens (Oldham, Trans **18**, 45-50, 19, 79-112). Hager (Trans **23**:5 236-237, 1952) gives a first-hand account of the species, covering her observations in 1949 at Pancake and Hockeridge Woods, near Berkhamsted. The description of cub play areas and predation on chickens to satisfy the increasing appetites of growing juveniles is familiar to all who have regularly watched foxes.*

*The dispersal of the cubs into growing arable crops is of interest: in this case into an oat field where a hare was disturbed and, later, a wheat field where 8 hares and a rabbit were displaced.*

*Recorded throughout Hertfordshire, Beds Wildlife (1987) describes foxes as 'widespread and common' and Dobson (1999) reports them to be 'abundant and increasing in Essex'. Burton (1974) had found the same status 25 years earlier in the outer suburbs of London and a few were also to be found 'in the inner suburbs, particularly near areas of waste ground and parks'.*

**Red fox** *Vulpes vulpes* **in short, well-marked summer pelage (Tewin).**

Laver (1897), a keen follower of the hounds in Essex, gives lengthy hunting anecdotes including: that of a vixen hotly pursued for many miles in the neighbourhood of Chelmsford which finally dropped a cub it had been carrying from its mouth; a vixen which was found with 4 cubs about 7m off the ground in a pollarded oak tree where 3 of the cubs were hand-reared afterwards; a dog fox chased onto a church roof where '3 or 4 couple of the hounds were passed up a broken buttress to complete the pursuit above the chancel and the fox was there compelled to surrender up his life without the benefit of clergy'; a fox chased on 19th February 1863 around Havering which ran 24 miles in 3 hours 7 minutes before being killed; and one in 1881 which had been raised (put up) at Parndon Wood which ran into Hertfordshire at Cheshunt and back to Parndon Wood in 1 hour 45 minutes - it went to earth and was dug out and killed.

Fox-hunting in Hertfordshire is also documented very fully, although by the 19th century its shooting estates, with easy access to and from London, virtually met each other across the entire countryside. Farmland was included in the game management which was carried out by gamekeepers. They ensured the survival of enough foxes for their employers to hunt. The pattern of woodlands and copses were passed down to us from a very strong field sports tradition which often caused conflict between its enthusiasts. Armstrong (1909) wrote:

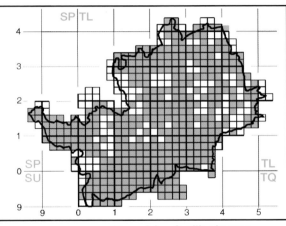

The red fox, familiar in most habitats.

**Increasing**

'Certain parts of Hertfordshire are pheasant-ridden, the country thereby having become less attractive from a fox-hunting standpoint since Lord Dacre's mastership (of the Hertfordshire Hounds), which covered the 27 years from 1839-1866. But the Bedford side (thanks to the Duke of Bedford) is still staunch to fox-hunting, though good wild shooting is also enjoyed.

'The Marchioness of Salisbury founded the Hunt in 1775 and hunted the slow hounds of that day ... In those early days the county was one with the adjoining Puckeridge, but separation was effected in 1799 ... To trace the history of hunting in Hertfordshire one must deal with the periods of Queen Elizabeth I and of Queen Anne, both of whom hunted the wild red deer in its natural forest lair. But the latter grand and courageous animal is too destructive of grain crops to be allowed to continue on or near cultivated lands: hence the noble antlered monarch has been swept away with the cruel, but necessary utilitarian besom of destruction,

147

**Major Russell Dore, Master of the Enfield Chace Foxhounds, hunting in Bramfield Forest, 27th February 1971.**

*only to inaugurate the reign of his carnivorous successor, the thief of the world - the wily fox. The Cecil family of Hatfield Park could not be left out of the ancient history, but respect for space induces the writer to go no further back than 1725, when kennels at Albury embraced both counties now known as the Hertfordshire and the Puckeridge'.*

*Armstrong lists a pack of hounds at Poles, near Ware, in about 1800 and notes that since 1896 Edward Barclay took over the Puckeridge hunt and later established the kennels at Brent Pelham near Buntingford, where the family still continues the tradition. By the 1950s the county was divided between this hunt (which links with the Essex hunts), the Enfield Chace and the Hertfordshire. The Whaddon Chase and the Old Berkeley were neighbours to the west and the Oakley and Cambridgeshire to the north. (The Enfield Chace was established in 1935 and the late Major Dore of Nyn, Northaw, was a driving force as master behind the pack for many seasons.)*

*One of the most detailed accounts of fox-hunting in the west of the county is given by Dorian Williams in his 'Pendley and a Pack of Hounds', which gives details of the history of his family and his own life spent hunting, with photographs of early meets, many people connected with hunting in Hertfordshire and shows the typical Jack Russell hunt terrier. (Williams developed adult education courses at Pendley and I attended Deer Society conferences there in the 1960s.) Many of the pictures are by the late Frank Meads whom I visited on 11 August 1972. He lived at Essendon and was the most famous hunt photographer, succeeded by his equally successful son, Jim Meads. Many of their photographs have been taken in Hertfordshire.*

*Williams' book gives very valuable background to the social and management aspects of chasing foxes with hounds and he described in deep sorrow how he experienced his first 'blank day' when in his second year as Master of the Whaddon Chase. Too many foxes were thought to have been killed cub hunting that year. Cub hunting is when the hounds are taken out in August to introduce new hounds to the skills of finding, chasing and killing inexperienced foxes of the year. 'The absolute priority in running a hunt is to show sport', he wrote.*

*Because fox-hunting is subject to even more heated debate than usual due to recent election promises by politicians, it is worth considering the activity about which everyone seems to have an opinion. The job of finding foxes is put down to the paid huntsman and others, including earth-stoppers who fill as many holes the foxes might go into as possible, and terrier-men who take the dogs to follow foxes underground. These are bred to corner the fox with noisy barks until it can be dug out, located by all the noise. Hunt followers must let the huntsman and 'whips' who control the hounds, do the work of finding a fox. Once the hounds have put one up, the fox must be allowed to get away before the riders can gallop after.*

*The excitement of jumping fences and following all manner of unexpected turns and unpredictable routes is the attraction. Historically, people have taken up fox-hunting as an activity as they ceased (usually through inherited wealth) to have to earn a living. Once the necessities of life were provided for, the fashionable activity of the day could be pursued. Many masters of foxhounds worked as hard at the job of running a hunt, with its essential kennel and stable staff, as they would have done if they were running a company. The paid huntsman who rides up front with the master has the job of locating foxes by 'drawing' woodland with his hounds. Followers are from every social background. Many follow the hunt on foot as well as those enjoying the horse riding.*

*Foxes were probably quite rare until the complicated social ritual of pursuit with hounds made their abundance a requirement of the local landowners. In the West Country, Parson Jack Russell described how the whole village would turn out to kill foxes if an active earth was discovered. He encouraged local people to preserve foxes and practice the sport of hunting with hounds. From about 1815 he developed and bred the little hunt terrier named after him.*

*Hunting is inextricably linked with the status and survival of the species in the county. By the 1960s it was possible to find, as I did, foxes on gibbets in the heart of the Enfield Chace country at Ponsbourne, near Newgate Street. This*

**The distinguished hunt photographer, Frank Meads, at his Hertfordshire home in Essendon, 11th August 1972.**

**This winter scene from** *They Meet at Eleven* **(1956), shows the Enfield Chace Foxhounds leaving Essendon in snowfall. Centre (light coat) is Ruth Murray, who has devoted her life to badger welfare.**

149

A snare set for foxes on the approach to a pheasant release pen in woods near Stevenage.

Before hunting in Dawley Woods and Bramfield Forest, the Enfield Chace Foxhounds meet at the Rose & Crown public house in Tewin, 27th February 1971.

would have been unheard of in earlier times. The protection of foxes for hunts is now clearly ignored in many areas and hundreds are shot annually in Hertfordshire. As foxes have become familiar in urban areas and breed in gardens, a more tolerant attitude towards the species has emerged. Many people are opposed to the organised hunting of foxes and demonstrate against the activity openly. The League Against Cruel Sports and more extreme hunt saboteur groups campaign to have the activity made illegal or disrupt the hunts when they meet. These divisions cloud many of the issues and instead of the entire conservation and countryside movements working for wildlife and their habitats as a whole, political influence is lost in a confusion of different fringe organisations and societies. Put together, all the people supporting the countryside would number millions, far in excess of the membership of any single political party. Only then would balance come to the arguments for preserving the countryside.

Roberts (Trans 7: 6, 171, 1893) noted that foxes had been credited from antiquity with the ingenuity of getting out of wells and that one had been found at the bottom of an ice house at Ashlyns, Berkhamsted. The fox was brought out, carried under the arm of a helper; 'The animal appeared to quite grasp the situation, did not attempt to bite, but merely looked up at him with its wonderfully bright eyes. On reaching the surface it was, of course, liberated'. (In our bat research we found the remains of rabbits and sheep in ice houses which had open access and have noted the scent of foxes or found their droppings in several cases, despite the depth of the well areas.)

The ice houses where evidence of foxes has been found are those with sloping brick sides which give a grip for foxes to scramble up and out, but at 3-4m depth they are still formidable heights to scale. The very deep, sheer-sided ice houses typified by two in the Hitchin area are protected by doors, but would give no chance of escape to the most agile of foxes if they gained entry.

The Nat His Mus Coll. has 3 Tring skins (1892, 1944 and 1948), 1 Cole Green (1964) and 2 Bayfordbury (1965) with 11 Hunton Bridge specimens all taken by N.Garland in 1969. The 1892 Tring skin was probably kept because it is very dark and the 1944 one because it was exceptionally large (HB 715mm, T 365mm, HF 155, E 190). The 11 from Hunton Bridge may seem a large total for one area, but one part-time keeper gave me details for an estate near Baldock on 30th August 1976 where 200 foxes were killed in the first year of control by a new full-time gamekeeper and if the count had included the previous 30 months, the total was 460. He used snares, spring traps, digging, gassing, shooting and poisons. (In the 1970s and 80s at Cuffley, Berkhamsted and Datchworth, the illegal use of poison also killed foxes and at least one badger was also found dead at Datchworth.)

Goodall (1972) gave figures of fox control on the Langleybury and Kings Langley estate land: 1,620 in 12 years. When keepers from Brocket Estate at Welwyn extended their control to Symondshyde Great Wood in 1950 they killed 130 foxes and in 1951, 131. Hunting by humans has been such an important influence on the ecology of the fox in Hertfordshire that many of our woods and copses have survived because they hold and encourage foxes. Artificial piped earths were dug for them to breed inside in many places. No doubt a compromise will one day be found. In the event of legal limitations on hunting with dogs, the spectacle of well turned-out riders, horses and hounds may have to continue by following a false trail or drag hunting. The trail is laid by a terrier dragging an aniseed soaked cloth, guided by a human, to reproduce the path a fox might take.

We must ensure that whatever management of foxes occurs in this new century, they will remain as part of the truly wild mammal fauna to be watched in the county and very much part of the folklore of the human species.

David MacDonald has shown how foxes regulate their own numbers so that all the expensive and often very inefficient methods of shooting, snaring and trapping are largely irrelevant. It is recommended to fence foxes out of places where they can do harm and leave them to control their own numbers, but for specific problems control by rifle at baited pits is humane.

Jim Meads has become as famous as his father as a hunt photographer. He was born at Essendon and went to Hertford Grammar School. He describes the end of a hunt, pictured below, as 'a sight not often seen and very rarely photographed which took me 25 years of hard running and much frustration to achieve'. It is from his book *They still meet at eleven* (1979).
(Frank and Jim Meads' pictures are reproduced by kind permission.)

Modern studies of foxes show that they are able to regulate their breeding success, although the mechanisms are not yet fully understood. Macdonald (1987) discusses this with reference to their social structure whereby only dominant females may rear cubs although all the vixens in a locality may come into oestrous. In places where there are few foxes, all vixens in a social group (signified by one dog fox and several related vixens) may be pregnant and bring up cubs. In

Fox attracted to food outside a hide and (below) two of the 9 cubs in one litter born in 1989.

Free-range hens protected by electric poultry netting above Tewin Orchard.

others, related vixens may help feed one vixen with cubs in the manner of kin selection (a theory which was first formulated by W.D.Hamilton and found in various carnivores). By helping her relatives to survive, the non-breeding vixen can thus help her own genes to survive.

Relentless persecution can thus have nothing more than a termporary effect on an area because as soon as a niche is left open, foxes dispersing from a non-control area will respond to the vacant area by having more cubs. In 1989 I recorded 9 cubs in one litter at Tewin next to an area of land where 14 foxes had been shot over the previous year. Most of the new litters of cubs were shot soon after they matured and began to venture away from the safety of the nature reserve where they were born. It is not difficult, however, to see how foxes can maintain their numbers by the mechanisms of social group support, adaptable breeding and their caution whenever they scent or see humans.

This makes control generally unnecessary, but protection of vulnerable livestock by fencing is essential. We have lost about 85 free-range chickens over 30 years to fox predation, but this has always been due to poor attention to fencing out the foxes. What generally happens is a rabbit will dig under the fence, unnoticed in summer cover, and a vixen with cubs will open up this route the next spring. It came as a shock to find a cock and 11 of our purebred Welsummer hens dead when I went to close their shed door one dusk, but I had not checked the fence line regularly. A hen had been partly dragged out of the rabbit hole under the wire. The breed had been slowly built up over 12 years and it is a setback to the poultry breeder when this type of loss occurs.

With nearly all poultry at present housed in fox-proof sheds, their significance in poultry farming is virtually nonexistent, but if egg production in cages is phased out by legislation, specialist small mesh electric poultry fencing will be widely used. Free-range in the dictionary definition is impossible in reality, otherwise all chickens would end up run over, 'trying to get to the other side'. However, mobile fencing is very effective and foxes are quickly deterred as long as the birds are locked up at night.

Macdonald shows that foxes in rural areas have a life expectancy of about 1½ years and most will die directly or indirectly due to human activity. Hunting with hounds, shooting, trapping, disease and road accidents are leading causes of death, and in urban areas Harris has shown that one-third of adult foxes have healed bone fractures from past road accidents. This increases the incidences of arthritis which handicaps foxes and makes feeding progressively more difficult. Macdonald gives a rough guide that a fox population can survive 60% annual mortality. Mange caused by parasitic mites has reduced urban fox numbers significantly in places.

I have watched foxes hunting with graceful springs onto small mammals in grassland on many occasions, but only once experienced a prolonged view of one in a bramble bush, gently pulling ripe blackberries off stems one by one until a walker approached on a path and the fox slipped away. These are just two aspects of feeding; in darkness earthworms and other invertebrates vary the diet. They will take every kind of food, including bird, mammal, fruit and carrion. In urban areas all manner of discarded human litter, especially fast food remains, ensure their survival in places of apparent shortage.

Although during analysis muntjac fawn hairs have been found in Hertfordshire fox droppings, adult does are very protective mothers. I have witnessed them chase foxes from cover where fawns were sitting (at Broxbourne and Tewin). It is more difficult for roe does to defend two kids, however. Badgers usually chase off foxes when feeding at places where food is put out for them, especially when badger cubs are present, but I have known an adult boar badger be chased for 50m by a large dog fox. The badger was low in its social group and never fed confidently. Generally even badger cubs will chase off foxes, although fox cubs often nip the tails or rumps of feeding badgers in the hopes of replacing them at the food.

You can expect foxes in any habitat which provides cover and feeding areas: an average Hertfordshire farm would have one family of foxes present, but the older towns will find higher concentrations in particularly neglected places. Our new towns, with high density housing such as Stevenage, are not ideal because of the lack of large, neglected, rambling gardens of the older residential areas.

Most of the finance for modern fox research has been in response to the spread of rabies across Europe which towards the end of the last century reached the west of France. However, the campaign on mainland Europe has had a great impact on the disease and its dangers have receded. The disease only died out in Britain early in the 19th century and despite the great progress with vaccinations we must realise that our present attitude to, and the status of, our wild mammals will dramatically alter should rabies become re-established in the wild carnivore or even bat populations.

Thanks to the *HMBG* I have been able to monitor sounds made by wildlife in the nature reserve as well as review visual events on a remotely controlled video. I have noticed in the past how foxes appear to prompt tawny owls into calling and made tapes when this has happened. When humans watch at night, however, they never know if their

Although most active at dawn and dusk, foxes often emerge in daylight and several pictures were possible of one stalking geese in Tewin Orchard around noon.

Fresh fox droppings, made up largely of rabbit fur, in snow and showing characteristic pointed ends (Tewin Orchard).

Fox footprint below Labrador dog track in soft mud (Tewin 1999). The fox is distinguished by fine nail prints, neat rounded pads and hair impressions between the toes.

presence in a wood may influence (a) the foxes (b) the owls, or both. With an intercom system you are completely detached indoors, 200m away.

During the January courtship of foxes in 1990 I listened much of the night and early hours of 11 January and at one point, with no previous calling by either species for about 30 minutes, a fox suddenly started to give the familiar 'warble' bark (as it sounds to me) as opposed to the harsh screams or sharp barks. At once a tawny owl started hooting and called almost in sequence with the fox for a time. The following morning produced the most remarkable view of foxes I have ever had. I had been in the bottom field checking earths for footprints and was actually holding a video camera as I re-arranged a tripod when I looked up to find a dog fox and vixen had emerged from the wood (which had been the centre of the noise overnight) and were now mating in sunshine on frosty grass.

I was out of view to them, but as the camera was operated by remote control I had to zoom in on the pair (which had now knotted in typical canine fashion) and rushed back to the cottage to set the recorder going. They were recorded for about 5 minutes between 9.15am and 9.30pm, but I was too slow to also get a transparency of them before they separated and ran off together. As vixens are only receptive to dog foxes for 3 days in the year, during January with its brief, often dull days and long nights, to be able to see and record the event in full sunshine was very memorable. The dog fox seemed to hurry away without warning and the vixen took a few moments to realise he had gone. She chased off after him, tail still arched over her back and fur expanded around the hind legs.

# (Pine marten)

## *Martes martes*

*Not listed in Oldham's Payments for Vermin paper and there appears to be only one reference to probably the last recorded pine marten, described in Lloyd (47):*

*'Though doubtless once common in the Hertfordshire woodlands, it has long been extinct. The sole record for the county appears to be that by J.E.Harting in The Zoologist, 1891 (p 456): 'A marten killed at Oxhey Wood, 26th December 1872, is preserved at Bushey.' A specimen in the collections of North Herts Mus is also reputed to be local.*

*Oldham wrote in 1910 (Trans **14**, 4: 58):*

*'The marten, apart from its beauty of form and restless grace, is of much interest to English naturalists. It was distributed throughout the wooded parts of England until about the middle of the last century when the game preserver wiped it out of existence almost before it was known to have become rare.'*

*This reflects a similar picture to that described by Laver*

Pine marten *Martes martes* in Scotland; rescued by Robert Coope and later released back into the wild.

154

*(1898) for Essex. Although he was optimistic that the species may have survived in the Epping Forest area, the last actual specimen was one trapped in April 1853 by a head keeper, in pheasant coverts at Loughton.*

*Dobson (1999) gives pre-1900 map locations for Essex and useful early information from 1768, 1810, 1812, 1845, 1853, 1881 and 1883. They are not included in Beds Wildlife's extinct mammals list (1987), but the county is mentioned in Hancox (also 1987) in a Mammal Society newsletter item on 'Pine marten recolonisation in Britain'. Hancox gives details from elsewhere including 1850 for extinction in Hampshire, but reported on a skull found in the excavated soil heap of a badger sett near West Meon, Hampshire in 1971. Although pine martens are associated very much with Scotland now, Hancox pointed out that they also disappeared from Kincardine by 1870, Aberdeenshire by 1915, but survived in Argyll, Inverness, Ross and northwest Scotland, North Wales (Caernarvon and Merioneth), parts of the Lake District, Lancashire and Yorkshire.*

*Howes gives full details for Yorkshire in Yorkshire Mammals (1985) and Velander's discouraging recent survey in England is reported in the same issue as the Hancox reference. MacNally (1979) shows how close the species came to extinction in Scotland where it is now watched by many and even fed on bird tables at house windows (as I have seen in several places) and he wrote:*

*'Harvie Brown, who left on record a valuable account of wildlife in the Highlands of that era, wrote in the Fauna of Sutherland and Caithness (1887): "The marten appears now to be of rarer occurrence throughout Scotland than the wildcat", and "The marten, being extremely unsuspicious of a baited trap, falls an easy prey to the professional vermin killer. In Assynt (Sutherland) it is now very rare, but in 1876, in Reay forest, one keeper had 15 skins awaiting the annual arrival of the furrier's traveller."*

*'Obviously the demand for skins in that era did not help any of our furred wildlife. Harvie Brown goes on to say "In Sutherland, between March 1831 and March 1834, as recorded by Selby, 901 wildcats, martens and foulmarts (polecats) were destroyed". In a later work, A Fauna of Skye and the northwest Highlands (1904), he was to write "At date of 1903 it is absolutely uncertain whether it (pine marten) is extinct or still lingers on", and 'The Dowager*

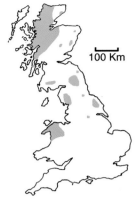

**Pine martens are locally found in the more remote parts of Britain.**

**Slow recovery of numbers**

**Captive marten 'Maddoc' at Tewin Orchard showing light winter coat moulting into summer chocolate brown colour.**

**Captive marten 'Marty' at Tewin Orchard showing typical agility jumping between tree stumps.**

Susie Clark with a marten, showing its throat patch as well as its tameness. Large ears and prominent eyes are also characteristic of martens. After leaving Tewin, martens continued in breeding programmes in wildlife parks.

Lady MacKenzie used to get in the 1860s, 30-40 marten skins every year chiefly from the natural pinewoods of Kinlochewe."

'Yet the pine marten did survive, perhaps only in one small pocket in the Torridon/Kinlochewe/Lochmaree area, and from this one small pocket it has spread throughout the northwest Highlands, right down the wooded Great Glen of Invernesshire, and it has reached as far south as Glencoe.'

Although pine martens have long been absent from Hertfordshire, their apparent gradual recovery in Scotland is welcome news. The species was clearly highly vulnerable to the development of the breach-loading shotgun and the increase in trapping on estates throughout the British Isles. I have watched the species to a limited extent in Scotland and Ireland, and, whilst it is a very difficult mammal to breed in captivity, I would give full support to any projects which would re-establish the indigenous pine marten in southern England.

I have seen groups of martens which visit homes in parts of Scotland to number 6 and 8 and more, behaving in this way for more than a decade, despite modern literature which suggests that they have an inflexible social organisation which never allows them to assemble in this way, even where food is concentrated. A free-living colony kept fed in this way should disperse naturally and our county includes many areas highly suitable for martens which are now protected. They would be a valuable predator on grey squirrels. Drey or magpie nest shooting would have to be made illegal unless poles are used to displace the animal so it can be identified as it leaves the nest in case the protected martens were present.

Poultry runs can be secured from aerial access by the type of electric fencing used for ground predators, but fitted as a top wire surround.

# Stoat

### Mustela erminea

Oldham only once found the stoat specifically referred to in the payments for vermin list, the amount being the same as for polecats, 4d:

'1732 paid Thomas Watters for A Stote ......4d'

Tom Gladwin's exceptional study of a stoat *Mustela erminea* with its prey, a rabbit.

He assumed that they were listed as with weasels as "&c", after polecats.

Lloyd (47) only credits the species with a single sentence: 'Fairly common still throughout the county despite many years of persecution by gamekeepers'. We do,

however, find far more references in the Trans to stoats than to weasels, probably because, due to their greater size, they are more often observed in the wild. Roberts (1892) gives the first records of their pelage changing to white in the county by quoting Brett's (1882) and Campbell's (1890) observations. He noted that in winter stoats in the north often turn white, but it was an unusual occurrence in Hertfordshire.

Campbell's stoat was shot on 2nd February 1890 and brought to him by a gamekeeper at Highfields Woods, Hoddesdon. It was a female with all-white fur except for the usual black tail tip and a few very slight streaks of brown about the nose. He added: 'I have met with stoats before in this neighbourhood during January and February with their usual coat pied with white, or all white except for the head, and I have looked forward to a severe winter to give me a specimen with its complete winter coat'.

Campbell exhibited his collection of stoats of various colours to HNHS in 1892 and there are 21 Hertfordshire (Tring) stoats in the Brit Mus Coll which represent 9 different colour phases from brown to the full ermine white, clearly selected from the thousands taken by Lord Rothschild's keepers or collectors over many seasons as particularly worthy of preservation. (They are shown on p159.)

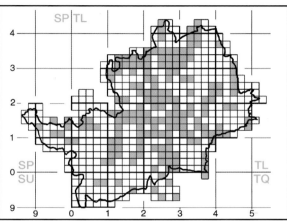

**Stoats adapt to most habitats and the species is well established throughout the county.**

**Stable, probably increasing in numbers with the revival of rabbit populations.**

Foster (34) records one ermine in Letchworth Museum and another shot at West Mill about 1925 'whilst trying to climb a wall dragging a rabbit after it'. He adds: 'W.P.Westell tells me that 2 stoats were brought to him in 1933, one of which was 'milk-white', the other 'cream-white' and Joseph Ransom, in his diary, said that he saw a stoat (4th March 1809), 'milk-white except its tail; my dog was near killing it, but it escaped into a mole's burrow.' In 1946 Foster published a short note on a white stoat killed by a gamekeeper on the outskirts of Hitchin which retained brown hair on a patch on the crown of its head and had brown rings or spectacles around each eye.

There are several white, or near-white stoats in N Herts Mus, but no recent ones, although there have been a few observations reported. In the severe 1962-63 winter I saw a completely ermine stoat in the Home Wood, Cuffley. Sleeman (1989) points out that the observation that weasels do not turn white except much further north than the stoat may be a reflection of the time each species spends above ground, exposed against snow. King (1989) explains the theories behind the change to white and concludes the same basic

One of Frank Henning and Chris Woodard's hand-reared stoats in Stevenage showing facial characteristics.

theory that it has evolved not to help catch a meal, because they do not hunt by stealth, but to avoid becoming one.

Clearly, the process of coat change fascinated early naturalists and sportsmen to whom anything novel or out of the ordinary was felt worthy of keeping by taxidermy. Museum collections tend, therefore, to be filled with the atypical rather than the normal. King devotes much attention to the moults and winter whitening of all types of stoats and weasels: growth of new hair is stimulated by the longer days of the spring as well as the shorter days of the autumn, but winter whitening is controlled by temperature and heredity.

In the Arctic, where the shortening days of autumn always herald the rapid onset of severe winters, the old coats are replaced quickly, within a few days. In milder climates, of which Hertfordshire is an example, the shorter daylight length of autumn days is just as predictable, but it is slower, spread over 4-6 weeks. King explains how the pituitary gland controls the production of melanin which gives the hair its colour and how cold temperatures can inhibit the production. She also shows from the work of Faidak (1977) that different parts of the stoat's body would turn white at different temperatures: the hindquarters and lower flanks only had to experience air at 2°C to change, but the head and back would not become white until minus 1°C had been reached.

This explains why we have had a variety of partially white as well as white stoats recorded in our county as winter temperatures may reach the threshold for change for certain parts of the stoat's body, but not for others.

To show how heredity is involved, King cites experiments in Britain, Switzerland and USA which found that stoats transplanted from warm areas stayed brown in freezing conditions (when all stoats around them turned white) and others taken from areas with annual subzero temperatures turned white, despite finding themselves in warm autumn conditions (where the local stoats were all brown).

Hertfordshire stoats are, therefore, likely to have a rather borderline inherited tendency not to turn white, but may do so partially or fully if we experience very cold winters which have temperatures below 2°C for several weeks. We should, after all, be grateful for the retention of these 'odd' specimens in our museum collections because they do give us the material which supports the modern research on this phenomenon of stoat biology and reflects the colder periods of our last 100 years quite accurately. Perhaps they would make good visual aids for lectures by meteorologists.

Other aspects of stoats recorded in the county tend to concentrate on their tenacity and lack of caution in the presence of man. Generations of gamekeepers have used the curiosity of stoats and weasels as a way of shooting them. As well as trapping them, they know that if they disturb one on their rounds it will frequently reappear from a temporary retreat and peer about for the intruder for long enough to be

29th October

2nd November

14th November

27th November

The rapid progress of the moult to ermine within a month - adapted from Hamilton (1939) in Ewer (1973).

shot. Whiteman (36) described them at Hexton as shot on sight by the gamekeepers and when one stoat was wounded and approached, it jumped up repeatedly at the man's leg. It attempted to climb up his body, but was finally knocked down by the man using his gun. The stoat was then shot as it made off.

Roberts (1893) reported that the Aldenham gamekeeper shot as many as 50 annually and on one occasion killed 3 juveniles of a litter with a stick when he came across them on a path. He went to fetch his gun, which was in the vicinity, and returned to find that the mother had carried off all 3 bodies. Although the use of mole runs is associated with the smaller weasels, a large stoat was caught in a mole trap at Knightlands Farm, Barnet in February 1891 (Trans **6**, 6: 196).

In more recent Trans, Sawford (**27**, 1:27) described how he had watched a stoat performing various acrobatic antics at Royston sewage farm (8th September 1967). Two other stoats were calling with a low murmur nearby and then leaping, springing and rolling continued for about 30 minutes. In 1971 Hughes reported having a stoat in her garden at Rabley Heath which approached her home and hissed angrily at the family dog before leaving (Trans **27**, 3:86).

I described the capture of rabbits at Hopkyns' Wood in 1979 where an adult was regularly seen hunting and Walton watched one swim to an island in the middle of the flooded pit at Frogmore (3rd April 1980) which was attacked by a lapwing that had a nest nearby. It was forced to retreat from the water by determined assaults by dabchicks only to meet the lapwing again (Trans **29**, 1:12). Newton watched stoats swimming in the Lea Valley especially between islands in flooded gravel pits on a number of occasions and Sleeman (1989) gives records of stoats easily swimming to offshore islands. King (1989) includes many such events in relation to sizes of different populations and predation of protected birds on islands. I have seen a stoat swim across a Scottish river with ease.

Stoats are shown in 39% of tetrads by Anderson (1985) and are described as widespread and frequent in Beds Wildlife (1987). Burton (1974) recorded them as found in the larger parks and commons in the outer suburbs of London, but (curiously) 'rare in Middlesex'.

Lever (1898) notes from Essex that 'persecution, from every quarter, seems to have little influence in diminishing its numbers'. On ermine specimens, he records one shot in March 1871 and adds: 'I have seen several perfectly snow-white. More frequently, however, they retain some reddish patches on the head and shoulders'. He recorded a stoat attacking a weasel, both of which were shot by a Mr.Kebby and mounted in the 'attitude they were seen fighting'.

Dobson (1999) gives ermine information and describes them

weasel

stoat

polecat

mink

pine marten

badger

otter

**Comparative sizes of the members of the family** *Mustelidae* **(after Robert Gillmor and personal references).**

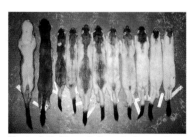

**Ventral (left) and dorsal views of large stoats in typical colour next to a set of 9 skins at different stages to full ermine white in Brit Mus (Nat Hist) Coll., South Kensington by kind permission.**

Stoat footprints which face each other (at John Card's Perry Green study area) reflect their nature: constantly retracing their steps when exploring new ground. Frank Henning and Chris Woodward's stoats did this when I was picturing them. The flexible body with long black-tipped tail shows well here.

*to be fairly common, but declining, in present day Essex.*

Stoats have great appeal and all my encounters with them in the wild have been unplanned. The nearest I have been to predicting views of them has been as honorary warden of Hopkyns' Wood Nature Reserve where regular visits are made to an area hunted by the species, although they occasionally visit our hens and the mammal table in our garden.

The first rabbit I saw actually being killed by a stoat was a young one which was rolling over and over with the stoat locked onto its neck, body curled round. When the rabbit's movement ceased, the stoat pulled it into a nearby rabbit burrow. It emerged after a short time and dragged the body out of view across a bridle way towards a copse, where I assumed it had young. The first indication of alarm had been an adult rabbit running past me, thumping a hind foot loudly to warn of danger. At that moment I looked up to see the juvenile caught. During the same year I frequently saw a stoat in this area and could almost predict that during an afternoon's work on my vegetable plot I would have a view of one across on the wood edge, particularly in late afternoon.

I have also noticed that stoats react to a period of rain in much the same way as rabbits: in September 1999, rain had lasted for most of the previous day and night, then further showers followed during the morning. Suddenly the clouds cleared and the sun shone. A number of rabbits emerged to feed on the field above Tewin Orchard. Then a stoat ran out, made an acrobatic tumble as if rolling where there were rabbit droppings and ran back into the hedge. Perhaps, like dogs, they like to roll in 'things'. It repeated this twice before disappearing into cover again.

In their recent books, King and Sleeman illustrate the 'wrapping' technique of both stoats and weasels in which the body is used to contain the struggles of a captured animal. The scream of a rabbit often attracts other predators (such as a fox or human) who may steal the food. Once the prey item is still, the teeth are released (usually from the neck) and the stoat may make use of a nearby hole in which to take the food for safe keeping. King records caches of up to 50 mice by single animals and explains the evolutionary value of this behaviour.

Stoats cannot be studied in the same way as badgers at known setts unless you are fortunate to find where a lactating female has young. Mustelids move their young as soon as they detect a threat to the nest site. Some years they seem scarce and I may only hear a rabbit scream out of sight in dense cover or find stoat (or weasel) droppings under corrugated iron sheets by small mammal nests.

Checking my diary I find that I now average about five encounters a year in the Orchard, but in 1979 stray dogs killed a stoat in the Reserve and another was run over on the road nearby; I had no record of them for two years following these deaths.

Small predators are vulnerable to many larger animals (as well as the gamekeepers) and one strategy I had noticed and not understood is explained in King and Sleeman: the lashing of the black tail tip. Stoats hunt above ground more often and more obviously than weasels. When a bird of prey attacks the black tip has been shown to be whisked up as the bird lands, both to distract and give a target away from the vital body. This explains why the black tip is retained even in ermine and King reports on Powell's experiments which showed how black tips to tails increase survival rates. I once frightened a stoat on the Gorhambury Estate near St. Albans which tail-lashed, but it did not occur to me at the time that this was a safety measure.

A stoat running with a rabbit which it had just killed.

The King and Sleeman books clarify much of the natural history of stoats which, like weasels, are linked to the successes of rodents and, especially in this country, rabbits. Before rabbits were present in Britain, water voles were a major source of food. Dependence on rabbits was well illustrated by Tapper's vermin-bag records of a Suffolk estate, which showed a sudden drop in stoat numbers during the 20th century when rabbit numbers diminished. King shows how the Russian fur trade could predict ermine catches by the water vole numbers caught the previous June, unless a low period for the voles coincided with a peak in smaller rodents. In Switzerland when the water voles virtually disappeared, so did the stoats.

Outstanding studies by Phil Farrer from Kings Langley which show both the long tail (which immediately distinguishes the stoat from the weasel *Mustela nivalis*) and the variable pattern to the throat patch.

Like badgers, stoats reproduce by delayed implantation and King shows how this ensures that all females can be mated before the family groups disperse. Packs of stoats are often described, as in Jefferies' 1881 account in his *Round about a Great Estate*. Reports also come from letters to the country magazines and BBC Radio 4 nature programmes: all refer to the family parties before a litter breaks up. King suggests that delayed implantation may indicate a closer relationship with pine marten-like ancestors whereas weasels, which do not delay implantation, are closer to the polecat tribe.

There is still heated debate over many of these aspects of mustelid biology and much is still to be found out. I have been able to enjoy the company of stoats at first-hand through Frank Henning and Chris Woodward in Stevenage, who exercised them indoors.

These orphan stoats were as cautious to explore new routes as weasels and repeatedly retraced their steps before going further. It is fascinating to see how a young one gets to know a new room and once a path is established how fast they can move through their territory. Polecats and weasels are also wary and scatter if surprised, but in my limited experience seem to explore a new room in a much more confident manner than stoats or pine martens.

Although it is true that they prey on birds as well as the

species of mammal considered harmful to human interests, their control by traps and shooting on sight appears to be a futile activity, worthy of becoming just a part of the history of game preservation and not necessary for its practice.

# Weasel

### *Mustela nivalis*

*Oldham, in his 1924 paper on payments for vermin, suspected that weasels and stoats were commonly referred to under the term '&c' listed with polecats. The price paid for them was 4d (about 2p), the same as for polecats, and he gives:*

1730  paid Wm Johnson for a Whezell        00    00    04

1735  paid for a Wheezell                          0     0     4
        paid Thomas Weeden for 3 Wheezells  0     1     0

**Facial details of captive weasel** *Mustela nivalis* **reared at Tewin Orchard after rescue by Patsie Shott (see p163).**

*Roberts (1893) described a Hertfordshire gamekeeper who killed a weasel with his foot when feeding his young pheasants. It had come close to him through the grass after the birds and he had seen others at the same time.*

*Lloyd (47) described them as widely distributed but never abundant. He saw them on the banks of Elstree Reservoir and recorded their leaping behaviour and a fight in Trans 21, 164 (1940). These are vivid, detailed descriptions in an otherwise neglected historical record in the Trans. There are 10 Hertfordshire (Roth) skins in the Nat His Mus, 9 for Tring itself and 1 for Wiggington: 1st August 1895 male; 14th January 1896 female(?); 15th September 1902 male; 22nd October 1902 male; 15th January 1903 male(?); 10th August 1903 male; 10th April 1904 male; 6th March 1905 male (a very large specimen with skull); 4th May 1905 male (very large); and 11th February 1913 male.*

*Foster (1934) noted that a weasel seemed to somersault and throw itself about as if in a fit of rage. A weasel we kept that had been found as a juvenile, abandoned before its eyes had opened, would show bouts of anger as it matured (see next section) and killed a female it was taken to be mated with (owned by Derek Reed of Tring Museum).*

*Laver (1898) recognised their role in small mammal control and regretted their persecution in Essex as vermin. Dobson (1999) shows a widespread distribution similar to that of stoats, but describes them as only 'fairly common, declining'. In Bedfordshire, Anderson (1985) had records from 38% of tetrads, just 1% less than the total for stoats. Burton (1974) also recorded them over virtually the same distribution as stoats in London, but noted that they were found further towards the centre, more abundantly in all areas and in a few localities in Middlesex.*

A weasel was by far the most exciting and rewarding wild mammal we have ever kept in our home. The juvenile was found still and cold on a path and picked up. It was taken to a friend, Patsie Shott, who kept it in an incubator before it came to us. The speed of weasels around known paths and runs in the wild is amazing: indoors I was reminded of this when I opened a door to enter the room where he was active. He could rouse, leave the couch, where he liked best to sleep, run across the floor about 3m, jump onto my leg and be on my shoulder before I closed the door.

If you set Longworth live traps for small mammals, weasels may also enter them as they hunt along pathways which smell of small mammals. You should never be taken by surprise because traps smell strongly of musk when you lift them and feel too heavy to contain a small rodent alone. Sometimes the weasels make a trap bounce about on the ground. This occured on three occasions when I was trapping round the orchard cottage at Tewin.

Whilst the joys of having a captive small carnivore, which looks like a microchip version of a pine marten are great, King's description of weasels as 'hair-trigger mousetraps with teeth' is very accurate.

She explains many aspects of weasels such as:

- the shape and long neck not only as an obvious advantage for entry into the narrow tunnels of small mammals, but to enable them to carry prey without falling over;
- the diurnal records (often from gamekeepers and ramblers) are explained by their hunting throughout the 24 hours, with eyes adapted to see well both in bright and dim light;
- a life linked with rodent success;
- the ability to shelter under snow and to continue to hunt in the warmer under-snow layer;
- taking over the homes of small mammals by eating the host and improving the nests by lining them with their own fur so that the thickness of the lining indicates how long a weasel has been in residence;
- their rapid digestion which can produce 19 scats in 24 hours so that dyed bait appeared as soon as 2-4 hours after consumption;
- the amazing ability of weasels to carry food items twice their own weight and bound away.

She also describes the old gamekeeper's trick for attracting weasels to live traps by mixing bait with rabbit intestines to give the irresistible scent appeal (that can also work for other predators); the life

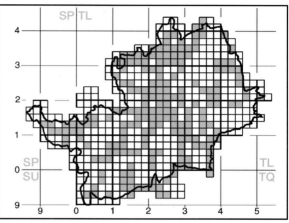

Weasels are found in most habitats.

Subject to cat predation, but stable numbers.

Droppings in a vole nest show that a weasel has taken over (Hoddesdon).

Whilst our male weasel would relax into almost hypnotic sleep when swung from the neck, David and Adrianne Watson's weasel, shown in the lower picture, remained alert. Note the short tail and no black tip.

expectancy of a year or less for males (although our second tame male was over 5 years old when it died); the observation that small predators do not live off 'the fat of the land' because for much of the time life is very much more chancy for them than for their prey - their numbers can be related to the basic factor of seed-fall as mouse/vole success is dependent upon the abundance of seeds.

She notes the frequent use of mole runs, and makes the important point that weasels do not dig their own burrows. When they have eaten a mouse and taken over its nest they begin by using the fur from the victim to line the nest, not using their own straight away.

I have never, however, found reference to one aspect of behaviour which we found in our own weasel: if very agitated at, for example, having to curtail his playtime in our living room and go back to his own enclosure, he could be made to relax if gently swung between the forefingers and thumb. (David and Adrianne Watson, however, kept a male weasel after our experience and repeatedly tried to emulate this behaviour without success. They also kept their weasel for over 5 years.)

A common parasitic nematode *Skrjabingylus nasicola* can kill weasels much earlier than this by invasion of the skull via the nasal passages. (It is thought that some of the strange fit behaviour of weasels, an apparent distraught frenzy, is brought on by serious brain damage in the later stages of the attack by this nematode.)

King described the observations of a Middlesex gamekeeper, Michael Hitchcock, who was noticed by a weasel as he stood by a heap of rotten logs. The weasel studied him for a few seconds at a range of 1m, then went into the logs and emerged carrying a tiny blind young one by the neck which she took to an alternative nest site along a hedgerow, out of view. She returned and repeated the procedure with a total of 6 young. Weasel young remain limp and passive whilst being carried and make no sound unless the mother bites them in the wrong place, such as the ear. German observers, King explains, call this condition *tragechlaffe* and they point out that it can be seen in adult females being carried about by a male during mating.

It was ironic that both our rescue weasels appeared to have been lost during a move between one nest and another, yet they never lost the skill of passive limpness. Both were cold, still and already attracting flies when found. Warmth is essential at such times, but we found both eager to eat meat and had well developed teeth. The instinct to go into a state of total relaxation may vary between individuals after adolescence, but could be related to the degree of tameness and frequency of handling in captivity. The strong, elongated neck is clearly as important for the transport of young as for the dragging of prey items into cover or back to a litter to feed on.

# Western polecat
## Mustela putorius

**Young hob (male) polecat** *Mustela putorius*, **Hopkyns' Wood, Tewin.**

*I was unable to locate any Hertfordshire polecat skins in the Nat Hist Mus (nor any pine martens), but Lloyd (47) refers to one at Tring and others in St.Albans. His details of the species, which was exterminated very recently for a mammal present since the last ice age, refer to Oldham's churchwarden's payments (see next page) plus:*

*'A polecat killed near Harpenden in 1877 and preserved in the County Museum at St.Albans (Trans XIV, 244); a skin in the Tring Museum labelled "Tring Reservoirs, 2nd September 1910, female", which is most likely only that of a feral polecat-ferret'.*

*He went on to report that in 1941 St.Albans Museum had possessed remains of 4 polecats (two mounted, a third very badly damaged and one skin). One at the Museum was killed at No-Man's Land about 1847 (Oldham, Mammals of St.Albans, in Trans, XIV 243-5). Vaughan Roberts stated that a specimen which he exhibited to the Hertfordshire Natural History Society (1891) was killed 'about 25 years ago' (about 1866) 'in this immediate neighbourhood' (Watford), (Trans, VII, 47, 1894). Polecats apparently existed in Buckinghamshire not far from the county border nearly until the end of the last century (see A.H.Cocks, 'Mammals' in V.C.H. Buckinghamshire [1905], and a note in The Zoologist [1890, 178] recorded 3 polecats from Bierton, Waddesdon and Stoke Mandeville - all near Aylesbury).*

*Foster (1934) gives historic information for the Hitchin area and Whiteman (1936) gives late 19th century records as well as those of the 1930s referred to earlier. They are not mentioned in the Beds Wildlife (1987) lists of recently extinct mammals.*

*Laver (1898) felt the species very rare in Essex and gives one killed near Roxwell about 1855 as the last confirmed record at the time of writing. Dobson (1999) notes that the last Epping Forest records were around 1880, but there were occasional reports from wooded country along the Lea Valley in 1900 and Frohawk considered that they were still present in marshes along the*

*We know from the lists of vermin payments that at least 30 polecats were killed each year in the county in the 1730s. Two hundred years later they were extinct, but reintroductions saw them firmly re-established in Hertfordshire by the 1990s.*

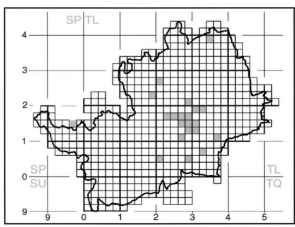

**Post 1981 polecat records in Hertfordshire.**

**Increasing**

**Polecat range pre-recovery (top) and post 1959 colonisation. Below a detail of where in the south, polecats (and other large mammals) are now unlikely to return due to road traffic density (after Birks & Kitchener 1999).**

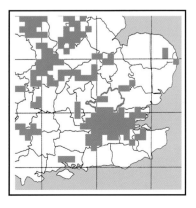

Thames in 1905.

Chas. Oldham wrote:

'The first mention of this animal in Hertfordshire is in the accounts for 1687:

"pd for six poulcats . . . . . . 00  02  00"

'The price then paid, 4d per head, was maintained with two exceptions (1690 "for a poulcate, 00-00-06" and 1731 "Paid John Hurdnall for 4 Poulcatts, 0.1.0") until 1768, and possibly later, but from 1769 to 1820 there are only generalized entries, eg from 1769-70:

"Paid for Hedgehogs Polcats and Sparrows - 01 01 6½"

and from 1818-19:

"Paid for Polecats and Sparrows - 01 15 0" '

'Fitchet', another name for the polecat, was almost as general in southern England as 'foumart' was in northern England, but never occurs in the lists. There are many variants of the modern name polecat: poulcat, poulcate, poulcatt, poult catt, poltcatt, polt catt, poalcat, polcat, polcatt, pol catt, polcate, pollcat, pollcate, pollcatt, pollcatte, poll cat, poll catt, pole cat, pole catt, polecatt, polecatte.

The following entries are cited to illustrate the numbers killed:

| | | | | |
|---|---|---|---|---|
| 1747 | Paid for polcatts . . . . | 0 | 4 | 0 |
| | Paid for 13 Polcatts . . . . | 0 | 4 | 4 |
| 1748 | Paid for Polcattes 5s 4d and for | | | |
| | Sparrows 7s & 10d in all . . | 0 | 13 | 2 |
| | Paide for Sparrows 7s 2¾ and for | | | |
| | Polleatts 1s in all . . . | 0 | 8 | 2¾ |
| 1751 | To 20 Polcats 6s 8d to 442 Sparrows | | | |
| | 9s 2½ . . . | 0 | 15 | 10½ |
| | To Sparrows and Polecats . | 0 | 13 | 10 |
| 1752 | To 12 Polcats 4s To 307 Sparrows | | | |
| | 6s 4¾d. . . . | 0 | 10 | 4¾ |
| | Paide for 148 Sparrows. . . . | 0 | 3 | 1 |
| | Paide for 2 Poleats. . . . | 0 | 0 | 8 |
| 1753 | Paide Sparrows & two polcatts . . . | 0 | 4 | 9½ |
| | Paide for Sparrows & | | | |
| | Eleven polcates . . . | 0 | 9 | 7 |
| 1759-60 | Paid for 6 polcates . . . | 0 | 2 | 0 |
| | Paid for Sparrows & Polcats | 0 | 7 | 9 |
| 1767-68 | Paid for Polcates | | | |
| | and Sparrows . . . | 0 | 9 | 11½ |
| | Paid for 3 Polcates . . . | 0 | 1 | 0 |

There is considerable interest in polecats and ferrets amongst modern naturalists and there is resentment that a tiny proportion of the human population were able to trap or shoot them to extinction across most of Britain. They are now recovering their range from a precarious, remnant colony in Wales and I have already described my own interest in *Mammal Watching* (1982).

I discuss in this book the uncertainty about the origins and

166

relationships shared by ferrets, polecat-ferrets and polecats. Polecats and ferrets freely hybridize and because ferrets are frequently lost in the countryside interbreeding in all parts of their distribution must be expected. This is even more liable to happen along the border country between Wales and England and if polecats are allowed to re-establish themselves in their former range (a useful contribution to rabbit control) there will always be occasional mixtures of polecats and the various domestic ferret forms.

During the 1970s, through the help of breeding animals from Prof. Russell Coope, Graham Welstead and contacts in Wales, we initially bred 24 polecats at Tewin. Two Welsh male polecats escaped and it was agreed with those involved in the breeding programme that these indigenous mammals, persecuted to extinction in the county for most of this century, should not be allowed to die out, but be added to from the captive stock. With individuals mixed to reduce risk of inbreeding, 7 areas had groups released into them.

At selected sites, up to 5 polecats (2 males and 3 females) were released together at a time into large rabbit warrens in early autumn. Food was left at each site on a weekly basis for 6 months to augment small mammals and rabbits caught naturally. The main dates of this activity were:

*1981-1982* two male Welsh polecats and 5 Tewin bred animals, then a further 3, at Tewin; 5 at Bramfield; 5 in the Broxbourne Woods complex and finally 3 near Essendon;

*1992-1994* release of polecats live trapped by John Wallace near Watton-at-Stone and 7 others; 3, then 2 more in Ashridge and 2 at the Broxbourne Woods complex again.

There followed records of road casualty polecats or polecat/ferret crosses from Welwyn Garden City (specimen in spirit at *Nat Hist Mus, Coll.* of Daphne Hills, 10th October 1986); a large hob (male ferret) from Watton-at-Stone seen by Christopher Woodward on the road side, 'very dark', 1985; 2 were reported caught in traps by a gamekeeper near Hertford in 1988 (verbal information via C.Woodward); and 1 male was found freshly run over at Bramfield by Diana Wallace in 1990. In 1991 no less than 3 were noted run over on the edge of Welwyn Garden City over a period of 3 months by Melvin Bedford and I found one on White Horse Lane, Burnham Green, in October 1991.

Since then road casualties from many central and west Hertfordshire districts, including Ashridge and the Hitchin area, indicate established breeding populations are now present, and in 2000 Brian Sawford told me that he had heard of 50 trapped on a north Hertfordshire estate. The polecat has clearly become re-established, even if the treatment they receive in certain places has not changed.

For their book *The distribution and status of the polecat Mustela putorius in Britain in the 1990s*, Johnny Birks and

**Polecat kitten development to show the fine white hair of a new litter which is replaced by darker coloured pelage by the time their eyes are opening at about five weeks (Tewin Orchard).**

**Mary Kourik exercising a hob ferret at Tewin Orchard.**

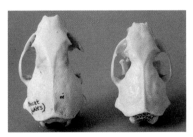

**Ferrets usually show a constriction in the skull (right) absent in most polecat skulls (left).**

Andrew Kitchener were given the Hertfordshire data and they show (including reference to up-to-date information on the distribution of the polecats) where reintroductions have aided its natural recovery and its movement out from Wales. They discuss at length the hybrid evidence in wild-living polecats found in the reintroduction counties. Apart from the Welsh individuals given to us to breed from, the Surrey ones from Graham Welstead had polecat-ferret ancestry and Russell Coope's first male was of Shropshire origin. In the future it is likely that hybrid features will disappear and Johnny Birks and Andrew Kitchener comment:

'...in the absence of constant and significant contributions of escaped ferrets to populations, polecat genes should gradually predominate in successive generations at the expense of ferret genes.'

Ken Walton's work on polecats has given valuable basic biology and distribution information for many years. More recently (before Sleeman's book of 1989 referred to earlier), P.R.S.Blanford produced a useful review of the literature on the species in *Mamm Soc*'s journal *Mammal Review*, **17**, 4: 155-198 (1987) and BBC Wildlife reviewed Weber's research in Switzerland, **7**, 7: 428 (1989). They are known to be nomadic especially along river valleys and eat small mammals, rats, rabbits, birds, amphibians, reptiles, fish and carrion. In Europe they have declined in places, yet the species has expanded north into Scandinavia (including Finland) and northern Russia. Weber radio-tracked 13 polecats in Switzerland and found they used various resting places: shrubs, piles of wood, farm buildings and holes in the ground. I found rabbit burrows used in Brecon in the 1970s.

Weber noted that the changes in diet were a consequence of their living accommodation rather than the cause: they sought shelter to conserve their body temperature in winter and often farmers were not aware that they were living in their barns and sheds.

The strong scents from polecats and ferrets seem different from each other to me, but this may be because individuals vary. The ferret smell seems the less appealing of the two to the human nose, if not to other ferrets, and Gotch (1979) explains their Latin name *M. putorius* as from *putoris*, a bad smell. The foul-smelling discharge from the glands under the tail, which I have only experienced at full blast, as it were, when a door partially closed on a polecat which had raced across the room in fun, can be incredibly pungent and long-lasting. Fortunately no harm came to the polecat, but the scent lingered despite extensive washing of the floor by the door. The old name of 'foulmart' compared to 'sweetmart' for the pine marten is understandable: I have handled captive pine martens which (to my mind) only give off the faintest of pleasant scents.

Polecat and ferret tails are a good guide to their peace of mind: when anxious about anything, the tail expands into an old style lavatory-brush shape, a feature common to other carnivores and even the edible dormouse. The play of hand-reared ferrets appears slightly different from hand-reared polecats, even of mixed blood. Ferrets are more bouncy and run backwards in teasing games, twisting the body as if with prey, whereas the polecat play seems more calculating and serious.

Polecats are very sensitive to airflow in their retreats and can detect hidden passages which ferrets seem oblivious to. Both have contented sounds in sleep rather as a baby makes when well fed and a little windy, but have sharp coughs after eating, especially when feathers have been consumed. They moan with frustration if food gets caught up and give squawks of annoyance or hiss when confronted with some aspect of life's minor frustrations. When kept together a polecat jill (female) was dominant to a ferret jill.

Interbreeding reduces the dark black or chocolate colour of wild polecats and the facial pattern loses its distinct dark areas. Coope considers hybrids from escaped ferrets as unimportant because they will always breed to the size and colour which survives best: much as the future generations of the multicoloured mink adapt in the wild to their original dark brown hue after release from captivity.

Although ferrets are frequently lost they find it difficult to cope in the wild, especially those mistakenly reared on the inappropriate bread and milk sort of diet so often given in the past. Over the years we have rescued several in poor condition, obviously not catching their own food, but others succeed and appear as large and vigorous as polecats, but pure white. They show no tendancy to tame even if regularly handled.

Birks & Kitchener (1999) consider interbreeding with ferrets is unlikely to significantly affect the recovery of the wild species. The skull was thought to be a good guide to origin, but a very dark polecat in the centre of the Welsh distribution has been found with this skull constriction, described as diagnostic for ferrets (J.Birks, pers.comm.).

Having now reared polecat kittens through to maturity and watched their play close-to on numerous occasions, a feature of their domesticity (which resulted in the working ferret) is the play-bite. Pine martens, foxes and wildcats were too large and stoats and weasels were too small, but polecats were just the right size to flush out a widespread food source, the rabbit, from its burrows. However, the polecat, which uses 'controlled' bites like the domestic dog when simulating kills in play, would not be suitable for the working version unless it was hand-tamed (handled from before their eyes are open).

In preparation for release our litters of polecats were bred in an enclosure attached to the house which allowed us to convert a small room adjoining into a play area. The advice in books is always to handle ferrets after they have eaten and our later litters of polecats were allowed to become so wild

**All modern Hertfordshire polecats were bred from this Staffordshire male from Russell Coope (top). In addition, polecats came from Welsh wildlife parks and Graham Welstead's Surrey litters. Pam and Graham Welstead (centre) with kittens, and (bottom) Anna Clark with jill and litter, all at Tewin Orchard. Lesley and Jim Harmer of London Colney also gave considerable help with the breeding programme.**

169

Polecats *Mustela putorius* **hunting under chicken sheds may flush rats and kill them after a quick chase (Tewin Orchard).**

we could not handle them even when they had full stomachs.

The play is a mixture of mating postures and rat/rabbit killing. They often hurt each other enough to cause loud yelps, but the only scars left were on the middle of the back where males may be badly bitten.

In the wild, our first family of 10 would have dispersed during the summer so that confinement as a family group beyond August was liable to provoke antagonism between the litter mates. Apart from the 'back-biting', other bites were controlled as nips or brief holds on the skin. A juvenile separated, handled and fussed daily, then spoilt with titbits of food, completely stops biting during handling.

Untrained polecats and ferrets will bite deeply to the bone under stress or when capturing prey. Without the half-bite or play nibble, and the response to being told off, ferrets never learn to adapt to life with humans. Just the same can be said for other carnivores, but it is a crucial feature of this small but very knowing species. Polecats climb freely and are breathtakingly fast when 'bouncing' from object to object in excitement or chasing prey.

Their nocturnal behaviour and colour is probably why polecats survived in the country longer than pine martens. They avoid human contact in the wild and released ones are not a threat to humans.

# American mink

## *Mustela vison*

**Captive mink** *Mustela vison* **at the excellent British Wildlife Centre in Surrey (see p272).**

*The American mink has been relatively slow to colonise Hertfordshire in contrast to a rapid expansion elsewhere in the British Isles since it was first brought to be farmed for fur in 1929. Some 700 farms were known by the 1950s and, after escapes or deliberate releases, breeding in the wild was first confirmed on the River Teign in Devon in 1956.*

*Despite several thousand now being trapped annually in Britain, mink are still spreading along water courses and the first records I received for the county were: one shot in 1969 at Sarratt Bottom, southwest Hertfordshire (Trotman); several seen on the Hiz to the north of Ickleford (Burton and Sutton) where 2 were shot near Ramerwick Farm in the early 1970s; a part skeleton of one*

170

from *Letchworth sewage works (9th June 1975) collected by B.Sawford (North Herts Mus Coll).*

*Lever's (1977) records go back even earlier: Wilstone Reservoir in 1962 and Wiggington in 1965. By 1980 one had been seen and another found dead at Oughtonhead, near Hitchin.*

*More sightings were made at Ramerwick Farm after May 1985 (Sutton) and the first River Beane record to the east of Stevenage came in September 1986 (Woodard). Records here continued for 2 years and tracks were found with further observations from Walkern 1988-89 (Bennett).*

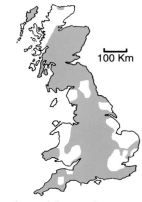

**American mink** *Mustela vison.*

Mink, like otters, exploit aquatic habitats and perhaps the first feature of the arrival of mink on a river is the loss of water voles from the site. Where there are otters there are water voles; where there are mink, otters and water voles are generally absent.

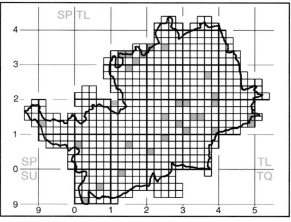

Survival by colour was discussed in the polecat section and it is surprising how quickly a colony of feral mink breeds back to a dark brown colour. Their small size allows them to exploit banks of rivers, streams and open water more easily than otters, which require larger retreats on secluded stretches of water. Both species like clean water with healthy, diverse food to catch. Mink are, however, able to subsist on a much smaller proportion of fish in their diet than the 80% suggested for otters; they will take all kinds of wetland birds and mammals.

Recent surveys by Jenny Jones and others have shown how water voles have declined in Hertfordshire as well as nationally in the last two decades. I once saw several water voles vacate tunnels and swim away rapidly where a mink was hunting the bank on the Essex marshes. It is now clear that water voles have disappeared from many water courses due to the arrival of mink and also as a result of pollution.

Dobson (1999) discusses mink distribution in Essex and gives Birks & Dunstone's 1991 British details of 1 litter of 4-6 young born in May and dispersal in August to occupy home ranges of 1-6km. Daphne Hills at the *Nat Hist Mus* has received 6 mink from Taylor's Lake, Bishop's Stortford, via J.Pretious of Abbey Cross Anglers and kept ticks from them. At the end of the 1990s nine were quickly trapped, but then numbers declined to one or two.

Hills has also pointed out to me that a reduction in skull size is found in the domestic mink when compared with wild populations, much as the constriction in the skulls of ferrets has been used to distinguish them from polecats. (As stated earlier, this is not invariably so.)

**The 39th mink caught by the Culmstock Otterhounds being retrieved, 13th August 1974.**

Mink will use runs on the water's edge and hunt out the local water vole populations as they colonise new rivers.

Anderson (1985) shows 20 records to have been received from 20 tetrads or 5% of the total for Bedfordshire. Although much of the published material on the losses of moorhens, coot, ducks, geese, frogs, newts, crayfish and fish seems to be exaggerated, there are major concerns, especially for water voles. It is true that these species have adapted to predation from all directions in the past. Mink will also take rats and rabbits.

It is to be regretted that mink have added another management problem to the environment: trapping with cages has been shown to simply cream off a surplus from a population when the young disperse from an untrapped area to establish a new territory. *MAFF* attempted to eradicate mink until 1970 when it wound up the campaign and encouraged occupiers of land to use traps. If traps were 100% efficient this would certainly stop the spread, but they are not, and the presence of mink along our waterways seems inevitable.

One way to deal with the presence of feral mink is to encourage the recolonisation of otters by building log holts and managing the river habitats sympathetically to cause a decline in mink naturally.

# Eurasian badger
## *Meles meles*

Badgers near Welwyn.

*A sett in the chalk at Ashlyns near Berkhamsted in southwest Hertfordshire is one of the earliest recorded active setts in Britain. Roberts (Trans Herts Nat Hist Soc, VII, 47, 1893) gives a picture of the treatment of badgers and expresses a sympathy for the species you often find in early accounts, frequently amongst the fox-hunting people and those who dug for badgers and foxes as a recreation:*

'*As mentioned in my paper on Terrestrial British Quadrupeds, badgers (Meles taxus) are not uncommon in Hertfordshire. In December 1891, I paid a visit to the celebrated badger earths at Ashlyns. I was taken to see them by Mr.Holliday of Haresfoot. He told me that his father, who had lived all his life in the locality and died some years ago at the age of 93, could carry his recollection and knowledge of the earths back for a period of about 100 years from the present time, and he knew that badgers had inhabited the spot as far back as memories and traditions went.*

'*The place in question is a large depression or wide pit in the chalk with beech trees growing in and around it. It may be natural or the ground may have been dug out at some distant period. The entrances to the main earths are situated*

at one side where the ground rises. The holes run in various
directions, but all terminate (it is said) in a large chamber
some distance off, excavated under the beech trees growing
on the high ground which forms that side of the depression.
Some three or four years ago a determined attempt was
made to exterminate the badgers in order to get rid of the
mange of foxes that used the earths. Great excavations were
made and vast quantities of chalk removed, but the attempt
had to be abandoned. I forget how many men were
employed, but I think they were at work for twelve days.

'The runs were found in numerous directions and at
considerable depths; one cutting made by the workmen that I
went into must have been eight or nine feet deep, and there
were runs all along the bottom. A chamber was also found
supported by a pillar left in the centre.
Foxes, badgers and rabbits all use this
great earth.

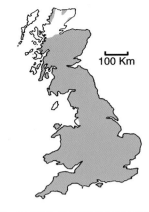

'Mr.Holliday told me that he had
frequently watched both fox and
badger cubs playing together outside.
We went to see another very similiar
but smaller earth, also in a depression
in a beech grove, with the holes formed
on the highest side and running into
the chalk under the roots of the trees.
Mr.Holliday entirely confirms
Mr.St.John's statement as to the
extreme cleanliness of the badger in its
abode. As inspections of these earths
gave one an excellent idea of the
resources of badgers and of the almost
impossibility of destroying them when

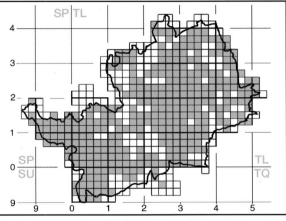

**Badger** *Meles meles.*

**Widespread, stable**

the locality chosen for their abode happens to be one well
adapted for their habits. The extent of their runs and the
great depth at which they occurred rendered even this most
vigorous attempt futile. I hope and believe that now they will
be suffered to remain in peace and that the prescriptive right
of such ancient inhabitants to their stronghold will be
respected.'

Roberts had already referred to badgers when he showed a
specimen shot at Long Spring, Cassiobury, Watford in 1878
to the Society. He extended Brett's 1877 description (see
below) with records of one captured at Odsey, near Ashwell,
and gave Brett's assessment of them in this area in 1886. He
concluded that badgers appeared to be overall 'not
uncommon' in the county. He thought that because of their
setts in old chalk pits and steep banks they would be nearly
impossible to dig out. 'They are comparatively harmless', he
said, 'and some persons nowadays are rather pleased to
have them on their estates,' which gave them protection in
places during an otherwise hostile century.

Brett's 1877 address to the Society is also worthy of

Erythristic (sandy) coloured cub with normal coloured litter mate, near Burnham Green. Eileen Soper recorded the colour form in the 1950s at this sett.

My first colour transparency of a badger, in 1963, revealed it emerging backwards rolling a ball of sandy clay between its front pads. All the spoil heap in the picture was excavated from a single entrance in a sett of about 12 holes, near Northaw, which appears much the same today. In contrast, the School Camp badger sett a mile away was gassed in the 1970s, bulldozed in the 1980s and now has a golf course built over the site.

reproduction for its accurate historic summary of the treatment of badgers:

'I am told they are common ...... at Ashridge and also at Ashlyns. Mr.E.Ellis tells me that, in 1870, "a badger was caught in a trap in the grounds at Aldenham Abbey. The keeper found it an awkward creature to deal with. He could neither take it nor liberate it. He then provided himself with a sack or bag, which he threw over the animal, and removed it to the stable, where he tied it in a loose box, and it was kept four or five days.

'He failed to domesticate it in any degree; it refused food and pined away, and died. It was a full-grown badger, and had a formidable set of teeth. Some years ago an earth of theirs was dug out at Aldenham Lodge and a litter of cubs found. An old man at Aldenham was a kind of purveyor of badgers for baiting. I am not sure whence he drew his supplies for his patrons, but probably not far away. In 1875 a female badger and three young ones were caught at the Temple of Pan, at The Grove, in Lord Clarendon's estate. They were placed by the keeper in an outhouse, and some one going there unexpectedly was so frightened as to run away, leaving the door open, and they all escaped, but one.

'I am told that the best run they had with the foxhounds in the Vale of Aylesbury last year was after a badger. They did not discover it till after the run was over, and they killed.

'Mr.Samuel Betts, of Hadham Hall in this county, says: "Some years ago, two, with their young ones, were taken in one of the Hadham Hall woods, and I had them stuffed. Since then none have been seen or heard of, and I believe they are now extinct in this part of the county. Those referred to were taken out of a fox earth, and, being such a rare animal, I have since felt very sorry that they were disturbed, but in those days everything had to give way to foxes, with which, however, I do not believe the badgers interfered at all."

'Mr.Forsdyke, senior, the keeper who has lived on the Cassiobury Estate 60 years, says that 30 or 40 years ago there were badgers in the Badgers' Dell at Cassiobury, and they sold them to a man at Croxley Green, who kept a public-house, and who used to have one placed in a tub, and dogs set on it. At about this time, also, I am told one was baited annually at Sandridge Fair, near St.Albans. There have been several Acts of Parliament regarding cock fighting and badger baiting. The last was in 1849, and these sports are now illegal.

'It is said that the "brock" or badger has legs on one side shorter than the other. I have brought a stuffed one for you to examine, and you can see if such is the case.'

Digging for baiting and destruction as a by-product of fox-hunting must have kept their numbers low even in more remote country districts during the 18th and 19th centuries. (Early Trans record one sold for baiting about 1840; one

174

*shot at Watford in 1878 was the first seen on that estate for 36 years; described as 'not uncommon' along the River Rib near Buntingford; 'rare' at Odsey, Ashwell, by 1883; frequent at Westmill, Braughing, where one was killed by a train (the line has been disused since the 1960s); and Plashes Wood (1882); present in Panshanger and in southwest Hertfordshire generally around Berkhamsted.*

*Whilst pine martens and polecats became extinct as gamekeepers trapped and shot predators on the estates, badgers appear to have survived, despite their greater size, because of the field sport interest in foxes.*

*They could have been snared or gin trapped even where setts were too difficult to dig out, but the requirements to preserve foxes for the hunts seems to have worked in their favour. By the time the employment of gamekeepers declined, and cyanide gas became freely available where the hunts*

*had less influence on a growing management of shoots by syndicates, badgers were firmly re-established in the county. The modern pressures upon them brought about by urban development, enormous growth in road use and a revival in interest in terriers are dealt with in the next section.*

Sand is favoured for the excavation, but entrances at this sett near Welwyn produce pure chalk spoil heaps at times when the badgers dig into a different layer of soil under the ground.

*Foster (1934) described badgers as 'scarcer, but still regularly found in the Hitchin district'. He had seen 3 caught in cat traps at Hexton Park where ducks were being reared for shooting: the eggs were being taken by the badgers. In 1927 a colleague had watched a family near Graveley and in 1928 one was found dead in a snare on Letchworth golf course where the greenkeeper had been trapping rabbits.*

*That badgers were often overlooked and gamekeepers can work in splendid isolation is shown by Whiteman's (1936) Hexton Parish observation 'although there were the 3 badgers caught by the lake (already referred to), and a large colony was in Meg Wood some years previously, there was no sign of them by 1936'. A footnote was later added: 'A keeper on the estate states that between 20 and 30 have been shot at various places since the 3 were trapped at the lake.'*

*Lloyd (47) summarized the early Trans records and was informed that they still bred towards Hastoe and in the vicinity of Wigginton. He gives the first mention of the Bishop's Stortford area and that Cranford deemed it 'not rare' there. (A badger had even been captured in the outskirts of the town.) He mentions 2 of the 4 Nat Hist Mus Coll, but says that Young reported these to be only from badgers 'turned out' there by Lord Rothschild, so that they may not have been from Hertfordshire originally. (I have*

An underpass for badgers and badger-proof fencing on the M25 near Watford. The strong fence wire is turned flat on the ground and buried (September 1986).

Wildlife culverts were first proposed by the author in Hertfordshire in 1969 (see Clark, 1970) and the schemes on Hertfordshire and Cheshire roads were followed by others elsewhere in Britain.

examined them and both have scars on top of the head, possibly from badger tongs or from dogs. They are of identical size and still have chalk in the hairs.)

There are 14 other skins in the collection, a rolled Tring one (male 1891) with distinct ginger tinge which is probably why it was kept, a flat Tring skin (female 1894), a Tring skin and skull (8th April 1973) and 11 of my own skin collection from road casualties, presented in 1988 and catalogued: 210-221. These are from Cuffley, Welwyn, Northaw, Berkhamsted, Little Gaddesden, Hitchin and Stevenage roads.

Lloyd refers to numerous place names in Britain from badger origins and gives Badger Wood at Ashridge and Badgerdell Wood at Kings Langley. (I made reference to old family and place names in my 1988 book 'Badgers': Broxbourne [Badgers' Brook] and the Tesco company coat of arms which includes two badgers as examples of good housekeeping. Tescos' headquarters is based in this area of the Lea Valley.)

A beautifully illustrated insight into the badgers of the Welwyn area of the 1950s is to be found in Soper's 'When Badgers Wake' (1955) and 'Wild Encounters' (1957). She reflects how common the use of Cymag (cyanide gassing) had become. This was when rabbit clearance societies were active in country districts. Even when myxomatosis almost wiped out the entire rabbit population, Soper records that badger setts were gassed because it was thought that the lack of this prey would make them turn to farm livestock instead. (It was not generally understood at this time that their major food item was earthworms, nor that in a dry summer, beetles and grain were the alternatives preferred.)

The Herts Nat His Soc presidential address by Phyllis Hager in 1956 (Trans 24, p201) was devoted to the badgers in the Chilterns around Berkhamsted. For the first time an increase in their numbers was recorded and she included a description of badger behaviour, diet and sett distribution. (The reduction of keepering during both world wars is viewed by many authors to have been a turning point for badgers this century because it enabled them to disperse into favourable sites and established themselves at a time when fox-hunting was suspended and only essential traffic used the roads.)

Hager noted that the typically steep banks in the hilly country about Berkhamsted were ideal for the construction of setts: Berkhamsted Common, Bourne End, Bolton Farm, Norcott Hill, Wendover, Pendley and Cholesbury are listed. Some of the setts could include 20-30 holes although not all would be in use and just 2-3 sometimes looked active. She recorded 2 badgers killed in single, isolated earths, one at Pancake Wood (1949) and one near the golf club on Berkhamsted Common (1947).

Daylight sightings of badgers had been made on

Duncombe Terrace, above Albury, around noon (1950); several badgers were seen sunning themselves in a dell at Dagnall; one crossed a field at Pancake Wood at 3.00pm (November 1955); one was chanced upon when asleep in Aldbury churchyard (about 1950); and one was disturbed at Potten End (14th January 1949). (The November and January records are curious because daylight activity is normally confined to summer and early autumn, in very undisturbed areas.)

Hager recorded badgers on roads at Leverstock Green (September 1948); Water End and Potten End (November 1948); Cow Lane, Pendley (10.00pm, 2nd December 1952); and there were sightings on 2 nights, a few days apart, about 1928 in the High Street, Stevenage. (The last sett reported by Tomkins in Stevenage New Town was in the hedgerow ditch between what was then Stevenage Girls' School [now the Music Centre] and the Fairlands Valley parkland where the funfairs are staged. This sett was active up to the late 1960s.) Hager ended with reference to 6 setts at Chorleywood where Turney had found them to often live unsuspected, close to human habitation.

From Essex, Laver (1898) reported that badgers had become scarce due to gamekeepers and witnessed a few baitings of badgers caught at South Benfleet in 1844. He quoted a description put to song of a hunt in Epping Forest 'where the beast was brutally ill-treated when captured'.

Dobson (1999) describes their status in modern Essex as 'common' and gives details of earlier persecution than that covered by Laver. He gives monthly road casualty figures, 1996-98 for 207 badgers recorded by the North East Essex Badger Group. This group and the national web of groups, including our own HMBG, has transformed the picture of badger persecution and helped inform the public. Dobson considers disturbance to badgers has been cut by a half in 10 years and badger numbers have correspondingly increased. (I visited setts in the 1960s with Bob Cowling, the County Recorder, and Bill Page in the early days of recording in Essex.) Burton (1974) described badgers to be 'abundant in the rural areas surrounding London, particularly in Kent. Also found in many of the outer suburbs where they will visit gardens to feed regularly. The setts at Richmond Park and Putney are probably the nearest to central London'. Reference to badgers in London is very thoroughly covered in Teagle (1969) and Paul Moxey comments on this paper on p295.

In Bedfordshire, a paper by Green & Woolnough (1978) gave historic parish vermin payment records and details of the survey of setts. Anderson (1985) listed their presence in 26% of Bedfordshire tetrads and the distribution has a southerly bias to the better drained hilly chalk soils. Beds Wildlife (1987) notes that 'it is interesting that the Luton and Dunstable area, which has the largest concentrated area of

Doreen and Frank Cooper lost their home at Kings Langley in 1985 because their bungalow was in the path of the M25. Their knowledge of the badgers and locations of setts was invaluable for the successful diversion of the wildlife from the new road.

A path for badgers and other wildlife was incorporated in this stream culvert under the Hoddesdon bypass. Details of this are in Neal 1977, 1986 and, with Cheeseman, 1996. (Dr.Neal, our greatest authority on badgers, was born at Boxmoor, Hertfordshire, on 20th May 1911 and died in Bedford on 5th April 1998.)

Dr.Peter Reynolds (Mammal News, Mammal Society, spring 2000) reports that wildlife overpasses (green bridges), landscape connectors or 'ecoducts', are increasingly being used to link habitats either side of roads. About 21 have been constructed in Holland, Germany, France and Switzerland, and 7 in North America, following the original British designs and constructions.

Badger cubs learn from their parents how to catch their staple diet of earthworms. Wet nights are ideal, especially when worms are mating and escape from the surface takes slightly longer than usual.

human population, also has the highest density of active setts'.

Green & Woolnough (1978) also gave survey details and an interesting historic section: 'The earliest record known of the badger in Britain is of fossil remains at Barrington in Cambridgeshire estimated to be 250,000 years old. Similar evidence is frequent in the middle and late Pleistocene periods. Remains dating from 1600-1400 BC have been found at Grimes Graves in Norfolk (Vine 1970), which makes it reasonable to suppose that the badger was also present in Bedfordshire at that time.

'The earliest Bedfordshire records are provided by the payments for vermin published in the churchwardens' account books. These payments were made under an Act of Elizabeth I giving authority for the destruction of "Vermyn" and laying down certain rules for their death. These accounts have been exhaustively researched in Bedfordshire (Elliot 1936).

'Renditions of the spelling contained within the accounts perhaps reflect the local pronunciation and/or poor spelling of the churchwardens. It should be pointed out that spelling was not standardised until the late 18th century. The following are some of the variations found: bager, bagger, badgares, bagongs, baggour, badgett, bagett, bagitts, baggotts, beget, bagert, barget, bagott, badgotts, badgits, badgitts, badget. The reward for a badger head was one shilling (5p), quite a considerable sum, which, with the same reward for a fox head, was the top amount paid although it is difficult to understand in the light of present day knowledge why the badger had such an unjustificd reputation.'

The first Mamm Soc national badger survey was launched on a county basis in the 1960s and there are papers on several, including Wiltshire, Norfolk, Bedfordshire and Yorkshire.

I made the following references to badgers in the HNHS Trans, apart from updating the distribution maps: an article on the conservation of badgers in Hertfordshire related to gassing, the sett survey, protection; the proposal in 1969 for road underpasses where badgers regularly cross, snaring and digging (1970); fight scars found in road casualty badgers above their tails, motorway underpasses planned, discussion on effects of Cymag on foxes, wasp nest consumption and other aspects of diet was discussed (1971); road casualty observations (peak around spring), feeding on acorns noted and the movement of some litters of cubs in early summer (1972); report on the Badger Survey Conference at Pendley and description with map of persecution (1973); erythristic (ginger) badgers, mange in a Berkhamsted road casualty, badger-digging case lost against Harlow digger at Hoddesdon sett because of claim to have been 'after foxes', bedding experiments, populations at known setts, fencing and culvert on new Hoddesdon and

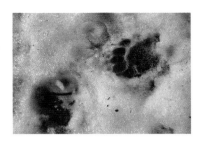

*Tring bypass roads, revival of records from Hitchin (1975); report of destruction by local farmer of famous Cuffley School Camp badger sett known to generations of children who grew up in the county (1977); more news of erythristic badgers, one found sleeping in a drainpipe, sett protection at Hoddesdon (this time from building), tracking badgers between social groups (1980); badgers in gardens, damage to sweetcorn crops, surveys in southwest Hertfordshire, M25 culvert and fencing first discussed for Kings Langley, 10 badgers from Hertfordshire road fatalities contributed to MAFF for TB survey and all proved negative (1983). I felt my initially repudiated evidence to MAFF fully exonerated when MAFF later found gassing totally unsuitable for badgers. Porton Down had never tested badgers to see if they died humanely when gassed. It finally emerged when they did the experiment (as late as 1980, due to the Zukerman Report) that they did not react in the same way as rabbits and foxes.*

The outstanding feature of the *Mamm Soc* county surveys, subsequently taken up by the badger groups, has been the relationship between geology and badger sett construction. Dunwell & Killingley's paper (1969): *The distribution of badger setts in relation to the geology of the Chilterns* is of particular local relevance. They showed that setts and the woodland edge coincide with the upper chalk where it gives way to clay. Here the badgers enjoy good drainage from the slopes, cover from the tree canopy and have quick access to feeding grounds in the fields which are where the middle chalk lies.

**Badger footprints are unmistakable thanks to their large pads and rows of toes. Although they are less active in cold weather, tracks can be seen in snow as well as winter mud. Sometimes a fox print shows next to badger spore and it is interesting to compare them (lower picture).**

They quote Likhachev (1956) who showed that badgers avoided digging setts in the impermeable loam in the Russian Preserve Forest where the plateau corresponded to the Chiltern clay. Of the setts he found, 93% were in ravines where sand was available.

Likhachev assumed drainage to be the vital factor and Gillam (1967) found all the wooded upper greensand slopes in Wiltshire to have setts. Green & Woolnough (1978) found in Bedfordshire that the densest concentration of setts was in the upper chalk and sand was often exploited for setts in the lower greensand.

Paget (1985) describes the distribution of badgers in Yorkshire as a close reflection of that for the earthworm *Lumbricus terrestris*, its staple diet, and these are to be found predominantly with grazed pasture at lower altitudes in more alkaline soils. The badgers are not, therefore, common on the gritstone Pennines nor the plateau of the North York Moors.

If I can express what Paget describes as the perfect sett site from the point of view of an estate agent: 'An old established sett in attractive cover, on a well drained slope, in workable rock for easy but secure extensions (with planning permission), adjoining extensive feeding grounds and plentiful earthworms with excellent educational prospects for cubs and minimal human interference.'

The southwest Chiltern Edge bias to the distribution of setts in Hertfordshire reflects all these features found in other counties. Clay frequently appears in spoil heaps at setts, but it is almost invariably in association with chalk or sand. Pure clay appears to be undesirable to the species because it retains dampness in tunnels and does not give adequate drainage. From long-term observation I have known many sett

**Detail of badger sett distribution in the Chiltern Hills showing how they follow the bands of Upper Chalk on woodland edges. There are woods and slopes on the clay plateau, but no setts are present there.**
**(After Dunwell & Killingley 1969.)**

| | |
|---|---|
| ●● | Setts |
| ■ | Clay |
| □ | Chalk |
| ⠿ | Woods |
| - - - | Chalk rock |

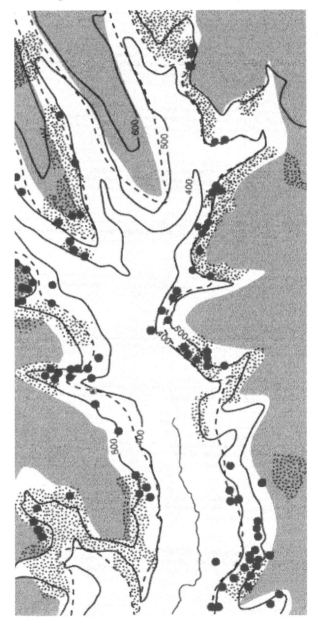

*Letter to Maureen Cullin, Editor.*

*Dear Badger Group,*
*Our visit to the Badger Hide on Monday evening with Diana Wallace was magical.*
   *5 Badgers, 1 Fox*
   *All in an hour*
   *Weren't we lucky!*
*I also want to thank the Badger Group for making the hide so easily reached by wheelchair. I have lived in England for 34 years and never seen a badger before so that made it an especial treat for me.*
*Yours*
*Mary Poole*

*(Badger Times, winter 1992)*

entrances to be developments of rabbit burrows and whilst these are often on the border of existing setts, soil samples from the burrows may be a source of valuable information to badgers before they commit themselves to more extensive tunnel excavations.

Although I was County Recorder for the *Mamm Soc* survey and, with many helpers, located over 300 setts by the mid 1970s, a much more detailed survey was organised by the *HMBG* in the 1980s and 1990s. The Group was originally established (with the Bat Group) for members of the *HMWT* with a specific interest in badgers. So much has been achieved by volunteers in the survey that it is now safe to estimate the actual total of setts at around 1,200 for Hertfordshire, most of which have the details of their size, soil and location recorded.

Mike Wainwright (1998) gives a very thorough account of the work of the *HMBG* and has published summaries of the badger road fatalities in the *HMBG* newsletters. I am grateful for his permission to quote from both. Members have a very good network of contacts so that when badgers are run over in the county someone in the Group is able to collect the body. About 100 badgers are known to be lost to vehicles annually, but many must also be injured and this is now the major control on the population.

The records accurately reflect the two most favourable areas for badgers: in the chalk of the hilly well-wooded parts of southwest Hertfordshire and in the gravels and chalk in the hilly, well-wooded eastern side. The database has over 1,500 surveys of some 1,200 setts undertaken since 1961 and the number of setts per 10km square can be illustrated.

When the numbers of holes per sett are compared, the impression that an increasing badger population would mean more sett entrances is shown to be false; the pattern of numbers is quite random. All who have surveyed setts will know of sites where there are numerous entrances scattered up a hillside, but actual activity is confined to only a few.

Entrances to setts become hidden in summer by vegetation but are often signalled by elder trees.

The droughts in 1989 and in the 1990s are believed to have caused more road fatalaties by forcing badgers to explore further for food, just as they did in 1975 and 1976. Roads also contributed in part to the second most important control: illegal digging or shooting by humans, because, in addition to individuals who live here, criminals can use the motorway networks to visit our county from areas where they have eliminated their local badger populations.

Deliberate human disturbance is much reduced but still continues and the public should always be vigilant and report all suspect behaviour. Prosecutions have largely involved local people: from Stevenage, the Lea Valley and Hemel Hempstead in particular.

**All five claws show on a scratched dead oak trunk which is near a crossroads of badger footpaths in rough pasture near Welwyn.**

**Badgers, like this one near Kings Langley, may sport worn nails, chewed ears, itchy throats and battle scars on their rumps.**

# Otter

## Lutra lutra

*Izaak Walton's famous description of an otter hunt was from the River Lea at Amwell which was a stronghold of the otter up to the 1970s. Published in 1653, 'The Compleat Angler' features much of the Lea Valley. (Walton was born in 1593*

*and died in 1683.) The next reference for Hertfordshire I have been able to find was one of Oldham's vermin lists for Welwyn which included 2 otters in 1706, presumably from the River Mimram.*

*John Carrington, 'the Hertfordshire Pepys', lived above the Mimram Valley at Tewin and he mentioned a live otter from the Lea, possibly kept to be baited like a badger, in his diary for 3rd November 1804: 'Saw the Otter Catched by Stanstead in a Ditch by some of the Ware Bargemen a-live.'*

*In 1877 Brett wrote (Trans 1, 9:23b): 'I presume that this animal was more common formerly than it is now, as we have two localities named after it - Otterspool and Little Otterspool. There is a curious pool at the former place interesting to geologists, but I do not know of any pool at the latter. The otter is not very frequent at Watford. Even old inhabitants have never seen a wild otter.*

**Memorial window to Izaak Walton in the Prior Silstede Chapel of Winchester Cathedral.**
**(The otter was in captivity at the Otter Trust, Bungay.)**

*'Alfred Dyson tells me that one was killed in the osier beds past Tolpits, 20 years ago. In 1875 a young one was killed in the Colne above Watford. George Francis recollects his father shooting one which escaped at Piccotts End, in the Gade, 60 years since.*

*'Arthur Hibbert, of Munden Park, tells me that a male otter was shot in February 1875 at Munden; it weighed 32lbs and a few ounces, and it was 4ft 2½ins long. It was shot after a heavy fall of snow had melted and the floods were out. The keeper had seen some strange tracks up and down the River Colne by Little Munden and he had found the head and tail of a large jack pike. Mr.Haylock was going through the Grove and, his dog bringing the otter to bay, he shot it about 100 yards from the water. The keeper looked out for the female but could not find her, nor did he see any tracks of any more. Lately, a large carp has been seen on the bank at Otterspool, partly consumed, as if it had been eaten by an otter. The same thing has been observed on a bank at Aldenham Abbey.*

*'It is a question whether the otter does good or harm to a stream. By doing good or harm, does he, I mean, increase*

182

or decrease the absolute weight of fish in a stream? There can be no doubt but that the otter destroys a large quantity of fish; but the fecundity of fish is so enormous that almost any loss can be readily replaced, and by taking out the larger fish he may actually be doing good; for the large ones do not grow in proportion to the food they consume. Growth is more rapid in the young, and the food consumed would go to produce more weight. Besides, the otter would naturally catch those fish which were least active in avoiding his pursuit. The swifter and more healthy would get away, and in this manner the breed of fish would be improved, according to the law of the survival of the fittest. I have no doubt the otter plays an important part in the plan of nature, and I hope he will not be exterminated from our county.'

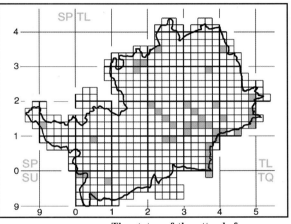

In 1881 Croft reported otters were present on the Lea. Evidence that they regularly colonised Hertfordshire from the Essex side, along the River Stort, was given to me by Lewis Watson (Trans **27**, 2 38, 1970), who saw 20 otters nailed to the door of a shed at Stanstead Abbotts, where the two rivers meet, in the 1930s. If gin traps (illegal since 1958) were set on prominent outcrops under the bridges such as happened here, few otters would avoid the danger because they range over such great distances. (I still have a gin trap I found set on a rock in a Scottish river, near Dunkeld, in 1964.)

**The status of the otter before recolonisation and all Hertfordshire records 1969-78, plus reports following reintroduction in 1992.**

The Nat Hist Mus has 9 Tring skins from the Roth Coll, which Lloyd (47) listed as:

| | |
|---|---|
| Male | Wilstone Reservoir, 4th May 1916 |
| Female | Tring Reservoirs, 25th March 1920 |
| Male | Tring Reservoirs, 13th January 1921 |
| Male | Tring Reservoirs, 27th April 1921 |
| Male | Tring Reservoirs, September 1922 (18lbs) |
| Male | Tring, 20th April 1923 |
| Female | Tring Reservoirs, 16th June 1923 |
| Female | Tring Reservoirs, 18th November 1925 |
| Male | Wilstone Reservoir, 29th August 1932. |

The data for the 1925 skin is now missing, so that Lloyd's list is helpful to complete the record. Lloyd assumed that these specimens (trapped or shot by the gamekeeper at the reservoirs) arrived along the Thame or the canals near Marsworth. He considered that otters had become rare in the county by 1947, but that the Lea and the Colne still harboured a few. He reported that one had been killed on the Stour (River Stort?) near Bishop's Stortford in 1930.

The otter became protected only in 1978 as it disappeared from much of England and is included in Schedule 5 of the Wildlife & Countryside Act 1981. In Europe the species is protected by the Habitats Directive 43/93 under The Berne Convention and there is now worldwide protection under CITES.

**Albert Sutton, who recorded the loss of otters at Ickleford due to water pollution in 1911 (see text).**

*Foster (1934) wrote that due to destruction of trout from pollution of the rivers, otters had ceased to visit many of their old haunts. The Ivel, he said, still had occasional visitors, but the absence of fish in the Hiz had caused the otters to be very scarce in that stream. Jim Sutton, who farmed all his working life at Ramerwick Farm, near Ickleford, has given me considerable help in the mammal survey and his father, Albert Truin Sutton (Bert), at the age of 95, recounted to me when the otters abruptly disappeared from the Hiz, which borders the Bedfordshire side of the farm. In 1911 the tannery in Hitchin polluted the river and killed the fish, many of which were caught up dead on the grille below their farm over a considerable period of time. Prior to this he had watched otters frequently and recalled cubs playing with an adult, presumably their mother. He never saw an otter on the river again: a remarkable record of environmental loss over such a long period.*

*Foster continued with local Hitchin area information by saying that several records were from the Radwell district where a Hitchin taxidermist had mounted more than 12 locally obtained specimens prior to 1900. He concluded with an entry in Lucas' diary for 5th November 1814: 'A very large male otter caught in the river between Ickleford and Arlesey was shown in the market.' There were reports of otters at Oughtonhead, near Hitchin in the 1930s and there is a specimen from the River Ivel at Shefford Mill (Bedfordshire) in N Herts Mus Coll. (1950).*

*Otters were always difficult to observe in the county and despite the concern of naturalists and certain farmers, there was clearly also every effort to trap or shoot them by some fishing interests and gamekeepers. Eastern Counties Otterhounds also made regular visits to our few small rivers and Tom Gladwin recorded two kills by the hunt in the 1950s, one at Roydon and one at Hertford. A kill by the same hounds at Stanstead Abbotts in their first meet after World*

**Eastern Counties Otterhounds: 'High summer on the Broadwater' at Hatfield from** *They Meet at Eleven* **by Frank Meads, by kind permission.**

War II was also reported to me by Lewis Watson.

When I started to collect the mammal records for the HNHS in the 1960s I made particular efforts to trace otters from the Ware/Stanstead Abbotts area without success, but a trickle of reliable records came in: up to 1964 a pair were regularly observed by a lock keeper on the Lea until gravel workings displaced them; one was seen playing in a water lily patch at Hatfield Water Mill (in the background of Frank Mead's photograph opposite), L.Lewis 1967; one seen at Cassiobury, Watford, eating a roach, via K.Jones 1968; tracks were seen at the same site, B.Ing February 1970; T.James found a partly eaten fish on the bank of the Lee Navigation at Amwell, 1970, presumably the work of an otter; a pair were observed at Digswell Park Lake by T.Gladwin; spraints were found at Wilstone Reservoir by C.Banks; 3 otters were seen at Codicote, on the Mimram, by PC S.Darton - all in 1971.

**River Hiz where it borders Ramerwick Farm, near Ickleford (see text). Mink have been trapped here in recent years.**

(I attended a hunt with the Bucks and Courtenay Tracey Otterhounds along the Ouse in Bedfordshire at this time, but spraints were only located in the upper reaches towards the end of the day and no otters were seen); there were no sightings reported in 1972, but the 1971 Darton record suggested a bitch with 2 cubs: the first contemporary breeding record I received. (He was a policeman at that time, fished regularly and chanced upon them when checking an empty property.) An otter from the Mimram was also seen by the road side at Archers Green near Tewin during a hard frost in November 1973.

I stayed with John and Joan Willett at their remarkable deer collection and private museum in Devon in 1974 and thanks to their hospitality was able to follow the Culmstock Otterhounds on 30th August. I had made a close study of the hunt records and found the followers to be very anxious about their local otter numbers. Although they killed their 39th mink of the season during the day, no otters were found. The hunt has one of the best documented records of its activities and continues as a mink hunt.

**Otters can keep a low profile on the water surface with nose, eyes and ears all in line, just above the surface. They can disappear from view in an instant and depart from the area under water.**

An otter was seen at Piccotts End close to the main stream of the Gade, 29th December 1974 (T.Holder); one was seen on the Mimram at Archers Green, Tewin, 2nd November 1975 (S.Darton); 2 were seen together on the Beane at Watton-at-Stone, 8th April 1976 (B.Sawford); one was seen on the Lea in 1977 near Enfield Lock; 2 were seen at Sarratt; a bitch and 2 cubs were observed when night fishing for eels on the Lea at Hertford during 1978 (G.Edmonds). This last record was the second

185

Kathy Kourik stands next to an undisturbed mound of bright green grass where generations of otters have left spraints as a marker on an Isle of Mull beach. It can take the form of 'jelly' (centre) or droppings (bottom), normally left at prominent places such as boulders or logs by the water.

modern breeding record and I later found during a field visit that a householder also watched 2 otters regularly here from her garden during 1976.

I was given an old record for the River Beane at this time: the late Jack Izzard, a neighbour in Tewin, told me that the only otter he ever shot was in Woodhall Park, near Watton-at-Stone, 'where the reed bed comes to the road side, by the culvert at Watton Green, in 1926, when I was 18 years old'.

At this point (1978) records for otters in the county sent to me ceased and the species was absent throughout the 1980s until they were reintroduced on the Lea and the Stort by the Otter Trust in 1991. A large native mammal species had thus become extinct in Hertfordshire, having been part of our fauna for some 10,000 years.

The home range and diet of the reintroduced otters, as well as the reason for the decline of the species in Britain and Europe, is described in Roche, Harris, Warrington & Copp (1995). The chemical dieldrin, PCBs and other factors have been put forward as the main causes for the decline (Mason & Macdonald 1983 and 1993) and there is no doubt that road traffic is likely to make survival very difficult for the reintroduced population in modern Hertfordshire.

Laver (1898) regretted the trapping and shooting of otters in Victorian Essex, but considered the species still widespread across the county. He quotes Daniel (1794) as recording a '40lb upwards of dog otter' snared between Ware and Hertford on the Lea as well as various ones taken in his own county. Dobson (1999) gives the modern distribution for otters in Essex and describes them as 'rare, increasing'. Recolonisation appears to be taking place from the north. (I found tracks on the estuary tide-line in the 1970s near Walton-on-the-Naze.) Beds Wildlife (1987) gives the last year that otters were recorded in the county as 1972. Before otters disappeared from much of England the Hertfordshire population was clearly dependent upon dispersal from Essex, Bedfordshire and Buckinghamshire. No mention of otters is made by Burton (1974) for the London area.

In ideal conditions, about 25 pairs of otters could have been supported on Hertfordshire rivers if we look at the county's river systems with modern knowledge of otter territorial and feeding requirements (Chanin; Mason & MacDonald; Jenkins, et al). Otters have always been more vulnerable than those of other larger carnivores compared to an estimated 3,000 foxes and 1,500 badgers. The reintroduced ones bred and dispersed in the 1990s, but they probably number less than 10.

They have been the first of our larger, modern carnivores to die out directly due to the following human impact on the rivers and countryside:

- evidence from recent research work cites river and stream pollution by the organochlorine pesticide

186

dieldrin, DDT, mercury, acid rain, nitrates;
- loss of holt nesting sites;
- hunting, which before it became illegal concentrated on the few rivers where otters survived;
- greater disturbance by humans through recreation (to a species which has learnt to be fearful of human presence over hundreds of years due to constant persecution);
- alterations in fish biomass;
- fyke eel nets, which are permanent lethal underwater traps;
- the type of river management which removes cover for otters to slip away into;
- major tree loss from our countryside in general.

Otters playing together.

Although these factors, and others, combined to make otters extinct from much of England, the introduction of cyclodiene pesticides into agriculture occurred at the time of the decline and it is impossible to know what cocktails of chemicals carried in the bodies of otters from polluted water may have reduced the effectiveness of their immune systems to disease.

Long whiskers help otters to locate prey in murky water.

This would affect their ability to breed and survive in extreme weather conditions. Chanin shows how evidence from the hunt records demonstrated that the declines coincided with each other across England, even in the most favourable otter country.

I knew from my reference to the Culmstock Otterhound Hunt records that in 1957 they had found more otters than at nearly any time in their 200 year history. Yet within a decade, when I went to follow the hunt to see what was happening, a hunt follower said resentfully to me that if the hounds nowadays got the scent of an otter, the master would take them off in the opposite direction until they found a mink. (Introduced mink were blamed at one stage for the otter decline, yet no evidence has ever shown this to be so and otters vanished in Hertfordshire at a time when mink were absent from much of the county.)

My investigation in Bedfordshire with the Bucks and Courtenay Tracy Otterhounds in 1971 had produced the same result three years earlier and the Eastern Counties

**Captive otter at Mole Hall, Widdington, Essex, in 1971. Other species kept at Mole Hall are shown in Harris (1968).**

Otterhounds had given up visiting Hertfordshire because of the blank days. Otters are so rarely seen that field work on spraints and tracks is needed to detect their presence. I had gained experience from estuary otters in Devon and at Irish and Scottish sites: when otters are present you can usually find their signs if you look in the right places.

There was clearly a small population in the Mimram and Beane tributary rivers to the Lea during much of the 1970s. Both the Tring and Lea Valley strongholds apparently lost their otters before these two isolated populations (in spring-fed chalk streams) also died out.

During the 1980s it was reported that otters survived in the protected waters of the Royal Ordnance Powdermill cut near Waltham Abbey. However, on my enquiry to Alastair Driver, the Thames Water Conservator, he confirmed in 1989 that they were absent from there and all of the 5,000 miles of rivers and streams of the Thames catchment area. He knew of only some small evidence of passage by otters through part of the sytem and that was in the Cotswolds.

Before the unannounced release of otters in Hertfordshire by the Otter Trust in 1991, I had written that our water quality and quantity must be ensured; the fish biomass must be adequate; bankside vegetation, resting places and undisturbed haven areas of banks must be provided to have any hope for their return.

Although there have been only about three ancient woods abutting rivers in the county for centuries (at Stapleford and the Hadhams), it is worth noting that Mason & Macdonald (1986) showed that 30-50% of ancient lowland woodlands in Britain have been destroyed since 1949 and many converted to commercial conifer plantations. Otters require species such as ash, oak and sycamore which provide good root system growth into rivers for their holts.

To make up for past damage to our river habitats, further artificial secluded holts should be constructed and log piles provided close to the water. Large eel tunnel traps (fyke nets) should be totally banned and access to roads fenced off. Otters wandering over bridges onto roads will probably always be a major problem. With conservation measures I felt that the investment of some £25,000 a pair to buy otters from a captive breeding programme for release seemed viable, taking into account that they need at least 10km of river and about 365kg of food each annually, of which 80% must be fish (Mason & MacDonald).

I estimated that the distribution survey may have been as

188

good an indication of the abundance of healthy crayfish and eels as anything else: the Mimram between Welwyn and Hertford, the Beane between Watton-at-Stone and Hertford, the Stort and Amwell Quarry areas would be the ideal haven sites for otters. As it has turned out, recolonisation from Amwell into the Mimram, where I would have first expected them to turn up, took nearly a decade and it may have been better to have released a pair on this river at the same time as those in the Stort and Lea. Panshanger Park would be ideal for further reintroductions.

*Having been present in Hertfordshire for some 10,000 years, since the last Ice Age, after 1978 otters became extinct here.*

There are fishing interests in all areas, but, as Mason & MacDonald concluded: otters are at least neutral to fishing interests and could very well be beneficial to fish populations by eating eels, which are major predators of fish. When he first moved to Tewin, Martin Symonds, who owns Tewin Fish Farm, told me how he would welcome otters at the farm (and has since put in pens including Indian otters amongst water fowl collections and deer on show).

*Otters reintroduced here in 1992 have bred in the wild and a slow return to vacated habitats is hoped for.*

Recolonisation from East Anglia via the Stort is a very long-term hope because road traffic is now so great in the county that exploration to other rivers is fraught with dangers. Expansion of the otter ranges in central England via Bedfordshire and Buckinghamshire is less likely, but the historic records of otters at Tring reservoirs give hope for this, as long as numbers recover well nationally.

The *HMG* has continued to monitor both the survival and dispersal of the originally introduced otters and their descendants. Training days have helped in spraint and tracking skills. My own survey area has been Archer's Green at Tewin where I had 2 records from the 1970s. Although I have never found spraint here, they have been located at Tewin Bury by Graham White, one mile upstream in 1999.

**Otter resting on a log.**

# Deer in Hertfordshire

*Our two indigenous deer, the red (the largest British land mammal, after which the county was named) and the roe,*

*disappeared around the 17th century without much published information apart from fossil records (eg red and roe deer antlers found in a gravel pit at Kings Langley [Trans 18, xvi-xvii and 216, 1927]). Both species have, however, reappeared as occasional visitors and, in the last 30 years, the expansion of the roe range has established them once again in the county. Roe are not successful as enclosed park deer, but fallow, red and, more recently, sika deer have all prospered at different times in our parklands. The deer usually seen in Hertfordshire today are muntjac and fallow.*

**Red deer stag** *Cervus elephus* **during the rut, Knebworth Park, near Stevenage, October 1972.**

*To understand our present populations we should look at the fashion for keeping deer on estates. The nearest royal park was just to the south in Middlesex, at Enfield Chace. Royal chases have records from the Middle Ages in which accounts, game bags and hunting details were carefully preserved; early authors were able to refer to them.*

*As well as the Kings Langley finds, the Trans recorded large quantities of antlers found there when moats were dredged around the 1860s. Excavations for the new retort house at the gas works in 1910 revealed probably post-Roman roe and red deer remains and deer (thought to be red) were found in a section at Watford Fields sewage farm in 1886.*

**A mature deer at Knebworth Park, 1975. The antlers of red stags are cast off and regrown each year.**

*Park deer featured in several Trans accounts. Brett (1878) reported that 80 fallow deer out of a herd of 300 enclosed in Cassiobury Park had died of an unknown cause, despite postmortem examination, and 150 had been lost from a herd of 600 in 1807. Forty ewes died with deer in a similar sudden death incident in 1821 and the postmortems suggested an excess of food. The venison was eaten with no ill effects on the people who ate it and I know of deer lost at Woburn in modern times when turned into a field with an exceptionally abundant crop of Turkey oak acorns (Quercus cerris). It may be that the deaths at Cassiobury also coincided with good acorn years. It was some time before the toxic effects of the acorns at Woburn, upon which the deer had gorged themselves, was suspected (via Dennis Talbot, then deer keeper). Turkey oaks were commonly planted in deer parks (Mitchell 1974).*

*Harting (1881) gave a summary of Hertfordshire deer parks past and present, but omitted Tring Park. (The summary is given on p198.) He points out that 'park', from the French 'parquer' (to pen cattle), signifies an enclosure. In Manwood's treatise on Forest Law, a park only differs from a chase in being enclosed. A chase, second to forest as the ultimate hunting ground, was an open place for keeping game. A park was defined as an enclosed chase which could vary in extent from a few acres to 2,000 acres or more. A park could only be created by royal licence, so that anyone who simply fenced off an area which contained deer, and thus turned wild animals into park stock, would suffer the full force of the law. (There was a modern example of this near Wheathamsted in Hertfordshire during the 1980s where objection was made to fallow deer and muntjac being enclosed in newly fenced grounds by a landowner.)*

*Harting describes the creation of parks after the Norman Conquest as licences were granted for enclosures until the notoriously strict forest laws were largely repealed. Thus the land was parcelled up amongst the nobility as a useful way of raising money for impoverished exchequers during many reigns until there were hardly any noblemen or 'gentlemen of position' who did not possess a park.*

*Civil wars caused many to be broken up and the deer exterminated. The decline was associated with the increasing value of timber and agricultural land. Daniel (1807) and Shirley (1867) show that the number of parks in England declined by over 50% over 60 years: Daniel gave 69 forests, 13 chases and 750 parks, whilst Shirley could only locate 334 parks still stocked with deer. (Red deer were kept at some 31 of these.)*

*Three of the 31 deer parks described in the Domesday Book were in Hertfordshire: at St.Albans, as part of the Abbey property; at Ware, which is described as containing wood to feed 400 hogs and a park of deer, together with a vineyard recently planted; and at Benington, which contained wood to feed 100 hogs and a park of deer.*

*Of the parks lost by Brett's day, Theobalds, near Cuffley, was one of the most important with red and fallow deer; even elk were kept in 1612 and were still there in 1624. The red were imported from Denmark in 1612, but there were still wild red deer outside the park at this time. Just to the northeast of Enfield Chace, Theobalds was the favourite hunting seat of James I and he gave Hatfield to Sir Robert Cecil in exchange for the park. The exchange enabled him to wall the park, hunting both red and fallow deer in Epping Forest, Enfield Chace and Hoddesdon Woods. He gave the 'dark' fallow to Epping Forest, which prosper to this day.*

*One of his guests, Lord Falkland, lost his life after a fall from a stand, which was the early version of a high seat*

**Roe buck in summer pelage (top) at Tewin Orchard, and (below) growing new antlers in winter. The winter coat is lighter and the pale throat patches show up clearly.**

**Muntjac buck in summer pelage and antlers in velvet.**

**Muntjac buck in winter (captive, Tewin Orchard).**

**Chinese water deer buck showing elongated canine (summer).**

constructed to shoot deer, but only when driven past rather than by the modern concept of cull plans where the stalker waits and selects appropriate deer below. A survey in 1650 put Theobalds at 2,508 acres. The property was valued at £1,545 15s 4d pa, deer £1,000, rabbits £15, timber £7,259 (exclusive of 15,608 trees marked for the use of the navy).

Panshanger, near Hertford, was listed as 500 acres with a herd of deer, up to the mid 19th century. Sawbridgeworth was 400 acres and, like New Place, Gilston, to the southwest near Harlow, lacked deer for many years. Hunsdon, near Ware, was an old hunting lodge of Queen Elizabeth I, and records show that in 1124 an annual gift of a doe deer was made to monks from the park herd. In the parish church is a brass memorial to Hames Gray, the deer keeper who died aged 35 in 1591. He is shown with bugle horn and broad sword having just discharged his crossbow at a stag. Death, shown as a skeleton, plucks the arrow from the deer with one hand and plunges a second into the breast of the keeper.

Other parks existed nearby at Widford, Eastwick, Thorley and Rye (just to the south of Hunsdon). Further north, Furneux Pelham, Wyddial and Throcking had deer parks. Hamels had deer in the 19th century, but Walkern was disparked much earlier. It was in the moat here at Walkern Park Farm, that a vast number of antlers were later dredged out. Stagenhoe, near Hitchin, had deer and there are good numbers of fallow still to be found around Hitch Wood and the farmland to the south of Buntingford, where Aspenden Hall originally had a deer park.

In Berkhamsted there was a royal park attached to the castle in the time of Edward I, and Pendley became enclosed in the time of Henry VI. Kings Langley, Brocket Hall near Welwyn, Tyttenhanger near Hatfield, Little Berkhamsted, Ponsbourne, Hertingfordbury and Shenley all had deer parks. Harting, writing in 1881, recorded some 40 deer parks of which only 10 survived 11 years later. It would be interesting to know whether a farming recession, change in fashion or another reason can be given for such a dramatic loss of deer parks.

Whitaker circulated 1,200 letters to survey the deer parks left in England and found only 9 (see page 199.) Just 5 fallow deer remained at Gorhambury and no red deer were kept in any of the parks. In the same year Roberts observed in the Trans HNHS that the Epping fallow were being conserved and were a uniform dark brown, unlike the dappled menil (normal) coloured deer of the parks. (I remember as a child in the 1950s seeing from my parents' car the dark Epping deer feeding close to the road side, but the increase in traffic over the next 20 years forced them to the perimeter of the Forest, as has been well documented by Chapman & Chapman [1975]. Eleven of 79 Epping fallow killed in road accidents recorded by the Chapmans were previously incapacitated, including missing legs, blindness and wire

Chinese water deer *Hydropotes inermis* doe with litter of newly-born fawns (Tewin Orchard).

Manchurian sika stag *C. nipon manchuricus* at Knebworth Park (1977).

*snares embedded in their legs. They show a young buck killed by a car which had already lost a hind leg in a previous accident and suffered a plastic ring stuck on the remaining hind foot.) The situation has improved in the last decade and the sanctuary at Theydon Bois now has over 200, as I saw on a guided visit with Paul Moxey and one of the deer keepers, Michael Collins, during a course we ran at High Beach Conservation Centre in 1999. It is a pity that the lethal road through the Forest has not been closed to traffic: it is such an internationally important environment here.*

*Laver (1898) quotes Harting's research on the Essex red deer and describes the hunting background to their presence. He also reports that red deer from Windsor had been used to restock Epping. He illustrates one of the Weald Hall fallow and quotes Harting's view that the Epping fallow have 'preserved their ancient character in regard to size and colour', i.e. small and dark, with slender antlers compared with the more palmated park types.*

*The disparking of the deer herds in the 20th century was accelerated by World War I and in 1937 Oldham produced an interesting account of the feral deer at Ashridge which reflects the different characters of the two indigenous species. Red deer (and roe) can be 'shot out' from an area if management is not imposed and poaching is rife, but the fallow deer can survive a certain amount of persecution by dispersal and become extremely wary. Oldham lists the deer sold when Ashridge came up for sale in 1921: 200 fallow, 100 red and 20 sika. In a deer drive 35 of the red were shot, but most of the fallow and sika survived and subsequent drives failed to reduce the herds appreciably. By 1936 between 300 and 400 fallow deer could be seen, but the red and sika were reduced to a few individuals and had probably died out by 1940.*

*John Wilson, then deer keeper at Ashridge, based in Thunderdell Lodge, wrote on the history of the Ashridge deer in East Anglian Deer News, No 6, November 1969:*

Fallow deer buck *Dama dama* showing pale form, Knebworth Park (1978).

Fallow deer bucks showing menil (spotted) and dark forms.

Tail pattern of fallow deer.

(Both at Knebworth Park, 1978.)

'The National Trust Ashridge Estate is situated on the Hertfordshire and Buckinghamshire borders, the county boundary running through the estate. At the present time the Estate comprises 4,000 acres, of which 3,000 acres are dedicated woodlands, heavily wooded commons and downland thorn scrub. Agricultural land accounts for the remainder. Surrounding the Estate is perhaps another 1,000 acres of woods and commons not belonging to the National Trust, in which deer are present.

'The first mention of deer at Ashridge was in 1286, when Edmund, Earl of Cornwall, enclosed it, later dividing the enclosure into two parks, one containing fallow deer and the other red deer. On the death of Edmund, the estate reverted to Edward I and an inquisition taken after his death records: "Park with deer, pasture for support of deer worth ten shillings and wood called Den Frith containing 763 acres." This wood exists today and bears its original name of Frithsden.

'Throughout the years that follow, references to the deer occur, as in: "Privy Purse Expenses, Henry VIII - payment of 7/6d made to a servant of Sir Edward Donnes for bringing of a bucke to the King at Ashridge."

'Then on 10th and 16th June 1643, despite two orders from Parliament forbidding plunder, parliamentary soldiers killed deer in Ashridge Park belonging to the Earl of Bridgewater.

'In 1681 Thomas Baskerville, visiting Ashridge, remarked on the herds of fallow and red deer and also to the pantry or buttery, "adorned with many heads and horns of stags". The Ashridge Steward's account book for 22nd January 1694 records "for cleaning the haybarn and taking hay to the deer in the Deer Park, payment to Hall and Ivory - one shilling." Apparently on 2nd February both men were paid two shillings for the same job. One week later, "payment to Clifton was made: one shilling for flaying a deer".

'Thereafter there is a continuous record of fallow and red deer in Ashridge Park, with one interesting addition in 1814 of white cashmere goats, which ran with the deer until the last one died in 1927.

'The number of deer kept in the park varied, but showed a steady increase. In 1914 there were 100 red and 300 fallow, whereas in 1921 there were approximately 150 red, 550 fallow and also 27 sika deer. At this time 50 calves and fawns were culled per annum, the majority of which were sold locally at 10/- (50p) per fawn and £1 per calf.

'When in 1921 Lord Brownlow, the owner of Ashridge, died his will directed the trustees to dispose of the whole of the estate to meet death duties. Immediately 11,300 acres were sold and in 1925 the National Trust acquired the amenity parts of the estate, which included the deer park. During the four years when the deer park was in the trustees' hands, fences were broken, deer escaped and eventually a local auctioneer was contracted for the removal

Fallow bucks seek shade in summer when flies bother them.

of the remaining deer in the park. *Thirty-five red deer were caught up and sent to Ireland. After several more unsuccessful attempts had been made to catch them, the remainder of the deer escaped and received the worst end of a free-for-all with shotguns, snares and deer traps. This resulted in the extermination of both the red deer and the sika (5 last seen in 1935) and the fallow were reduced to their lowest ebb.*

'*The Forestry Report dated 1931 said, "It is understood that the deer will probably disappear within a very few years." However, this was not to be. The fallow increased again up to the outbreak of World War II. Thereafter their numbers declined until syndicate shooting was stopped on the estate and control was placed in the hands of the keepers by a committee who were sympathetic towards the welfare of the deer.*

'*The latest census was taken in March 1964 and showed 86 fallow deer present on the estate. This comprises of 30 bucks of various ages, 41 does and 15 fawns. From these figures the following year's cull is assessed. All road and other casualties are taken into account and classed as part of the cull. The majority of road casualties are does, so shooting of does has not taken place as yet. From time to time complaints are received of damage done by deer on farmland, allotments and gardens, but the estate is fortunate in having tenant farmers who tolerate the deer and confine their complaints only to serious damage, when action is taken by the keepers.*

'*The quality and condition of the deer is very good. Some of*

A young fallow in Knebworth Park prances on all four legs, springbok fashion, due to my presence with 400mm telephoto lens.

**Red deer**

**Fallow deer**

**Sika deer**

**Roe deer**

**Muntjac deer**

Deer tracks: the above images are 50% of full size for an adult male.

the bucks bear excellent heads and culling is confined to 'wasters', bad antler formation and bucks 'going back'. About 50 of the herd are the common dark variety, 40% black, the remainder menil and white, including one four year white buck.

'Other species of deer on the estate are muntjac and water deer. There have also been two doubtful reports of Siberian roe recently. The muntjac were first seen and shot on the estate in 1926 and are now generally widespread. The hard winter of 1963 took a heavy toll because this species found it virtually impossible to feed. A nucleus was left. These deer are not shot on the estate since damage to forestry and farm crops has not been significant yet.

'Chinese water deer are certainly present on the estate in small numbers, but prove to be elusive. Dew ponds and woodland ponds have been opened out by the Conservation Corps for other purposes, but at the same time are proving very popular with the deer. Mineral licks have also been provided and these measures seem to be having the desired effect in keeping the deer confined to the woodland and common areas.

'The public show great interest in the deer at Ashridge and there seems no reason to doubt that their future welfare is assured.'

Foster (1934) felt unable to give any information on wild deer because none had been present for decades in the 10 mile radius around Hitchin he described (despite Kings Walden Deer Park and its escapees, which the Preston and Whitwell herds no doubt originated from).

Berry (1957) gives valuable background to the modern herds in east Hertfordshire by stating that in a memorable storm in March 1916 a tree fell and breached the wall of Woodhall Park, near Hertford, through which a few fallow escaped. Some years later they had become established at Bramfield, near Hertford, and at Meesden and Langley. By 1935 they were reported from Scales Park and Clavering Park, so that all the area hunted by the Puckeridge Foxhounds from Meesden to Hatfield Forest (Essex) showed fallow.

He gives Cambridgeshire, Essex and Bedfordshire records and concludes that the deer show no sign of deterioration. The herds were, if anything, increasing in size, despite spasmodic efforts to reduce their numbers by hunting, shooting and 'other, but less orthodox, methods'. Hatfield Forest still has fallow present, but I have found evidence of poaching there in the past where butchery on the spot has taken place: limbs and head were hidden in an area of undergrowth.

J.Morewood Dowsett (1942) referred to the mixed fortunes of the deer in Enfield Chace:

'The earliest records of a park at Enfield are 11th century when the manor was owned by Geoffrey de Mandeville.

196

*Immediately to the north of the town of Enfield there was an extensive tract of land, measuring about 8½ miles from east to west and including parts of the adjoining parishes of Edmonton, Hadley and South Mimms. This was termed Enfield Chace.*

*'Like a forest, a chase was unenclosed and the property of one of the king's subjects, so that offences committed therein were generally punishable by the common law instead of the enactments of forest legislation.*

*'To all intents and purposes, Enfield Chace was a park within a park, the core or inner portion being composed of the Ancient Great Park, which was sometimes called "le Frith". Around this there was a far larger outer park (parcus extrinsicus). In the troubled reign of Edward II, Enfield Chace was forfeited to the Crown. A certain Richard Pounz was then the keeper of the park, and in 1324 the king ordered him to permit the prior of St.John of Jerusalem at Clerkenwell to take five bucks between Midsummer and Michaelmas and five does between Michaelmas and Lent (with dogs or archers at his pleasure) from the outer park, in accordance with the ancient grant of William de Mandeville, Earl of Essex. It was stated that this park had always belonged to the manor of Enfield so that no hogs were allowed in the Chace during the fence month (June) when the does were fawning, while all hogs and swine had to bear their owner's mark and the king's.*

*'Writing of Enfield Chace in 1596, Borden says: "A solitary desert, yet stocked with not less than 5,000 deers." This appears to be an extraordinarily large number for a hunting ground so near London, but Borden's figures receive confirmation from the warrant issued to John West, keeper of the West Baily Walk in Enfield Chace in 1608, for it authorises him to spend £30 per annum to provide hay for the deer. Since hay was given to them only in the winter months when they could find no good green pasturage, we may infer the presence of extensive herds.*

*'Like so many other royal hunting grounds, Enfield Chace suffered severely during the Civil War. The attempt by Charles I to revive royal hunting rights which had remained in abeyance for centuries caused universal indignation which came to a head in the damages done to many a forest. Enfield Chace was no exception, and the killing and snaring of deer and the destruction of timber was carried to such excess that the Council of State was compelled to intervene. A letter from this body to the Earl of Salisbury in 1649 urged the application of the common law to the persons whose offences had become notorious, suggesting that they would not cultivate such an inordinate taste for venison if the meat had to be purchased at the price of a heavy fine.*

*'A survey showed that the Chace still had an area of 7,904 acres. The deer, whose herds had shrunk considerably during the war, were valued at £150, but the oaks, apart from*

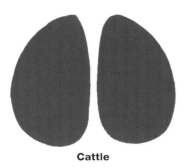

**Cattle**

**Sheep**

**Goat**

**Pig**

**Tracks of farm animals also at 50% of full size for an adult male.**

(Based on the author's drawings in *The Field Guide to British Deer*, **Deer Society 1971.**)

**How to make a plaster cast of a deer track.**

*Carefully remove twigs, leaves or mud that have fallen into the print. Forceps or photographer's blower brush are useful at this stage.*

*Mix plaster of Paris with clean water in plastic bowl.*

*Press card (or tin) strip round track and avoid air bubbles by pouring plaster carefully onto side of track.*

2,500 trees reserved for the navy, were worth £2,500, and the hornbeams and other trees were valued at £12,000...

'After the Restoration the Chace reverted to the Crown and much money was spent in replanting trees and restocking the deer. In 1662 a warrant was issued to the "Masters of the Buck Hounds and the Toils" to take such deer from the parks of the Earl of Essex, Mrs.Sadler, Mr.Butler and Sir Henry Blunt as they should think fit and convey them to Enfield Chace or elsewhere, as ordered by Lord Gerard. The Earl of Essex in question was the son of one of Cromwell's chief generals and a keen hunter, for it stated that he died in September 1646 as the result of a fever brought on by overexertion at a stag hunt in Windsor Forest.

'The Lord Gerard, who had the job of restocking the deer, was the new ranger and chief keeper of Enfield Chace.

'Three keepers were appointed under him and the old order of things seemed to be securely re-established. After the death of Charles II royal hunting grounds began to languish all over the country. Enfield Chace was disafforested in 1777 in the reign of George III.

'Eleven years previously its mightiest oak had been felled; its bole measured thirty feet in length and contained three tons of timber, the diameter of the butt being three feet...

'If you travel to London from Cambridge by train, you will pass on the borders of Hertfordshire and Middlesex a station called Hadley Wood, and there is a real wood there. A Hertfordshire guide book states that it is the last remnant of Enfield Chace.'

A summary of Harting's 1881 and Whitaker's 1892 lists of Hertfordshire deer parks is as follows - although Harting missed out Tring Park, it was included in Whitaker's.

### Harting's list of existing parks, 1881:
Ashridge, Cassiobury, Gorhambury, Grove Park, Hatfield, Knebworth, Moor Park, Putteridge, Rickmansworth and Woodhall. (Total 10)

**Disparked:** Aspenden Hall, Bedwell, Benington, Berkhamsted, Brocket Hall, Cheshunt, Eastwick, Furneux Pelham, Hadham Parva, Hamills, Hertingfordbury, Hondon, Hunsdon, Kings Langley, Manor of the Rye, Offley Place, New Place (Gilston), Panshanger, Pendley Park, Pishobury, Ponsbourne, Roxford, St.Albans, Sawbridgeworth, Shenley, Stagenhoe, Theobalds, Thorley, Throcking, Tittenhanger, Walkern, Ware, Widford and Wyddial. (Total 34)

Harting gave the following information on those which survived.

**Hatfield**, with the red deer and fallow deer originally kept in separate enclosures because of a treatise published in 1616 which insisted that they should not be mixed and which was later found to be erroneous, united to form 314 acres with just fallow deer. (Feral fallow are still *present in the woodland here and red deer have been re-established in the park during the 1990s.)*

**Cassiobury**, *near Watford, about 670 acres, originally 700-800 deer, later 300-400 fallow deer. (Large losses of deer at certain periods of the park's history may have been connected with over-stocking because 1 deer to 1 acre has become the general rule of thumb for a herd.)*

**Grove Park**, *adjoining Cassiobury, about 100 fallow on 300 acres.*

**Knebworth**, *about 140 fallow on 280 acres.*

**Gorhambury**, *St.Albans (no stock details).*

**Moor Park**, *Rickmansworth, 250 fallow on 500 acres.*

**Ashridge**, *by Berkhamsted, red and fallow, part of the grounds in Buckinghamshire.*

**Woodhall**, *near Hertford, 300 fallow on 400 acres.*

**Rickmansworth**, *50 fallow on 200 acres.*

**Putteridge**, *Lilley (on Bedfordshire border), 'well stocked' on 450 acres.*

### Whitaker's list and notes 1892
*Made 11 years later and showing 1 less park than Harting's survey, but including Tring and giving the totals for deer present, by then, all fallow.*

**Cassiobury Park.** *Owner, the Earl of Essex. Acreage, 1,028 acres and 38 perches. Fence, wooden park fencing. Water supply natural, the River Gade. Number of fallow deer, about 150. Average weight of bucks, 14 stone and 8 lbs. Average weight of does, 60 lbs. The park is splendidly timbered. Fine avenue of limes, oak and cedar. The River Gade intersects the park. Undulating and exceedingly picturesque.*

**Hatfield Park.** *Owner, the Marquess of Salisbury, KG. Acreage, 530 acres. Fence, wire. Water supply both natural and artificial. Number of fallow deer, 200. Average weight of bucks, 17 stone and 8 lbs. Average weight of does, 8 stone. This park is fairly wooded with avenues, and game coverts.*

**Moor Park.** *Owner, Lord Ebury. Acreage, 500 acres. Fence, park paling. Water supply natural. Number of fallow deer, about 225. Average weight of bucks, 15 stone and 8lbs. Average weight of does, 7 stone. Heavily timbered; a large quantity of very old oaks. Imparked in the reign of Charles II. A considerable difference of elevation between the higher and lower portions of the park.*

**Woodhall Park.** *Owner, Abel Smith Esquire, MP. Acreage, 447 acres. Fence, brick wall. Water supply natural, River Beane, trout stream. Number of fallow deer, 300. Average weight of bucks, 125 to 130 lbs., dead weight. Average weight of does, 70 lbs. Birds, swans and wild ducks. Fine elm, ash, beech, cedar, oak, fir, walnut, chestnut, lime and hornbeam.*

**Knebworth Park.** *Owner, the Earl of Lytton. Acreage, 400*

*Check by gentle finger pressure to see if dry. This usually takes 15-30 minutes depending on how much water was mixed with plaster,*

*Cut out soil round plaster and remove complete. Pull back card and pack carefully inside newspaper.*

*Very gently wash off mud under tap. When dry, colour track or background and add details.*

**(Based on the author's drawings of a cast made of a muntjac track, Cuffley, in** *The Field Guide to British Deer,* **Deer Society 1971.)**

acres. Fence, oak paling. Water supply artificial and natural. Number of fallow deer, 150. Average weight of bucks, 80 lbs. Average weight of does, 50 lbs. Well timbered and undulating.

**Tring Park.** Owner, Lord Rothschild. Acreage, 350 acres. Fence, one half stone wall, the rest paling. Water supply artificial. Number of fallow deer, 60. Other animals or birds, 25 kangaroos, 14 emus, 8 rheas, 70 wild geese of nine different species. The park stands high and undulating; surrounded by woods, chiefly beech.

**Gorhambury Park.** Owner, the Earl of Verulam. Acreage, about 300 acres. Fence, oak slabs. Water supply, pond called Brickhill Spring. Number of fallow deer, 5 only remain. Other animals, sheep and bullocks. Oak and beech trees and a young plantation of cypress.

**Grove Park.** Owner, the Earl of Clarendon. Acreage, about 250 acres. Fence, oak paling and iron fencing. Water supply natural. Number of fallow deer, about 100. Average weight of bucks, 11 to 12 stone, clean. Average weight of does, 7 to 8 stone, clean. Undulating ground, well timbered; the trees are oak, ash, elm, walnut, beech, chestnut, thorn, lime and conifers of various kinds.

**Rickmansworth Park.** Owner, John William Birch, Esquire. Acreage, 200 acres. Fence, oak paling. Water supply natural. Number of fallow deer, 52. Average weight of bucks, 17 stone and 8 lbs, dead weight. Average weight of does, 7 stone. Pond water, about one acre. Some fine old trees.

**Total number of parks in 1892: 9 (1,242 deer, all fallow).**

Deer populations increase by one-third each year without predation of any kind. Wolves were once the major control on their numbers, but they became extinct here due to persecution by humans. We have always been a major predator of deer, and modern management of herds is by high velocity rifle from high seats (above) when reduction is necessary.

Knebworth red deer were partly descended from Warnham stock with its distinct, complex antlers. J.G.Millais illustrated the eleven successive heads from a single Warnham stag (right). They were in his personal collection and shown in *The mammals of Great Britain and Ireland* (1906).

200

# Red deer

## Cervus elaphus

Hertfordshire was first listed as a county in the Anglo Saxon Chronicle in 1011 and is named after our largest land mammal, the red deer or 'hart', which is the old name for a stag more than 5 years old. For the county bearing this title to have no wild red deer left uneaten by around the end of the 13th century (Whitehead 1964) says much about our willingness to share our habitats with large, untamed

**Knebworth Park at dawn during the October rut (1977).**

herbivors. We have not been a nation fond of sacred cows, but it is shameful that no wild red deer were allowed to survive in the county.

Tradition has it that where the county town of Hertford stands at the confluence of the rivers Lea, Beane, Mimram and Rib, the wild red deer herds used to cross; thus 'Hart-ford' or Hertford in modern spelling.

As Branch Johnson explained in 1952: 'The name of Hertford is said to have been derived from a natural ford over the Lea, used, at the period when the district was thickly forested, by harts. Hounds circle and bay (or howl) the deer when cornered. The calling of hounds during hunting is often referred to as "music" in the old hunting accounts. Modern images of the county emblem never include the hounds. The name was retained when the Local Government Act changed or merged many others in 1974'.

Despite the historic extinction of the wild deer, red deer were kept in Hertfordshire parks, but by 1950 Whitehead recorded that no deer at all were being kept in or out of enclosures, and the last red deer would have been those in Ashridge which died out in the mid 1930s.

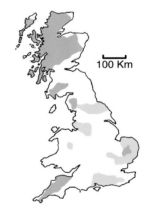

Hingston (1988) records how red deer were later reintroduced into Knebworth Park in 1972. A founder member of the Deer Society, I had a small role in their management at this time and there were sika, fallow and, for a short time, rusa (C.timorensis) present, too. Most of the deer were obtained from catch-ups at Warnham, Woburn, Savernake Forest and Whipsnade Zoo. Of these, only the red deer survived in the park by 1990 when there were 100 in the herd. The deer keeper, Wocko Watkins, gave me the details for 1999: over 100 red deer,

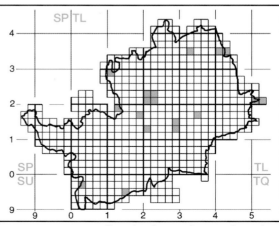

**Occasional away from parks and deer farms. Deserves a greater presence in the county.**

Red deer stag with 'hard horn' (top) and velvet in June (bottom). (Both of Knebworth Park deer.)

A vagrant stag at Bramfield joined cattle during the rut, October 1968, due to the lack of wild red hinds. It was later shot when it continued to 'bully' the cattle as substitutes for hinds.

kept with 30 Japanese sika (*Cervus nippon*).

*Deer farming commenced in the county in 1985. By concentrating on artificial feeds the old rule of thumb of one red deer to one acre could be exceeded.*

*At Furneaux Pelham Hall, Buntingford, Hingeton gave 210 red deer plus yearling stags on 100 acres with a planned herd size of 500. Red deer could also be seen from the road side at Sandon in the 1990s and the prevalence of deer farming will fluctuate depending, of course, upon market forces. A herd can increase by a third each year, but there are disease implications, especially when a species is concentrated on the same ground in large numbers: a recent concern was over bovine tuberculosis which has long been the veterinary headache of cattle management.*

*Dansie gave a summary of the species in Hertfordshire in Deer, 1:8, 313-315, February 1969: he lists three of the more recent, but always infrequent appearances of wild, or newly escaped, stags: (Welwyn, Bramfield and Peters Green) and notes the lack of hinds. Lord Brocket had told him that the Hertfordshire crest was selected from his own armorial insignia before the last war and that he derived his name from a 'brock' or third-year red stag. (A brock is, of course, also one of the many names for a badger.)*

*Beds Wildlife (1987) lists 6 escapees seen from Woburn or Knebworth in the previous 15 years. Laver (1898) gives the history of red deer in Essex and notes how the Epping herd was removed to Windsor around 1827, but some had also been reintroduced there at the end of the century. Dobson (1999) records only one breeding herd left in Essex, confined to woods in the north of the county. He gives details of sightings since the 1960s as well as historic information, but concludes that, outside captive herds, the species is one of the rarest and most localised of their mammals.*

The occasional wild red deer stags which turn up alone in the county usually make themselves known amongst cattle during the rut. These individuals travel great distances from the Essex borders, possibly even from Thetford populations or the feral groups associated with the surviving Essex deer parks. Usually the stags, unable to find hinds, 'bully' (mount) cattle and are shot by farmers.

The most recent red deer in Tewin, about 20 years ago, gives an example of the fate of such a large and obvious species. Initially a report came to me of a roe deer seen in Tewin Wood. The colour, size and lack of obvious tail suggested that this was a roe and with no antlers seen, I put it down as an unconfirmed sighting of a deer larger than a muntjac.

A week later I was called to help a neighbour, Alan Davis, then farm manager at Tewin Hill Farm, because he had seen a deer with its lower jaw shot away. We located and eventually cornered this very distressed animal in a pit, where it was

202

humanely despatched. The jaw was hanging and had bled profusely. Because of this injury, the deer had been unable to feed. It was a young male red deer, half-grown, and was probably with the parent hind when she was shot. How soon after being left on its own the deer was also shot at it was impossible to say, but this does reflect (a) the mistreatment of deer when certain people come across them and (b) how deer can easily be misidentified, even when very clear, detailed descriptions are given.

**Three red deer hinds with a yearling (right).**

Views of red deer are likely to be brief and in the rut. This is the most interesting time to view both park and wild red deer, although caution is needed if you want to get out of your vehicle to approach stags. The roaring and fighting make splendid spectacles.

Perhaps if large areas of forest were re-established in the northeast of the county, wild red deer may be able to survive with compensation paid to farmers when crops are attacked. (Carrots are a favourite food to select at night.) Ashridge is another suitable area with a long history of red deer. Wardens would be essential. The observation has been made before that 'it would be good to put the hart back into Hertfordshire'.

# Fallow deer

### Dama dama

*Technically, fallow deer could be described from the fossil record as indigenous (see Chapman & Chapman's Clacton and Swanscombe finds and European evidence), but they retreated during the glacial periods and the absence of remains from both Mesolithic and Neolithic sites in Britain indicates that there were reintroductions at some stage.*

*Despite modern evidence of Roman introductions, there is some doubt about the age of a fallow bone from an excavation at St.Albans (see Appendix 1). It is a single, shed antler base and there is no indication of any other extensive introduction of fallow deer here. Firm evidence of the presence of fallow deer comes from hunting accounts and records in the early Middle Ages, so importation by the Normans probably saw the main establishment of the species in the county. As Chapman & Chapman point out, the Norman kings and their nobles were passionately fond of hunting and sited many of their residences close to the royal forests. They also ruled Sicily and southern Italy where fallow parks had probably been maintained since Roman times.*

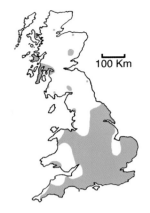

100 Km

The relationship of fallow with our deer parks has already been given in the general account. Until the second half of the 20th century they were by far the most numerous species of deer living in the county, possibly since the 11th century. Roe deer declined through relentless persecution to total extinction from all of England by 1800.

However, fallow lived almost always in entirely enclosed, managed herds. It was not until the final breakdown of the dwindling park tradition during the 20th century that two areas in Hertfordshire (southwest and northeast) established large wild populations. By 1950 only 140 parks with fallow deer remained in England, Kings Walden Bury near Hitchin being the only one to survive in Hertfordshire (Whitehead 1964). In his 'Deer and their Management' (1950)

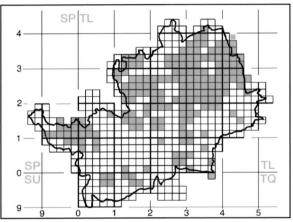

**Fallow deer** *Dama dama* **are most plentiful in the north and west of the county.**

**Stable**

Whitehead noted that of the 1,424 fallow listed by Harting in 1892 at 9 parks in Hertfordshire, none were left by 1949.

Whitehead also noted that the woods in Scales Park, near Royston, harboured a fair number of fallow, but when the estate was converted into an aerodrome in 1941, the deer scattered into the surrounding country. (The world wars also affected certain carnivore species with less keepering and dispersal due to preferential wartime activities.) He noted that Foster had reported no feral deer in the Hitchin region (1934), but Kings Walden still retained a herd of over 50 fallow into the 1960s. Hingston (1988) records that Kings Walden was disparked in 1975. Other notes by Whitehead (1950) included the herds being given up at Hatfield and Knebworth in the 1914-18 Great War. Both estates have deer herds again now.

The fallow deer reported from Northaw Great Wood (Clark 1966) were those observed by the wardens and the most regular sightings were in the harsh winter of 1946-47. Tracks were seen in 1951 and odd reports of 'large deer' continue to this day. These are almost certainly descendants of the Hatfield Park feral population, but there is a possibility of colonisation southwards from the Woodhall Park escapees already described (Berry 1937). The Woodhall herd finally dispersed after further gale damage to the fences in 1943.

A buck with large antlers was killed by a train close to the south entrance to Bayford tunnel in 1961 and occasional sightings are made in Ponsbourne and Broxbourne Woods.

Fordham (1967) noted their presence at Sandon, in (inappropriately) Roe Wood and at Scales Park. These populations appear to have consolidated in the years since then, with regular reports of 20-30 in single herds and over 80 were counted by Trevor James in one group at Scales Park in 1991. There was a sighting of a fallow doe between Wheathampsted and Harpenden, 23rd May 1971, indicating dispersal from the Ashridge herds, where, in 1972, 168 were counted by twice that number of people who took part in a March survey. Thirty-five of the fallow were adult bucks; (30 muntjac, 1 Chinese water deer, 6 foxes and 2 weasels added to the variety of sightings for the day).

By the 1970s the deer park at Knebworth had been re-established with fallow, sika, red and a few rusa deer at large in the newly fenced grassland areas. The subsequent park escapees augmented existing wild groups in the area. Deer 'leaps', of which the most familiar is probably at Ashridge (near the monument drive) were a way of getting escaped deer or wild deer to enter or return to a park without letting others escape. The deer jump down into the park at a tempting gap in the fence which has, in fact, a constructed depression, too deep to leap back out from.

Miriam Rothschild refers to the Tring fallow deer in her biography of Walter Rothschild (1983) and points out that when the family bought the property in 1872, fallow deer had been kept in Tring Park continously since Charles Gore's ownership of about 1670.

Beds Wildlife (1987) reports occasional strays and the map indicates a concentration of these from the Ashridge area, a few linked with Woburn and in the Potton Wood area near Hatley Park as the border merges into Cambridgeshire. Dobson (1999) describes fallow as now common and increasing in Essex despite the continued losses on Epping Forest roads. As well as Epping, Burton (1974) lists Lullingstone Park for London as having a small herd living in a wild state and names Richmond (with red deer), Greenwich and Battersea as parks where fallow survived.

An alert fallow deer buck in Knebworth Park. Wild bucks, away from enclosures, are particularly secretive in summer as their new antlers grow.

Fallow deer can thrash and ringbark unguarded young trees in plantations as they rub their antlers clean prior to the rut (near Walkern).

As the historic survey has shown, the present distribution of fallow deer relates to the establishment of numerous deer parks on our country estates, but we owe their survival to their ability to disperse when poached or when estate management begins to threaten their numbers.

Like fallow, the introduced muntjac deer are able to exploit cover and disperse if regularly persecuted, whereas Chinese water deer, also established here this century, favour exposed, tall grass ditch or reed areas and may be eliminated, like red or roe deer, with sustained effort.

Fallow deer demonstrate, therefore, an exceptional survival strategy of dispersal into small family groups if frequently shot at or chased. They are very cautious and shy, yet able to cope with the growing pressures of dogs and people in a diminishing countryside, away from major traffic arteries. Road traffic inflicts an indiscriminate toll on numbers and causes retreat from their old-established territories (as Epping

**Fallow buck in velvet at Knebworth Park showing the black on the rump and down the centre of the tail in the menil colour variety.**

*Paul Moxey has pointed out to me where fallow deer rest next to a busy public house car park and picnic area at a roundabout. The deer appear to have ascertained that the traffic slows as it approaches the roundabout and this is a safe place to cross and lie up during the hours of daylight.*

Forest on our eastern borders shows). Chapman & Chapman's paper (1969) shows one fallow deer was killed every 3½ days.

Food found in the stomachs of road casualties mainly consisted of grass together with acorns, apples, chestnuts, wheat and leaves of beech, holly and ivy. Bracket fungi have also been found in the rumen. Of the colour varieties, all in Epping were dark apart from 4 which were of the spotted (menil) shade. Dobson's (1999) figures show an even greater road toll now (opposite).

(Hertfordshire Police records, via Inspector Kourik, show all species of deer figure in about 365 road traffic accidents each year; on average another deer is knocked down and killed every day of the year in the county.)

The present fallow deer herd areas in Hertfordshire also concentrate between the major vehicle routes. They will, however, cross country roads in line and often it is the second or third animal which is struck as a driver concentrates on the leading doe and fails to prepare for the followers. A major outer ring road driven through Hertfordshire, beyond the M25, would be particularly disastrous for our fallow deer population which almost forms a parallel circuit to the M25 in the rural areas, some 20 miles to the north.

The Lea Valley urban development has proved a barrier for any mixing of Epping deer with the Hertfordshire populations in the southeast. The deer distribution to the north of Bishop's Stortford has no barriers and the herds are present in good numbers across the Hertfordshire/Essex borders in this rural, arable farmland with scattered woods.

It is possible to see groups of up to 30 deer as far south as Watton-at-Stone, but the Stevenage/Hitchin/ Letchworth urban areas now form a significant obstacle in an otherwise continuous distribution across the north of Hertfordshire. Threatened development on green belt land to the west of Stevenage will reduce fallow habitat yet further, will increase road traffic accidents and is one of the worst examples of how the protection of our countryside has fallen into the hands of those who care nought for wildlife.

The characteristic herd on the move has a mature doe leading it, so that if disturbed she runs with a trail of mixed aged deer behind. Occasionally I have announced to groups of fellow ramblers that there are fallow footprints across a bridleway only to turn the corner to find a flock of sheep. Regular routes for feeding and escape are followed and the large footprints are distinctive on paths. Hoof prints are very variable and illustrations are only a guide.

The novice local deer watcher might start with dawn and dusk forays to Ashridge during the rut, between September and November. The *HNHS* has held many field meetings there around October, led by the local expert Brian Barton. He points out the browse line on the trees and the field signs, and he has extensive local knowledge of the rutting stands where bucks hold their territories. He also has considerable historic knowledge of the area which was so nearly sold as building plots earlier last century.

Thankfully the National Trust now owns most of the Ashridge woodlands and other areas of outstanding countryside here. My best views of the deer have been with Clive Banks at Ringshall Coppice and Brian Barton on the Berkhamsted Common side. Brian's sound recordings are a valuable local archive and, when combined with Clive's pictures, make up one of our best known and popular local natural history lecture teams.

The colours of our wild fallow herds are very variable, with frequent white individuals. The woods are favoured for food and safety, but fawns are frequently dropped in grassland. There is concern for the losses of young of all our deer species as less hay meadows remain, due mainly to silage cutting which takes place earlier when the grass is lush. Prior (1989) gave roe deer as the most vulnerable to this change in farming because births peak around 20th May when mowing is at its height, but red, fallow and sika drop their young over the next fortnight.

Muntjac births are scattered throughout the year and another danger is from well-meaning people who find a fawn on its own and imagine it has been abandoned. My wife, Anna, has hand-reared both muntjac and roe picked up in this way. Everyone should avoid contact with solitary fawns because they are almost invariably *not* abandoned. If a doe fallow is killed on a road, its fawn may be recognised by finding a hungry, anxious young deer stumbling about, sometimes calling for its parent, up to a day or more later. A silent fawn, crouched still on the ground, is in good order and is being

**Fallow deer fawn in Knebworth Park. Under no circumstances should they be approached or touched. They are left like this by the adults between feeds.**

**Recorded road deaths for the Epping Forest area between 1979/80 and 1995/96 (from Dobson,** *The Mammals of Essex* **1999).**

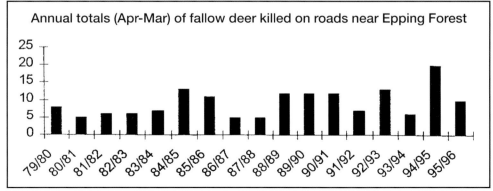

Annual totals (Apr-Mar) of fallow deer killed on roads near Epping Forest

properly looked after.

Hopefully, a way of saving fawns by flushing them to one side ahead of mower blades on farm machinery will be invented. Deer love to sunbathe on the edge of woodland and fallow relax to ruminate in this way unless persecuted in an area. They graze out from cover and so develop the habitual paths which are a good guide to local activity. Signs of fraying by the bucks, where young trees are beaten and rubbed by their antlers and their heads, are relatively obvious. Thanks to John Tomkins, I have been shown a heavily frayed tree within 200m of the borough boundary of Stevenage. The rut is by far the most exciting time to watch the herds, when bucks return to their old-established territories, often with a focal point of an old tree or stand of trees, to which the does are drawn by his scent and belching calls. All deer scrape at the ground with their hooves at times and this is another feature of such sites.

# Roe deer

## *Capreolus capreolus*

*Lloyd (47) is brief and to the point: 'A former denizen, though long extinct. Antlers have been found in alluvial deposits in the Colne Valley before 1911. A left-side antler still attached to the frontal bone was found by Oldham at a gravel pit in Kings Langley in 1927, with bones of red deer and ancient cattle (Bos primigenius) and recorded in the Trans, **XVIII**, 216, 1929.'*

*Whitehead (1963) is certain that roe did not become totally extinct in England, as was thought by others, and confirms that the Lake District, possibly Northumberland and Durham, too, have indigenous populations of what is the oldest deer species still present in Britain. He describes the mixed history of roe as beasts of the chase, which were relegated to warren status in 1338 when the Court of the King's Bench decided 'that the roe was not a beast of the forest, but of the warren, on the ground that it drove away the other deer'. (Whitehead points out that there seems no evidence to support the suggestion that roe drive away other deer and it may be that the reverse is the case, such as where sika introductions have resulted in a marked decline in the roe population.)*

*He notes that there were no Middlesex or Hertfordshire reports confirmed, but that in 1951 there was a report of a possible Siberian roe at Welwyn made by Lord Brocket. Beds Wildlife (1987) refers to this latter species, introduced by the Duke of Bedford: 'three seen near Woburn Park in 1950, now extinct', which suggests that the Welwyn deer had* dispersed in much the same direction that muntjac had colonised the county. The future natural return of roe to Bedfordshire is anticipated in Anderson (1985), but the species has long been absent from the county, too.

Whitehead thought that when the reintroduced roe were present in Epping Forest during the 19th century, they may have also strayed into Hertfordshire and these deer would account for the regular Broxbourne Woods reports: Tom Gladwin saw roe in this area occasionally during bird watching visits in the 1950s and 1960s. Michael Bland, a member of the Deer Society, reported 4 roe seen regularly at Baas Hill feeding near a farm during the very harsh weather of the 1962-63 winter. (None were seen subsequently, but fallow were sometimes also sighted and muntjac almost daily.) As well as the actual roe deer found at Northaw, referred to below, Betty Yandell, another Deer Society member, saw a doe roe cross the road near Thorntons Farm, Northaw and in the 1980s, David and Adrienne Watson reported more sightings from Broxbourne Woods. There is, therefore, ample evidence that roe have had a small, but surviving presence in southeast Hertfordshire over the past 40 years.

Glendinning (1989) names fallow and roe deer, fox and pine marten to have been hunted by Queen Elizabeth I in Hertfordshire during her visits to Lord Burleigh's estate at Theobalds. Laver (1898) notes that roe disappeared from Essex by 1594 and records their reintroduction to Epping Forest in 1884. At the time of his writing, Laver had estimated over 20 roe were present in the Forest and the figure was growing. Dobson (1999) describes them as 'scarce, increasing' and shows the Essex distribution to be confined to scattered individuals, mostly in the north.

Burton (1974) noted that roe were spreading towards London, had been seen in suburban gardens and were established in Surrey.

Roe are now entering Hertfordshire from the Chilterns on the Buckinghamshire borders and Dr.John Jackson (pers. comm.) reported resident roe at Hockeridge and Pancake Woods and a buck found dead at the nearby Rossway Estate (1997).

Single observations have came from Wheathampstead, Harpenden, Kimpton and Markyate. There have been reports from the Great Munden area by more than one observer.

Such an infrequent, elusive species, easily confused with others, is frustrating to the recorder, but an actual specimen

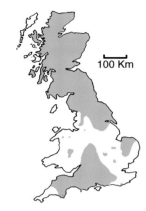

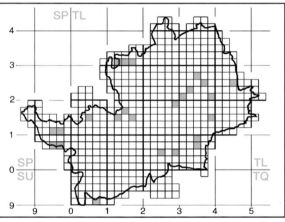

**Roe deer** *Capreolus capreolus* **are returning slowly to the county.**

**Local**

**The antler velvet is shed in the spring (Tewin Orchard).**

Top: **Roe deer buck.**
Centre: **roe deer doe showing tuft of hair in tail region.**
Bottom: **roe deer doe showing large ears and white patches on either side of nose.**
**All captive (Tewin Orchard).**

finally came to light as I described in a letter to *Deer*, 1:5, 179 (1968):

'Mr.John Castle of Little Heath by Potters Bar, tripped over the antlers of a complete roe deer skeleton in dense bracken in Northaw Great Wood in September 1959. He picked up the head and kept it at home. When he read a letter of mine in *Hertfordshire Countryside* magazine saying that roe had not been recorded in Hertfordshire for about 50 years, he had the antlers mounted and kindly lent them to me to measure and photograph: the length: 256mm; span: 116mm; round coronets: 175mm measured as indicated by Richard Prior in *Roe Stalking* (see photograph on p258).

'Mr Castle was certain he saw 3 roe, not together, but barking to each other, on the border of a field near the Great Wood (no date recalled) and saw the occasional fallow in the district from time to time. He sees muntjac on most days during his work in the grounds of Queenswood School, which is very near the Great Wood.

'I include a map of the position of the wood to pinpoint the location. It would be interesting to know if anybody has any ideas as to where the roe came from.'

Between 1997 and 1999 I have seen roe hoof prints close to the northeast side of Northaw Great Wood and keepers from the Hatfield Estate have since seen roe here in spotlights during rabbit control. Twin roebuck, orphaned when their mother was run over in Dorset, lived at Tewin Orchard for over ten years before being killed by two Dobermann dogs, let out regularly to hunt at night around the parish, unsupervised.

They later killed a doe muntjac in the Orchard, an act witnessed by me when I approached them thinking the sounds were coming from fox cubs fighting. (In 1998 two boxer dogs were also frequently allowed to roam and were observed to attack a muntjac and a badger on separate occasions in the Orchard. They killed poultry and also disrupted viewing for people who had journeyed to watch wild animals at ease from the hide.) Two roe does were brought to mate with the twin bucks without success. The stress of repeated handling can be fatal to the species. This extreme anxiety in their nature may explain why they are unable to adapt to parkland management.

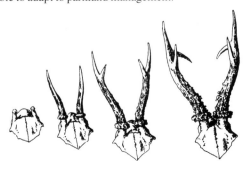

**Antler development in roe deer,
(after Kurt Hennings 1909).**

# Muntjac deer
## *Muntiacus reevesi*

*Percy Hickman, who succeeded in the same post of estate gamekeeper as his father held at Broxbournebury during the first half of the 20th century, showed me the tail of the first muntjac he ever saw in Broxbourne Woods. He had shot this one in 1938 (plus about 25 since) and said that the 1938 specimen 'caused quite a stir locally'. Judging by his account, muntjac bucks continued to arrive as individuals until they were breeding locally.*

*Wormley and Cowheath Woods appeared to have become a stronghold by the 1950s when Major F.R.Dore, then the Master of the Enfield Chace Foxhounds, noted in a letter (17th February 1953) to Whitehead (1964) that the hunt from time to time came across the deer when drawing the coverts in this part of Broxbourne Woods.*

*He thought that they may have escaped from a travelling menagerie which had its headquarters by Wormley Woods, although he considered they were more likely to have escaped from Woburn, 30 miles to the northwest. Lever (1977) quotes escapes from Major Pam's Wormleybury collection (the menagerie Dore was referring to) in the 1930s as being a second source of muntjac. He also gives a pre-1936 record from Ashridge.*

*Whitehead gave localities for much of Hertfordshire: Offley, Hitchin, Hemel Hempstead, Gorhambury, Bricket Wood, Knebworth, Bayford and Standon for the period up to 1964. Their colonisation was unobtrusive and there was a lack of published information in field guides until the Mamm Soc Deer Group (which later became the Deer Society) produced accurate illustrations of tracks and signs. It was the first deer species I tracked (near Northaw at Nyn Park), and later watched, in 1962. In suitable areas with dense undergrowth their numbers multiplied, probably most rapidly on the estates where foxes were strenuously controlled so that fawns survived well.*

*The 30 recorded on the Ashridge deer count (11th March 1972), described in the fallow section, and Dangerfield's (1971) report that they were 'regularly shot on keepered*

**Widespread, increasing**

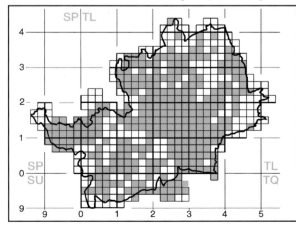

Spotted muntjac fawn (top) and adult muntjac doe (both at Tewin Orchard).

Watercolour of doe and fawn muntjac by Eileen Soper (author's collection). Eric Hosking (see p265) also pictured wildlife at the Soper's reserve, 'Wildings'.

estates' indicated large concentrations of deer in suitable habitats. I had attended one such shoot on the Knebworth Estate, February 1967, to help catch-up individuals for Dr.Oliver Dansie's study: 27 adults and juveniles were killed and 4 caught up and released after being measured and marked for future recognition. Records of shoots are not usually published, but sometimes this information has been forwarded to the HNHS survey and 16 were noted as shot on the Brocket estate, 28th June 1986.

As well as regular road casualty records, one was killed by a train near Bayford tunnel in October 1969 (McCready). Dogs kill them, as in the case of a whippet at Northaw Great Wood (1968) and two Alsations at Tewin (1981), for example. They regularly appear in urban areas as well as suburban gardens, such as in Hitchin (1965) and St.Albans (1978). A buck jumped through a window into a house in York Road, Hemel Hempstead (1975).

Like foxes they favour overgrown, neglected gardens to retreat to, and the high density accommodation in newer towns such as Stevenage is more slowly colonised. However, where overgrown woodland and established parks exist in the New Town wards, such as in Monkswood Way and at Shephalbury, they have become an occasional sight and are now clearly breeding within the New Town boundary.

The sudden appearance of muntjac in the middle of traffic, on a roundabout, or in a shopping centre, is usually the result of dogs chasing the deer from their usual regular beat round favoured feeding areas. Although they live in small family groups of up to 4, even 5 (doe, buck, fawn, previous fawn or fawns), dispersal can also find young animals in very unsuitable places. (I have seen nearly as many cases of aggression between does as between bucks.)

A book was devoted to the species in Hertfordshire by Eileen Soper (1969) and it is a very valuable as well as beautifully illustrated account of their colonisation of her large garden nature reserve in 1961. This refuge, in which they quickly became established, was created by Eileen's father, George Soper, a master at rendering the English countryside in wood engravings and watercolours. Eileen carefully recorded the arrival of the introduced species of deer and grey squirrels. The demise of native species in the garden is noted, too: dormice, red squirrels, red-backed shrikes, wrynecks and nightingales, all referred to in her books and diaries. She had regular visits from the great wildlife photographer, Eric Hosking, and records in her diary his use of hides in the garden.

The antler cycle of muntjac was the cause of heated correspondence in the pages of Deer (1972-1973) before it was fully understood. No dates are given for the introduction of muntjac to Woburn or the spread of the species in Beds Wildlife (1987), but their distribution is now widespread and dispersal was discussed by Dansie in an article in Deer **2**,

212

4: 618, (1971). The appearance in central Hertfordshire around Welwyn (1942) is given in Deer News **1**, 9:37-41, (1966). Anderson (1985) had received records from 36% of tetrads in the Bedfordshire survey.

Dobson (1999) describes the arrival of muntjac in Essex and gives 1958 for the first recorded resident population at Coptford Hall, Margaretting (Chapman 1977). By the mid 1970s they were present in many woods and they are now widespread across the county. Burton (1974) noted that 'this introduced species is particularly abundant in woods around Potters Bar, Hertfordshire, and may well spread and establish itself in the London suburbs. Other species of deer, such as sika, can be seen in parks and occasionally escape'.

Lloyd (47) makes no reference to muntjac as being present in the county, although we now know that their appearance was already being noticed by people who worked in the countryside as early as the 1930s. Whiteman (1936) gives no information on deer of any kind in his mammal chapter for the Hexton parish (where muntjac and, occasionally, fallow are now present), although one would expect colonisation of the Ravenburgh Castle area at the time he wrote, as the species was rapidly spreading along this favourable tract of country at that time. Their route would be through woodlands in the Barton Hills, Offley, Welwyn, Bayford and Broxbourne districts, to the edge of the Lea Valley.

Fordham, Trans **26**: 4, 210, (1967) reported that the first muntjac seen at Odsey, near Ashwell, was early in 1962 and the species has been present in the neighbourhood since then.

Details of a relatively tame individual in Broxbourne Woods seen by Michael Barrett, one in a garden and a winter fawn, followed 7 months later by a summer one born to the same captive doe, are given in the Trans, **27**:3 88, (1971). A St.Albans inner-city resident muntjac and antler details are given in the Trans, **27**: 4, 163-4, (1972); injuries and deaths by foxhounds are referred to in the Trans, **27**: 7, 329, (1975) and flattening behaviour in the Trans **29**:1, 14, (1983) is also illustrated in my book Mammal Watching, (1981). Colour variations away from usual winter/summer coat changes are seldom noticed, but Tomkins reported seeing a melanistic muntjac in Box Wood, near Stevenage, 21st November 1981, Trans **29**:1, 14, (1983).

Perhaps the most recognisable feature that muntjac have contributed to our countryside is the sound of their regular, distinct barks, often repeated at 4 second intervals for long periods in the darkness. Max Bryant, Vicar of Cuffley and Northaw when I lived in the Parish, reported to me that his normally boisterous Irish setter dog would become very anxious and retiring when muntjac began to call near his cottage on the edge of Nyn Park, Northaw. Many people who live close to woodland are still surprised to find that the

**Muntjac antlers: year 1 (top); year 7 (centre); and year 9 (bottom).**

**Head of Indian muntjac buck** *Muntiacus muntjac* **drawn by Wilhelm Kuhnert (1865-1926). Larger than** *Muntiacus reevesi***, the species which is now present in Hertfordshire, they have longer pedicles and antlers. Indian muntjac were also released at Woburn but did not establish themselves in the wild.**

distant calls they hear are not made by a dog or a fox, but this small, introduced deer.

Philip Kingsbury gave the delightful story of when he was carefully counting muntjac barks in Ashridge. They had passed the 70 mark at the usual regular intervals when a door of a nearby house in the woods was opened, a voice roared 'shut up' and the deer immediately fell silent.

We found that all our tame doe muntjac had a deeper bark than the single buck we kept. This may have been an individual variation, but he fathered 15 fawns before his death at 17 years and his higher pitched voice did not appear to have any significance; I have since noticed this in wild deer.

Although the does give birth in all seasons of the year, bucks establish an annual antler cycle which casts the small exposed bone around May and June, with growth in velvet to September. Velvet is rubbed clean and the antlers are distinct from September to May. A male fawn begins to grow long pedicles (from which the antlers will emerge) at about 5 months and they are fully formed in another 4 months. A winter buck fawn may grow small caps on the pedicles in its first autumn, but a spring juvenile does not have fully developed pedicles much after the autumn and will not start to grow his first simple head of antlers until the following May.

The first road casualty muntjac I was able to examine was in 1961 on the 'Switch Backs', Nyn, Northaw, and it had the simple angular bone with no coronet: a typical first 'head'. The two booklets on muntjac by Oliver Dansie first published by the Deer Society in 1970 and then in 1983, show the advances in knowledge of the species, especially its antler cycle, between the two dates. The work was largely based on studies in Hertfordshire with collected road casualties, dead specimens from shoots on estates and netting exercises where the deer were marked, measured and released.

# Chinese water deer
## *Hydropotes inermis*

*The presentation by the Duke of Bedford of 32 Chinese water deer to Whipsnade Zoo (1929-30) brought this species to an open parkland setting close to the Hertfordshire border and it is from this area that the nucleus of our records is received.*

*Whitehead (1964) describes the arrival of the species in Woburn from China early in the 20th century and he reports how the deer came to also establish themselves around the park, principally in the direction of Ampthill and Flitwick during World War II.*

*He makes no mention of them in Hertfordshire, apart from a hand-reared one in Hitchin in 1952. Lloyd (47) had no information on the species and its spread from Woburn and Whipsnade has been much more restricted than that of muntjac. Only one was counted in the Ashridge deer census of 11th March 1972, but the impression given from people who shot deer in west Hertfordshire and south Bedfordshire was that they favoured the borders of woodland and are often put up from open ditches where they like to sit in long grass. I now know from keeping a colony at Tewin that they prefer to graze in open grassland much more than muntjac, which look insecure when crossing fields away from scrub canopy or woodland.*

*Their greater size and preference for more open areas allows easier management on estates and their number can be rapidly reduced by shooting. Initial colonisation is often unnoticed, however, and Cooke & Farrell (1983) describe how the Woodwalton Fen population was present for 8 or 9 years before they were correctly identified in 1971, despite being on a national nature reserve regularly visited by naturalists.*

*Cooke & Farrell mention the confusion between these deer and roe and having kept both species I can confirm the similarities in many respects, although their colouring and behaviour is quite different. (One of the Woodwalton bucks was reported as 'a lion' which resulted in frenzied activity by the local police. The deer was hit and killed by a car, but such errors in identification are becoming a little less common as the public is becoming more able to identify animals correctly.)*

*The known distribution through southeast Bedfordshire, Essex and Cambridgeshire into East Anglia and The Fens in particular, appears to be patchy and local in reality, with open, long-grass areas certainly favoured. Although they find wetland ideal for cover and escape, they do not show an excessive love of water, but Whitehead (1972) gives the range of the species in East China and Korea where it is most plentiful in the reed swamps and grasslands of all the large rivers. Formerly abundant in the great reed beds of the deltas and estuaries of the Fuchun Kiang and Yangtze Kiang, he mentions that they seldom congregate and are generally seen alone or in pairs.*

*Inside the perimeter fence of Whipsnade Zoo, especially on the southern farm side, the deer certainly do congregate during the rut. Regular visits have been made over the last*

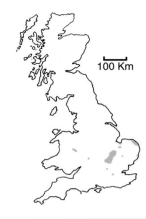

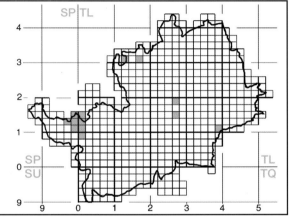

**Chinese water deer** *Hydropotes inermis.*

**Local and scarce**

**A hand-reared Chinese water deer fawn strikes out with a forefoot to stimulate milk flow (Tewin Orchard 1981).**

The four Chinese water deer fawns shown on page 193 and feeding (above), as sub-adults in the summer of 1983 (Tewin Orchard).

Hoof prints of a buck in soft mud.

20 years by Clive Banks, Brian Barton and myself to watch their rut in December. We often lead local groups on, or close to, Boxing Days or New Year's Days as HNHS and HMG early morning meetings. Although the deer will range freely within the park, their assembly in very large groups in the vicinity of the farm cannot be compared directly with behaviour in the natural state.

Cooke & Farrell found that when their grazing areas disappeared under water, the deer left the swampy ground to forage on arable land and they did find a tendency to congregate on good feeding areas early in the year.

(At Tewin an unmated, tame doe came into oestrous long after the usual December rut when a buck from Woburn was introduced to her pen in late January. She became pregnant and produced 4 fawns.) The highest grouping seen at Woodwalton Fen was 9 during a time of food scarcity, but they do not herd in the manner of fallow or red deer, and of 2,195 sightings logged in 1976 to 1979, 61% were of solitary deer.

Although Anderson (1985) reported records received from 24 tetrads, Beds Wildlife (1987) describes the species as local and uncommon in southwest Bedfordshire. The distribution map shows an area still relatively local to Woburn and Whipsnade. There is no record of them in Essex so far (Dobson 1999), but the Rye Meads colony (see below) is close to the border in the Lea Valley.

In 30 years our distribution map of Chinese water deer has hardly altered and a natural southern or eastern spread seems unlikely because of roads and unsuitable habitat. The two isolated tetrads shown in north Hertfordshire are from the colony we kept at Tewin Orchard, central Hertfordshire, now dispersed in the wild.

The hand-reared doe and her five fawns mentioned above left the Orchard and Hetty and Diana Wallace reported seeing one among wheat on John Wallace's farm between Watton-at-Stone and Stevenage. No records were received to the south, but to our surprise the doe returned after an 8 months absence and walked up to us, fed in the Orchard, and after 2 days disappeared again. These deer were probably the source of the colony established in the 1990s in Rye Meads (on the east side of map).

Chinese water deer have features which distinguish them from all other deer in Britain: the bucks have long canines but no antlers, and the does have multiple births of up to 7 fawns though usually 2 or 3 young are seen with the does. Cooke & Farrell (1983) describe successful pregnancies in first-year does and a gestation of about 180 days.

The rut progresses in its activity with an increase in the deer's 'yappy' barks and more aggression between bucks. Fawns can be dropped from as early as May. Cooke & Farrell give a mortality of 25% in the first 3 days at one farmland study area, and at Woodwalton Fen losses from the foetus stage to maturity at 6 months were estimated as higher than 90%.

Multiple births are able to produce population explosions, as recorded at Whipsnade Zoo and Woodwalton Fen, but this is balanced by periods of high mortality from disease and harsh weather conditions recorded at the same sites. We experienced a muntjac buck killing a water deer buck with slashes from its canines. No defence appeared to have been offered by the Chinese water deer, which has thick hair, but easily torn skin when compared with that of the muntjac.

Orphan deer, such as this Chinese water deer fawn, will only thrive with correct feeds, such as sow's milk replacer, and stimulation to defaecate and urinate.

The buck muntjac had entered the Chinese water deer pen shortly after the birth of a fawn he had fathered and a doe muntjac had come into oestrous. In the wild, the Chinese water deer would be expected to retreat at speed from aggressive encounters, but the most malevolant expression of any mammal I have seen was on the face of a Chinese water deer doe when approached by another. They chase and use their sharp hooves to attack others, especially as territories are being re-established in November with the onset of the rut.

Like roe, the tiny tail only really shows up when they stand to defaecate. The facial expression reminds me of a triangle of 3 large black buttons: 2 eyes, 1 nose. In walking past individuals sitting in the grass, a series of movements of the head indicate an ability to detect movement rather than detail. They lose you, then relocate you repeatedly as you pass by. A fox or dog follows you with a continuous head movement.

The rather yellow winter coat, which falls away in lumps if caught on twigs, moults to a sleek, foxy red/brown in the summer. Like roe, the fawns are spotted for a short time after birth. One aspect of does missed from accounts of the deer in this country is the presence of an enlongated canine, but the tooth does not develop to the same visible extent as in the buck. Vietmeyer (1986) describes the small inguinal gland present on each side of the groin in both sexes, the only known instance of such a gland among deer.

Alert Chinese water deer doe, May 1980 (Tewin Orchard).

The deer are active in daytime and particularly around dusk. They hear very well and take flight at any threatening disturbance. Food is a staple diet of grass and some plants such as chickweed, with an increase in browse from bramble, thorn and trees in harsh weather.

# Human

## Homo sapiens

Walter Rothschild, the precocious zoologist, aged 10. (Portrait by J.B.Millais 1878, by kind permission of Miriam Rothschild.)

The Trans have not neglected humans and Oakley's 'Early Man in Hertfordshire' is listed by Kingsbury in his index as an essential source paper. Oakley lists (in Vol 22, 247-257) some 50 Palaeolithic sites with artefacts present in most, 4 Mesolithic sites and about 30 Neolithic finds. Hicks (1889) wrote a general paper 'Prehistoric man in Britain' (Trans 5, 147-154) and Standling summed up in his presidential address (Trans 9, 85-100, 1894) that 'humans were a wonderful animal doomed to extinction by having too big a brain'. How perceptive he seems to have been.

Sir John Evans' 20th anniversary address to the HNHS (26th February 1895) is one of the most valuable illustrated accounts of any species published in the Journal of the Society and ranks in importance with the anniversary address by Sir Edward Salisbury (28th March 1923) on 'The effects of coppicing as illustrated by the woods of Hertfordshire'.

Walter, Lord Rothschild, and Herbrandt, 11th Duke of Bedford, both contributed enormously to our knowledge of animals and left land, property and collections to the nation so that future generations could continue to enjoy and study their achievements.

All research into humans in the county should include reference to our Hertfordshire archives and local study collections in County Hall, Hertford. From the bewildering array of books and other material I have particular favourite references and recommend Rook's readable 'A History of Hertfordshire' (1984), re-printed 1998, which puts events and people into an environmental context and has a useful bibliography of the main historical references for the county.

Spicer's 'Tyme out of Mind' (1984) is a good background to the new town story of Stevenage and how the garden cities have incorporated the existing village structures. The last chapter in Rook's history is a valuable summary of Ebenezer Howard's work and the green belt ideal. As Rook says: 'There is no excitement or majesty, but it works. The spacious park-like layout, adequate gardens and cottage-style dwellings became the inspiration of countless inter-war suburbs'.

Munby in 'The History of the Hertfordshire Landscape' puts his finger on the problem of writing about Letchworth: 'The most striking thing about Letchworth (the first garden city) is that there is nothing striking to see. The difficulty ... is that so many things that were done for the first time have become commonplace since.' The black squirrels, the foxes,

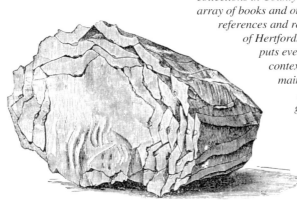

Sir John Evans' 1895 paper included this illustration of how flakes were struck from a core of flint. Both cores and flints are readily found in the county and are enduring evidence of early human populations.

218

muntjac and hedgehogs survive as a result of Howard's ideals and at a time when the green belt is under siege, these aspects should be familiar to us all.

Robinson's 'Hertfordshire' (1978) is very good for its chronological summaries from 8000 BC to the present time, which makes dipping into various periods for reference very enjoyable. A notable example of local histories of villages and towns is Hine's 'History of Hitchin' (1927) and his editorship of the 'Natural History of the Hitchin Region' (1934).

Other particular favourites of mine include: Whiteman's 'Hexton: A Parish Survey' (1936), which has a foreword by Hine that must rank as one of the most pompous ever written; Wilkerson's 'Two Ears of Barley' (1969) about the village of Barley; Wayne's 'A Foot on Three Daisies' (1987) about Pirton; and Anne Ashley Cooper's 'A Harvest of Hexton' (1986).

Bronze Age axe from the very comprehensive display of prehistoric material in Hertford Museum.

The Ashley Coopers have been very generous to mammal research in Hertfordshire by allowing access over many years to particular sites of interest which survive largely due to their careful protection. The book by Anne Ashley Cooper is an outstanding account of the history of the communities in the county linked with the farming and rural life, as well as being specific to Hexton. There is also great charm to the Pirton book by Wayne and I cherish one sentence on page 2: 'So the centuries rolled by and the Stone Age, the Bronze Age and the Iron Age came and went.' That is the way to write history and deal with all those wretched problems of research.

What is so valuable about these books is their records of everyday life of village people as well as the nobility and politicians. It is the country people who have observed and influenced the lives of our wild mammals, birds, reptiles and amphibians just as much as those who own land or legislate for what happens to the environment.

W. Branch Johnson's books and Thwaite's 'Periodicals and Transactions relating to Hertfordshire' (1959) are very important guides and my visits to County Hall in lunch hours as a schoolboy introduced me to their bound set of the Trans of the Herts Nat Hist Soc for the first time.

The urban influences on the south and southeast of the county are reflected in the valuable rural accounts such as Molly Hughes' 'A London Family between the Wars' (1940), which on a personal level includes amusing references to my grandmother in Cuffley, and the Speakman books on Epping Forest in Essex, which also refer to the mammals and birds in Hertfordshire around Goffs Oak and Cuffley. This is especially relevant in his account of the life of the poacher Curtis, as told to Speakman in 'A Poacher's Tale' (1960). 'A Keeper's Tale' followed (1962), and 'A Forest by Night' (1965) tells of the Epping Forest badgers just before human

Flint axe from Plate XIII, *Hertfordshire stone implements*, referred to in the anniversary address to the *HNHS* by Sir John Evans, 26th February 1895, at Watford: *The Stone Age in Hertfordshire.*

pressure through traffic and interference transformed the area.

The 20th century has seen stories told by a number of people who took up farming or worked smallholdings from outside the established farming families. A book which captures the life of the small farmer really well is by David Tree, who describes in 'Pig in the Middle' (1966) life at Baas Hill, near Broxbourne, years before the 'good life' ideas of a 'return to the soil' became fashionable. (It was in connection with their badgers and bats that I first visited the family in June 1968.)

Harman's book 'Seventy Summers' (1986) accompanied a BBC television series and beautifully described the life of the author and the changes in farming in the Chilterns in the 20th century on the border between Buckinghamshire and Hertfordshire. Reference is made to the recovery of badger populations since legal protection and he contrasts pre-myxomotosis rabbit populations with recent trends.

Clifton Reynolds wrote of his farm life at Chipperfield, near Kings Langley, Hertfordshire, in 3 books on 'Glory Hill Farm', also in this border country with Buckinghamshire.

The 'Highways and Byways' series is, perhaps, best remembered now for its illustrations and the Hertfordshire volume (1902) is distinguished by F.L.Griggs' superb line drawings.

Thanks to the Phillimore series of Domesday Book County Paperbacks (1976), Hertfordshire's entry (vol 12) is available with modern English text facing each facsimile of the original 1086 AD statistical survey. The famous census shows how the distribution of humans in Hertfordshire has shifted from a northeast concentration, with some growth round Tring and St.Albans, to its present weight of population in the south and around the garden city and new town developments. This leaves the once busy northeast to be a rural farming area; an extraordinary reversal of the dominant mammal's distribution.

Davis in 'The Deserted Medieval Village of Hertfordshire' (1982) discusses the reasons for growth and contraction. The national population was 7 million between the 11th and 14th centuries and the pressure on wildlife at this time would have been considerable as marginal land was cultivated and

The aerial view drawing of Clifton Reynold's farmhouse, Glory Hill Farm at Chipperfield, shows the traditional orchards and buildings of the 1930s.

new settlements were built. Village life was dominant, but the deterioration in climate, harvest failures and animal plagues (principally rat, mouse, vole and sparrow) resulted in a fall in the numbers of humans even before the famous population crash of the Black Death.

Wood devotes considerable space to Hertfordshire in his 'Domesday: a Search for the Roots of England' (1986) and shows how the habitats around Great Wymondley and Codicote are particularly unchanged since the census. He also refers to Hatfield and St.Albans in his very readable, well-illustrated account.

To the naturalist walking in the Hertfordshire countryside, the impact of man on the environment can be obvious or subtle. The creation of marl pits where chalk was dug to dress the fields is described by several of the above references. These have become wilderness treasures in a farming scene which has to make space for mechanisation and ever greater efficiency to survive. Every church and churchyard reflects natural as well as human history just as every field and wood has human as well as natural influences indelibly marked on it, even when not at first apparent.

Major events such as the Black Death and the World Wars left a population which demanded changes in personal liberty and attitudes. Human society records its natural death rate and accepts that accidental deaths also occur. It is, however, surprising that when the annual loss of life by violent accidents on Hertfordshire roads is published (which averages some 80 dead and 5,000 injured) this attracts little sense of outrage. Unnatural death at any period should be a cause for concern and Ashley Cooper lists 200 witches killed in the eastern counties alone between 1645 and 1699 at a time of lax law and order.

Changes in family fortune are reflected in Ashley Cooper's list of animals which moved into Hexton House when it stood empty for 30 years in the 19th century: starlings, jackdaws and bats flew in and out, while rabbits and foxes were said to live in the cellars. The use of ferrets is ancient, but records of rabbit captures are infrequent: 28 rabbits in 3 hours in 1909 (selling price 6d [2½ p] per rabbit) and the barter and exchange system of village life is also described by Ashley Cooper for Hexton. She makes the point that due to the stringent green belt policy, only 10 new houses had been allowed to be built in the village in the last 45 years.

The Pirton history 'A Foot on Three Daisies' describes 27 species of mammals recorded, of which 3 have been lost (polecat, otter and red squirrel) and 4 gained (mink, muntjac, Chinese water deer and roe deer). Amphibians are listed but no mention is made of reptiles. One of the World War II war efforts described was the collection of rabbit skins. At times of shortage the advantage of being able to obtain wild food is another feature of village life. Cyril

Farming and conservation have always gone hand-in-hand on the Wallace farms in Hertfordshire. Diana Collingridge, neé Wallace, (top) has served on the *HNHS* Council and her father, John, is shown (standing, right) next to Tony Rook during an archeological dig in a Broom Hall Farm field (13th July 1985).

**In association with local farmers, *HMWT* manages the Mimram water meadows with cattle to maintain the diversity of wildlife. Two examples of long-established farming families are Zena and John Barton (top) at Warrengate, and Ivor Williams (lower) who farms with his brother, Vaughan, at Tewin Bury.**

*Burton regularly sent in records from Pirton for the HNHS surveys.*

*For a portrait of two notorious Hertfordshire poachers, the feature on the Fox twins in Whitmore's 'Hertfordshire Headlines' (1987) is very good. It is a fitting introduction to an account of the farming and game rearing with which the fate of our wild animals has been so closely linked.*

There is much historical information available on this species which is established throughout the county. Sexes can usually be distinguished due to the greater facial hair in the male (popularly shaved off on a daily basis) and more muscular body; the females usually have wider hips for child-bearing, more prominent mammae and softer skin. Many different racial origins are represented in the county and all stand erect.

More frequently they are seen away from their habitations seated inside metallic boxes of various kinds, hurtling about the county and exchanging a wide range of gestures with their hands. At such times they may express verbal communications to each other, often on mobile telephones, from a vocabulary mostly learned in childhood.

Language and the written word have been vital to the development of remote communication between individuals of the species. Books, for example, are a unique form of package design which continue to be widely used as the most aesthetically and convenient form of information storage for general use despite the development of word and data processing through computers, electronic mail on the World Wide Web (or Internet) and the communication of material via radio and television, including transmission via satellites.

There is usually one child at birth, but twins and larger numbers are recorded. The young are weaned at about 6 months, crawl at about 8 months, walk upright at about 14 months and talk at about 2 years. These stages may be reversed in advanced years or induced on a temporary or sometimes semi-permanent basis, by commonly circulated forms of drink. Due to brewing by fermentation or distillation, alcohol is widely produced and freely consumed. There are many kinds of other addictive drugs, but apart from medical applications and tobacco, these are generally illegal and risk the user being detained in a special kind of accommodation which limits freedom of movement and communication.

There is no fixed rut or mating time, although a greater tendency to this behaviour can be observed in spring. Mating is generally kept to the retreats or homes, but great ingenuity distinguishes the species in this area and the motor vehicle has been a major form of human conception in more ways than one.

Winters and loss of forest shelter have made permanent buildings the favoured habitat in the county and the social groups are generally family based with a preoccupation to give indications of territorial success expressed through clothing, scale of home range and possessions such as motor vehicles. Those with space around their homes create reproductions of the countryside where all manner of exotic plants are grown and vegetables may be cultivated.

It is possible to locate many large country gardens a few metres or up to 250m from where garden cuttings and waste are dumped. Wheelbarrow paths through the undergrowth can help track the source of the remains and may reveal the actual home range of the dominant male or female. (As in fallow deer, typified when a herd escapes across a field, female dominance is a feature of this species. This is especially obvious when couples of different sex seek garments made by others to cover their bodies; a stressful activity known as shopping.)

Farming is the most vital form of cultivation, where large areas of land provide food in the form of crops of animals or vegetable matter, harvested to be sold to other humans. It is the progress in this area rather than medicines to treat illness which has allowed humans to live longer, healthier lives than in former times. However, the advantages or disadvantages of the reliance on chemicals in farming, excessive use of medicines and the growth in illegal drug abuse in the last 100 years have all become matters of heated debate. Genetic modification of crops, like the experiments with African bees in South America, may cause the alteration or extinction of species and alter the environment irrevocably.

The media now highlights the traces found in human bodies which may show 500 man-made chemicals in a single cell of a healthy 30 year old, contrasted with a pre-1900 human body which is free of man-made toxic chemicals (L.Johnson & J.Ingham, *The Express* 6th January 2000). The scene for modern species loss was set in 1962 by Rachel Carlson's *Silent Spring* and the most significant recent extinction in the county was the loss of the otter, now known to be chiefly as a result of chemical pollution of the water environment. They have since been reintroduced.

Humans live by a complex system of earning currency (or money) to represent the exchange of goods, employment, ownership and credit, but the importance of farming in the communities has changed so that whereas 150 years ago 84% of the population was involved with the land, less than 3% is now. It took 2½ hours to earn enough money to buy a loaf of bread (which is still the staple food) 150 years ago, but today, on average, it takes only 6 minutes. It took 7 days to cut, thresh and process one acre of corn then, but this now takes one human hour. By the use of fertilizers, the soil in which crops are grown is 5 times more productive than just 50 years ago. Not many humans are engaged in production now but from their education they can apply numeracy and literacy skills to earn an income with which to buy products made by others.

**The role of farm manager includes a complex mixture of skills and responsibilities. Mick Lloyd of Tewin Hill Farm was pictured during a ploughing match on Ivor and Vaughan Williams' land next to Dawley Woods (2000).**

*The number of humans killed or seriously injured in road accidents per 100,000 in 1998 in Hertfordshire was 111 (The Times, 22nd April 2000): the seventh highest total in all English counties. 1998 is the first year for which regional differences have been published. Berkshire has a figure of only 40; North Yorkshire tops the survey with 165 per 100,000 people.*

In terms of the environment, members of the service team like Gary Cooper (left) and Trevor Turner are performing one of the most important jobs in society. They are shown working in Tewin during the winter snow of 1999.
It is vital that more refuse is recycled and the district councils continue to increase facilities. In East Hertfordshire district, for example, over 50,000 dustbins are emptied each week at a cost of £1.7 million per year.

*People in Hertfordshire produce over half a million tonnes of household waste each year; HCC estimates it is enough to fill the Titanic five times over. Street cleaning costs over £700,000 and we maintain the 'thin veneer of civilization' exhibited by humans at a cost of £133 million for the Hertfordshire Police Force.*

At one time those who could not work or pay their way, young or old, those with special needs, with ill health or overtly criminal in their behaviour, were kept at the public expense, in the workhouse or in prison. Income support is now given in a variety of ways, with some humans employed to support others, and a variety of systems now attempting to help people to cope by their own efforts. Ill health is treated through a system of trained doctors and nurses in hospitals where people are cared for when they need special attention beyond what can be achieved in their own homes.

Defence of territory on land, sea and air at one stage required all able-bodied male humans to enter one of the 'forces': This was called National Service and lasted for two years. The compulsory service taught basic life skills and was particularly helpful to those who had avoided doing much for themselves or thinking of others in the community up to that time.

There has been a return to learning how to make tree houses and tunnels by those who prefer not to earn their living in a formal way and one useful benefit of this activity has been the review of road building. Road construction, if allowed to proceed unchecked, would leave no habitats unaffected and little wildlife would therefore be able to survive.

Hertfordshire has a large transitory population, much influenced by London's population. Modern genetic research shows that humans are all related to common ancestors in Africa where *H.sapiens* colonised outwards from about 150,000 years ago to inhabit virtually every part of the planet. Over population by humans at the expense of the destruction of habitats of other species with no adequate resistance to this corruption of resource is a feature of the species. Extinction of other species by human activities is now accelerating at an unprecedented rate.

The political representatives of humans appear to be unable or unwilling to achieve successful conservation policies, exemplified by building on green belt land in Hertfordshire. Systems of taxation paid by a majority of the population support very expensive administrative systems which govern the population.

Inventions and scientific discovery are also acclaimed, but not usually supported in the lifetime of the people involved outside corporations. Laws have evolved from early tribal taboos to restrict unsociable behaviour. There is a curious tradition in Hertfordshire whereby the poachers of game, such as the Fox twins and Kate Nash, are better remembered than the protectors. Even notorious murderers, such as Walter Clibbon, have posts to remember them by and thieves of the highways like Richard (Dick) Turpin and Katherine Ferrers (The Wicked Lady of Markyate Cell in west Hertfordshire) have motion pictures made about them. Yet who can recall the names of the police, magistrates or judges who spent so much time protecting their communities from the activities of these people?

Humans, particularly the males, can be very aggressive and concious of territory due to testosterone, a potent steroid hormone, but can be creative and sensitive to the arts. Whilst the artists of either sex are considered of little social worth in their lifetime, their work (in cave paintings, image making of all kinds, poetry, plays, music, story writing, architecture and great feats of engineering) are the best remembered of all human activities.

*Access to the countryside requires responsible behaviour and fly-tipping, for example, is increasing. Stolen cars burn at such a high temperature that specimen oak trees have been destroyed where such cars were torched.*

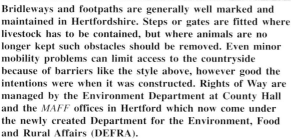

**Bridleways and footpaths are generally well marked and maintained in Hertfordshire. Steps or gates are fitted where livestock has to be contained, but where animals are no longer kept such obstacles should be removed. Even minor mobility problems can limit access to the countryside because of barriers like the style above, however good the intentions were when it was constructed. Rights of Way are managed by the Environment Department at County Hall and the *MAFF* offices in Hertford which now come under the newly created Department for the Environment, Food and Rural Affairs (DEFRA).**

# Farming and game rearing

**These longhorn cattle maintain pasture habitats for wildlife under a joint scheme run by *HMWT* and Hertfordshire farmers.**

The relationship between human history and our book theme discussed in the previous chapter is aptly summed up in part of Wilkerson's *Two Ears of Barley* about the village of Barley:

*'A medieval site came to light when I was digging out a ferret that was laid up. I dug through a patch of very dark soil. It did not seem significant at the time, but now I realised that it was worth investigating.*

*'The interest that had been aroused by burrowing in the soil led on to a search for ancient records connected with Barley. The pleasures to be obtained by perusing musty documents are not readily apparent, but a 400 year old survey comes alive when one finds in it the names of fields walked over every day, and the same names as men in the village today.'*

*24 June 1822, William Cobbett writes in his journal:*
*'The custom is in this part of Hertfordshire to leave a border around the ploughed part of the fields to bear grass and make hay from, so that, the hay now made, every field has a closely mowed grass walk ten feet wide all round it, between the corn and the hedge. This is most beautiful! The hedges are now full of the shepherd's rose, honeysuckles, and all sorts of wild flowers; so that you are upon a grass walk, with this most beautiful of all flower gardens and shubberies on one hand, and with the corn on the other. And thus you go from field to field, the corn, underwood and timber, the shape and size of the fields, the height of the hedgerows and the trees, all continually varying. Talk of pleasure-grounds indeed! What, that man ever invented, can equal these fields in Herts?'*

Ashley Cooper and Wayne reflect in their books the agricultural character of rural Hertfordshire noted in the previous section. The medieval strip cultivation system, where individuals owned a section but farmed to a common system, is particularly well explained in the book *A Foot on Three Daisies*.

The changes in agriculture between 1200 and 1500 were slight, but with the enclosures after the 16th century, more sheep were kept and the records show that at Hexton, Pirton and Barley wealth could be reflected in the number of cows, pigs, sheep and working horses a villager owned.

Strip farming was succeeded by men working on a paid basis for tenant farmers or landowners, and in Hexton the common field system of strip farming disappeared after 1767 as a result of the Enclosure Acts. Anne Ashley Cooper points out that although better farming practices followed, the cottagers lost their grazing rights. Hexton was listed in 1767 as: *'1,527 acres of common field arable, and 473 acres of common'*. At that time a man with a six-acre holding, a house and his common rights could keep two cows, one heifer, one calf, several pigs, and poultry, and so provide cheese, milk, eggs, vegetables and bacon for the family for the year.

Anne Ashley Cooper describes the crop rotations developed at the end of the 16th century, the straw-plaiting cottage industry, the corn depressions, the importance of horsepower and the development of allotments and how rabbits shot at harvest were a farmer's perk. She reminds us how vital were the skills of the haystack makers to protect the crop from weather and vermin damage, and illustrates the major changes in modern farming reflected in Harman's *Seventy Summers*.

From Hexton estate maps of about 1918, Anne Ashley Cooper lists: 500 acres of pasture; 800 acres of arable; 286 acres of woodland; 1,686 acres in total with about 100 acres of rough and lanes, yards and village. In modern Hexton these records can be compared with: 73 acres of pasture;

1,101 acres of arable; and 334 acres of woodland, plus the 150 acres of 'extras'. The loss of ponds provided for stock on the pastures and the growth in arable areas would have favoured hares at the expense of amphibians and bats especially.

The harvest stories in Wayne's book on Pirton include reference to about 500 rats killed from 6 large stacks when the stored crop was broken up to be threshed. Sparrows and moles were a constant cause for concern so that lists of payments for killing them survive with particular reference to 1748, 1749 and 1777 when the moles were so troublesome that a John Walker was given a 3 year contract for 7 guineas plus 5 shillings to buy him mole traps: '*And if the said John Walker Doth Not Kill The moles according to This Agreement the said John Walker Is To forfeit the said Money.*'

Young's classic *General view of the Agriculture of Hertfordshire* (1804), reprinted in 1971, is a delightful picture of the land, estates, tenures, buildings, farms, implements, fences, hedges, gates, arable techniques, crops, grassland, gardens, orchards, woods, plantations, wastes, cultivation improvements, livestock, economy, means of transport and miscellaneous observations at the start of the 19th century. Carrington's diary of country life in Hertfordshire (see Johnson [1973] in the bibliography) was also written at this time. Tomkins (1975) published a fascinating account by John Parnell of his visits to Arthur Young's farm near North Mymms which includes lengthy descriptions of the fences and hedgerows.

All these old accounts illustrate a very thorough and planned approach to an industry which occupied more than 80% of the population. The areas of clay with flints gave the county a reputation for being very expensive to farm because ploughshares wore or broke so quickly. The soil map (p22) shows the chalk, clay, loam and poor gravel which left so much more woodland in the south of the county. Ironically, modern farming can transform these difficult soils and the gravels used in the construction industry nationally have been anything but 'poor' to those who have been able to extract them for profit.

Although Young summarises the farms in the late 1700s as '*none above 1,000 acres; 500 acres forms a large one; perhaps the size most common is from 150 to 400; but there are many much smaller,*' he gives no total figures for crops or livestock in the county.

About hundred years later, however, Harpenden's Richard Lydekker FRS, gives interesting statistics of crops and livestock for the county in *Hertfordshire* (1909) (Cambridge County Geography Series).

Of the 402,856 acres (or 630 square miles), Lydekker gave 329,641 as under cultivation in 1905; 1,917 were orchards; 26,568 were woodland; 1,657 are listed as heaths and common grazing grounds; 116,700 were under corn; 32,702

**Fallow deer share Peter Cannon's farm at Hyde Hall near Buntingford. He pauses in front of a rutting stand in 1992.**

*Thomas Cox of Stanborough Farm (near Welwyn Garden City) born in 1735, sometimes recorded the misdeeds of his farm labourers in the farm account book. In June 1760 he wrote: "Onn Satterday night Thomas Warriner lay out all night long", and in August "William Collins wheant out and did not come home till 7 o'clock at night". On 6th December 1760 "Thos. Grenhams stole my faggotts and the sheppard and I saw him". An amusing incident is recorded for 14th November 1764: "I ordered John Barbar to gow to fitche the children home from schoule. He said he would not gow for theam nor would not. I ordered him to gow to work in the field a great many times befor he would gow and att last he wheant and I wheant three or four oures after word. He looked a boute him and did not dow his work as he ought to dow. His answer was and so it may be. I asked why he did not mind his business, why did he stand still att almost everything that be. His answer was he would stand still when he liked." He asked what I looked over hedge for to wach him if he work." But John Barbar was still employed in 1765, so this incident must have blown over.*

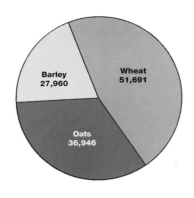

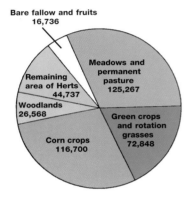

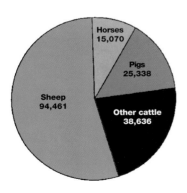

**Lydekker's diagrams for Hertfordshire farms (1909).**

were green crops; 36,831 included clovers, sainfoin and grasses; 3,315 were lucerne; there were 54,589 meadows, 70,678 pastures and 544 devoted to small fruits.

Of the corn, 51,691 acres was wheat, 36,946 oats and 27,960 barley. More than half of the whole area of the county, he noted, was still under the plough, a large proportion exceeded in only six other English counties.

A particular fruit grown was the Hertfordshire black cherry and orchards were situated near the homesteads of most of the older farms. Market gardening was increasingly lucrative, Rothamsted (near Harpenden) was already world renowned as an agricultural research station. Corn and straw was supplied to London as well as fresh fruit and vegetables.

Elm, oak, beech and ash were the most common timber trees. The undergrowth of mainly hazel in woods was cut about every 12 years.

Livestock is listed as 94,461 sheep (about 234 to every 1,000 acres) of the breeds Hampshire Downs, South Downs and Dorset, the latter favoured for its early lambing. The county was not noted for its horse breeding and they numbered only 15,070. Cattle totalled 38,636 and pigs 25,338. Shorthorns were the favourite type and although the chalk districts were not specially suited for dairy purposes, farms near the main railways despatched a considerable amount of milk to the big markets of London. (From 1901 to 1905 horse numbers had remained much the same, but whilst cattle had increased by 2,000, sheep had reduced by 2,000 and pigs by over 6,000).

Writing of Knebworth, Munby *et al* (1953) noted: *'During the first three-quarters of the nineteenth century Knebworth farming continued to develop along traditional lines, though with considerable changes in ownership of the farms. Then in the mid-1870s bad weather and cheap corn from America brought on what proved to be a continuing crisis for British farming. Hertfordshire farming families were forced to sell up and move out in large numbers. Only the Tompson family at Norton Green Farm survived the deluge. They have been there 160 years. Scots farmers were attracted by the low rents and the nearness to London. One of the first to come was steward on the Knebworth Estate, Matthew Gray; he was followed by others, the present Mr. Muirhead's father, who took over Deard's End in 1882, Mr. Wallace at Swangley's, Mr. Corson at Knebworth Lodge Farm, and others'.*

John Wallace (see p243) has pointed out to me that the popularity of Ayrshire cattle in the county was due to the influx of Scottish farming families (like his own) over 100 years ago, who kept the type they knew best.

At Cuffley and at Tewin there are also farming dynasties from Wales and both Williams and Thomas have been familiar names as well as helpful neighbours to my relatives in both localities.

Major modern environmental concerns are about how loss of habitat on farms and the use of chemicals has affected animals. I have found that farmers protect many sites with no publicity, because they know that certain undesirable people will steal rare plants and devastate habitats if they are too open with information. Farmers have been required by governments to increase food production; they have been advised to use chemicals and paid to remove hedgerows. We are lucky in the county to have excellent farming practice in all parts - habitat damage is unusual.

Interesting records have been made of Brook Farm noting the changes over the last 60 years, reflecting what has probably happened at many Hertfordshire farms. I am indebted to David Thomas who allowed me to take photographs at the farm, and to his son Gareth who has made his extensive 'A' level project about the farm available to me. I had also kept notes about the farm from 1966 with Alan Burn who recorded crops and field names.

David Thomas (top) and Gareth Thomas at Brook Farm.

A field on Brook Farm and (bottom) Cuffley Brook further upstream in Northaw Great Wood.

Gareth Thomas' diagrams show the changes at Brook Farm between 1941 (when his grandfather J.I.Thomas moved there) and 2000. I have compared the 1898 Ordnance Survey for the farm, then known as Cuffley Farm, and the field patterns are much the same as Gareth's 1941 details. Changes continue apace and the recession in beef prices means that the carefully developed herd will soon be gone, just as the dairy cattle ceased to be viable a few years earlier.

Hedgerow losses were also monitored very well by Gareth and clearly meant less habitat for small mammals and birds. There are, however, still many left and Cuffley retains more hedges than many other parts of the county: the 'horsey-culture' of the south around the urban and wealthy village areas means hedgerow survival to enclose stock in contrast to the arable northeast. Rackham (1986) illustrates the history of hedges remarkably clearly and records 200,000 miles to have been planted between 1750 and 1850, *'equal to all those planted in the previous 500 years'*. This would have resulted in a massive boost to all species of animal which thrive in hedgerow cover, exploiting its food, shelter and protection for nest building. As Gareth points out, the loss of certain hedges became essential to manage the farm profitably, but a family farm retains a great deal of cover whereas a site taken over and run by a remote multi-national

Aerial view of Brook Farm, Cuffley, in 1991. The farm boundary is shown in red. In recent years extra land has been managed (see p232). The farm borders Cuffley on the left and Goffs Oak on the right. How the field shapes evolved is shown in a series of diagrams (see pp232-233).

agri-business simply clears it for intensive contract cultivation.

The larger mammals are more numerous in the area of the farm due to badger protection and the arrival of muntjac deer, although hares are diminishing generally. Foxes and rabbits flourish in the area which has always been something of a stronghold for amphibians and reptiles. Recent diseases involving farm animals have many long-term consequences, and diversity in the countryside has diminished. The loss of livestock from the farm following a long tradition of milking herds and beef cattle has in turn reduced insect food in a stream valley otherwise very favourable to the larger bat species, for example.

Gareth's hypothesis was that the governments of the day and the European Community policies have had the most influence on the management of Brook Farm since 1941. His grandfather recalled how the introduction of the Milk Marketing Board in 1933 had been a 'life-saver' to many farm businesses. All milk produced on each farm was bought by one body, eliminating the worry of a free market. In 1941 there were 26 fields and about 6 were small paddocks unsuitable for arable crops. The diagrams show the activities

230

and space allocated. One field was lost to industrial development and further land taken on from Burnt Farm on the southern border. These changes are illustrated. The M25 motorway now marks the boundary to the south, just above the county boundary with Middlesex.

The full text of Gareth Thomas' project is an invaluable historic record of this part of Cuffley as well as a detailed account of farming practice from personal experience.

Community Forests are a very welcome development, although adequate funding appears to be lacking. As many areas of farmland are less profitable, woodlands and fruit orchards should be planted to encourage wildlife so that species such as dormice do not disappear.

However, in the last 50 years all farms have experienced subsidised hedge removal so that the wild flower, bird, butterfly and mammal populations, to name only the types of wildlife most noticed, are now greatly reduced. This all relates to the success or failure of dormice, for example.

The Dell, Cuffley, which was a beautiful sandy wilderness of pits with the archaelogical interests associated with flint hand tools, was bulldozed in the 1980s and illegally fly-tipped with building rubble. It had been a site for slowworms and grass snakes, as well having all the shrub features close to ancient woodland associated with ideal dormouse habitats. There was a flourishing badger sett which was part of their chain of earthworkings (where the sand appeared) to link with Thorntons Farm and along the valley edge into Nyn Park at Northaw. All these animals have been lost to the area.

In such a place, the purchase of the land (by local people, or the County Council, or the Trust) could bring in a tree planting scheme with open glades to transform the area into woodland with dense hedgerows to link the communities of Northaw and Cuffley. It would be easy to create walks full of wildlife for all to enjoy. Cuffley village could again be surrounded by a tree belt of oaks, hornbeams, hazels and also fruit trees in community orchards, which is much as it was for over a thousand years: a clearing in the woods of the ancient Enfield Chace.

The first sett where I watched and photographed badgers in part of Northaw Great Wood, adjoining Cuffley Brook and the School Camp, suffered a similar fate as the Dell and was bulldozed without warning. Aerial pictures reveal the loss of a corner of the SSSI (Site of Special Scientific Interest), where the brook was apparently re-aligned during the earthmoving. I had left Cuffley by this time, but I know of no action taken by the planning authorities over either site.

If we continue to allow the habitats to be reduced to little more than suburban parks, arable prairies and neglected old coppiced woodlands, developed with housing up to their edges with the resultant cat, dog and human damage to the ecology, we should not be surprised if we lose more and more species from the county list.

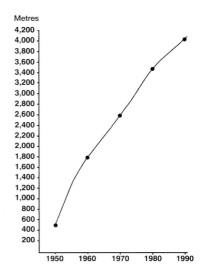

**Brook Farm: cumulative total of length in metres of hedgerows removed between 1941 and 1991.**

*When public footpaths and access to the environment generally are suddenly denied to prevent the spread of disease, we realise just how fortunate we are to have this network of routes to walk and ride. A system of joining and extending routes to give a more logical network would transform the way the countryside can be enjoyed.*

# Brook Farm

The modern farm, which now manages additional land south to the Middlesex border, is shown here (right). The evolution of the post-1941 farm is illustrated in sequence starting below left and continues on the opposite page. The gradual creation of larger fields becomes more obvious and the actual amount of land reclaimed by the hedgerow removal is shown in the field diagram which covers the whole period (p233 bottom right).

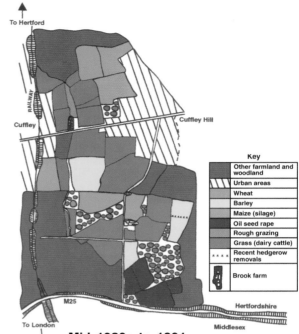

**Key**
- Other farmland and woodland
- Urban areas
- Wheat
- Barley
- Maize (silage)
- Oil seed rape
- Rough grazing
- Grass (dairy cattle)
- Recent hedgerow removals
- Brook farm

**Mid 1980s to 1991**
This area is farmed to the present day and takes in the additional management of Burnt Farm fields.

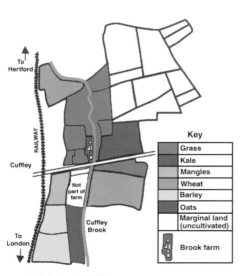

**Key**
- Grass
- Kale
- Mangles
- Wheat
- Barley
- Oats
- Marginal land (uncultivated)
- Brook farm

**1941 to 1950**
Field shapes and land use.

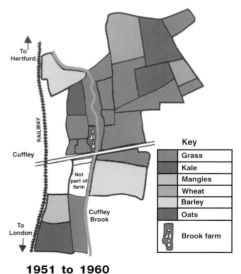

**Key**
- Grass
- Kale
- Mangles
- Wheat
- Barley
- Oats
- Brook farm

**1951 to 1960**
Field shapes and land use - marginal land taken into cultivation.

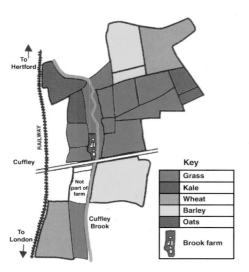

**1961 to 1970**
Field shapes and land use.

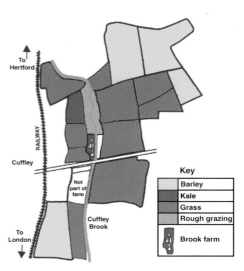

**1971 to 1980**
Field shapes and land use.

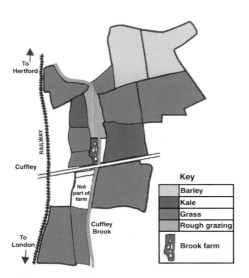

**1981 to 1985**
The simplification of fields on the
northeast shows clearly by the mid 1980s.

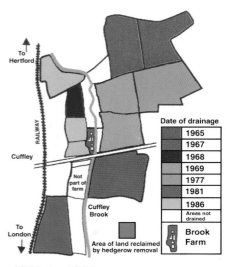

**1941 to 1991**
Drainage schemes and land
reclaimed by hedgerow removal.

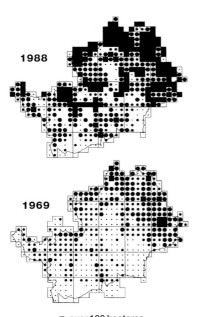

**1988**

**1969**

- ■ over 100 hectares
- ● 51-100 hectares
- • 26-50 hectares
- · 1-25 hectares

**Comparison of the distribution of wheat production in Hertfordshire in the years 1969 and 1988.**

Elsewhere in Hertfordshire crops and types of farming have come and gone. The county has long featured the special cultivation of watercress due to its spring-fed, clear chalk streams and was said to produce the best of this crop in England. Many have gone, but were excellent sites for water voles and water shrews.

The railways distributed the neatly tied bundles of cut cress to the Midlands and beyond as well as London. Lavender was a speciality of Hitchin where lavender water had also been produced for 80 years previously.

Farms are traditionally associated with all aspects of the domestication of mammals from the sheep dogs and farmyard cats to the stock in the fields. The history of domesticity was given by Juliet Clutton-Brock (1987).

Those animals that responded to domestication have become part of the human farming or household scene. All are hardy, have an inborn affinity with humans, are comfort-loving, breed freely and are easy to tend. Clutton-Brock examines these factors in the light of modern knowledge, although I disagree with her statement that deer will not feed or breed readily if constrained in a pen: muntjac make a very good job of both. Francis Galton (1865), who summed up the haphazard trials and errors of domesticating every wild mammal possible, ended with the prophetic words on those animal species which humans did not find suitable: *'As civilisation extends they are doomed to be gradually destroyed off the face of the earth as useless consumers of cultivated produce.'*

Clutton-Brock points out the unique and paradoxical feature of humans in that they are a tropical, omnivorous primate whose exceptional success as a species began to accelerate only when they became social hunters in a subarctic environment. Hunting and the development of the wolf/human relationships, so well described in Lorenz's *Man meets Dog* (1954), has resulted in all the domestic breeds of dog known today: variations of the wolf ancestor, selectively bred for particular activities. (In terms of the working day, it could be said that until recent technology farmers chose the wrong way of life: they had to work much longer hours than hunter-gatherers, even in arid regions.) To see how the breeds of dogs appeared a century ago, Walter Rothschild's Museum at Tring will reward the visitor with a large selection of breeds preserved by expert taxidermy, some of which, such as the bulldog with much longer legs, have altered considerably.

Clutton-Brock points out that although economic progress was once totally dependent upon horses, they were the last species to be domesticated: sheep and goats came first, then cattle and pigs.

The cow, so much a part of village life in Hertfordshire down the centuries, gives the most versatile range of resources and every part of the body can be used by humans.

234

Although we think of Roman Britain as very remote from us now, Ashley Cooper pointed out in the Hexton book, discussed earlier, that the Romans were present in Britain for 400 years, the same time span as from Elizabeth I to our own era; a very long part of our history. The Romans, in particular, Clutton-Brock shows, made great efforts to re-organise the animal world to suit their own inclinations and fashions. Even frogs were introduced to places in their Empire so that croaking could be heard where none existed before.

Baker (1990) has produced a table of these from which can be summarized, with Lever (1977), the mammals which have found niches in Hertfordshire:

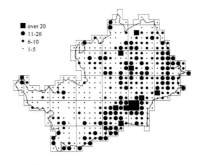

**Ponds.**

| Species | When established | Notes |
| --- | --- | --- |
| Rabbit | 11-12thC | Warrens for food, escaped. |
| Grey squirrel | 1890 | Deliberate releases since 1876. First established at Woburn, Beds. |
| House mouse | 10thC BC | Accidental, as trade developed, via foodstuffs. |
| Black rat | 3-4thC | Found associated with Roman remains. Now extinct here. Ware was the last stronghold. |
| Brown rat | 1728-29 | Thought to be introduced via shipping from Russia. |
| Edible dormouse | 1902 | Only species deliberately released and established first in Herts: Walter Rothschild, Tring. |
| Coypu | 1932 | Escaped from fur farms, now extinct here. (Never really established in Hertfordshire although noted in Lever (1977) for southwest Herts (p146). |
| Mink | 1953 | First bred in fur farms in 1929. (Escapees were late to establish in Hertfordshire about 1975). |
| Muntjac | 1900 | Woburn & Whipsnade escapees. |
| Chinese water deer | 1900 | Woburn and Whipsnade and some other park escapees. (Lever [1977] gives 1940s for Herts and Bucks borders) |

Full details of the distribution of broad-leaved, coniferous and all woodlands, urban development, golf courses, parkland, mineral workings, barley, grassland, field beans, oilseed rape, dairy and beef cattle, pigs and sheep are all given in Smith, Dee, Fernside, Fletcher & Smith, *HNHS* (1993) from which the above and the diagrams for wheat opposite are reproduced by kind permission.

The black rat is believed to have caused a greater number of human deaths than all the catastrophes of wars because it is a carrier of disease transmitted by its urine, faeces and fleas, (but when total human deaths by an animal are calculated, the mosquito leads by far, for killing by the transmission of malaria).

Nigel Agar, in the chapter he contributed to *The Hertfordshire Farmer in the Age of Industrial Revolution* (1991) points out that Hertfordshire has been a farming county throughout most of its history, and with the possible exception of the paper-making industry of the southwest, the first industrial revolution of the 18th and 19th centuries passed it by with regard to manufacture. The common businesses of Hertfordshire (strawplaiting, malting and brewing) were closely linked to agriculture.

However, Hertfordshire has had a central role in the 'industry' which grew up around hunting and shooting. The management of country estates is a major form of employment in its own right, although at a much greater scale a century ago. Due to its proximity to London the county became much sought-after by town-based sports people and for syndicate shoots. It is also home to the firm of Gilbertson & Page established in Hertford at the end of the last century, and which now concentrates on the manufacture of dog food. The firm, often referred to as *Gilpa*, became one of the most familiar names in the world of game rearing and published the *Gamekeeper* magazine. I am most grateful to the firm for the material reproduced here from old catalogues and early magazines.

'G & P' always worked to reform the old practices which so often harmed protected species, and the magazine (which later became *Gamekeeper and Countryside*, then *Countryside* and finally *Dog and Country*) encouraged a humane, conservation viewpoint despite the harsh early traditions. They have now sold all their interests in game-rearing equipment and the magazine has disappeared after many years of dedicated editorship by Edward Askwith. They continue to sponsor food for wildlife on the reserve at Tewin Orchard.

Two past employees of Gilbertson & Page, Ray Crisp (left) and Cyril Myford. One of Ray's jobs was to prepare the secret mixture of 'Renardine' repellant. Cyril had been pest control officer for Hertfordshire under *MAFF*.

The history of game preservation (which is also the history of the second oldest profession, poaching) is well described in Trench's *The Poacher and the Squire* (1967). Domestication and hunting have gone hand in hand with the development of man as both hunter-gatherer and farmer. Sporting techniques are all related to our oldest hunting skills such as throwing which represents the same dexterity as controlling a spear.

Trench describes the necessity of hunting in England prior to game laws, although nothing is known of game preservation in the Roman occupation. Saxon law did not restrict the pursuit of game by anyone in the lower social groups and even allowed the following of hares (but not deer) into royal woods. The Normans, however, introduced game preservation in the French style and imposed harsh penalties on those who transgressed the forest laws. Trench points out that William the Conqueror was obsessed with the sport of hunting, so that the economic aspects of feeding the royal household and preservation to combat famine were only

AT STUD.                    Flatcoated Retriever.
## " PONSBOURNE PETER "
Reg. K.C.
By "Bryn Asaph Crack" ex "Gwyn Judy."
Use this dog for keen working stock and outcross.
BRYANT, Gamekeeper, Newgate Street, near Hertford.

A typical 1950s advertisement for a working retriever in the magazine which was published monthly in Hertford town.

a part of the consideration.

James I, so closely linked with our county through Theobalds and the Enfield Chace, made a proclamation in 1607 because he felt the forest laws had become disregarded due in part to the lack of care during the reign of Elizabeth I. It threatened future offenders with the full force of the law, and Trench gives details of Hertfordshire deer poachers:

*'Thomas Smith of Hoddesdon in the county of Hertford, oatmeal maker; Robert Sawyer, constable of the hamlet of Hallingfield in the parish of Waltham Abbey in the county of Essex, husbandman; Robert Cordell of Hallingfield, labourer; Robert Dernishe of Hoddesdon, husbandman and Robert Spicer of Broxbourne, husbandman with others unknown, on Thursday, 26th April last, past in the night riotously assembled armed with defensive and offensive weapons to kill, maim, wound and beat all keepers and others as should withstand them and with nets, buckstalls and such like engines to take and carry away the buck and other deer that they should take.*

*'They entered into the park and enclosed ground of Your Majesty's subject and servant, Sir Edward Grivell, knight, called Harold Park in the parish of Waltham Abbey, pitched their nets and by their cunning brought the herd of deer into their nets, took sundry bucks, broke their necks and took them away which the said Grivell had specially preserved for Your Majesty's pastime .... The said persons are extraordinarily contemptuous and exceeding arrogant and presumptuous'.*

Wild deer had disappeared from most of England by the 10th century when bird shooting became fashionable. Fox-hunting and the preservation of other animals guaranteed that there would be sport where these species (along with badgers for baiting) had been previously killed at every opportunity.

Gamekeepers became very important not only for rearing the game and protecting it, but for showing the employers and their guests how to use the guns. Endless stories exist of events in the shooting field and Trench quotes a Victorian incident reported in *The Times* when the then Prince of Wales peppered a friend as he was 'caught short' and bent over behind a bush:

*'Lord Clermont, having had too hearty a breakfast, sat in a resting position behind a furze bush. Two of the Prince's dogs scented the noble peer and came to a point. His Royal Highness let fly at the furze bush, wounding Lord Clermont in the defenceless portion of his body. The Prince's gun hung fire, or the snipe would have received the full charge. Twenty-three and a half grains of Number 4 shot were extracted from his lordship's bum'.*

Enemies of game became 'vermin' and the ingenuity shown by humans in inventing all manner of traps is comprehensively dealt with in Bateman's book *Animal Traps and Trapping* (1971). The gin trap, which held a mammal by

**John Card with part of his extensive collection of gin traps when he lived near Much Hadham (April 1985).**

# TRAPPING SIEVES

(With handle to fold.)

For sifting fine soil upon the pans of Traps. Can be easily carried in the pocket.

**7/-** each

**Often gin traps were set around the entrances to fox earths and badger setts. The trapping sieve was used to sprinkle soil over the traps to hide them. A victim caught by the foot on one trap would be likely to then set the others off as it struggled to escape.**

Pheasant poaching, by its very nature, is a private activity, but has always been a feature of country life. Melvin Bedford has given special permission for his pictures to be used here. It is many years since he would do the round of pheasant roosts with a folding .410 shotgun, much as he would do his milk round in Cuffley. He would keep to the legal shooting seasons and humanely 'drop' the birds as they roosted asleep above him in the branches. He never encroached on land where pheasants were reared. The favoured tree roosts, used year after year, were mostly on the village road sides. A keen badger watcher, he and his family attract a wide variety of birds to feeders and tables in their garden.

the leg with sprung, toothed, steel grippers, was made illegal in this country nearly 50 years ago.

An animal caught by its foot in any circumstances suffers acute distress. As well as having pity for our own wildlife, it is sad to think how the wolves and other species in North America have been trapped by hundreds of thousands of gins, taken to colonies with the first settlers and then produced in vast quantities locally as demand grew. They became popular, along with snares, because they do not damage the pelt of the animal, which is usually killed by blows to the nose or head if still alive when found.

For all aspects of sport, the Lonsdale library, published earlier this century (eg the *Londsdale Keeper's Book* [1938], *Tegetmier on Pheasants* [1911], Gilbertston & Page's own little Victorian book *Poachers versus Keepers* [no date] and the various books on poaching by Hawker, Rider Haggard, Vesey-Fitzgerald, Nial, Watson and Bedson) give vivid pictures of the lives on both sides of the fence.

There is no doubt that game preservation was the reason for the extinction of so many predatory birds and mammals, not only from Hertfordshire but much of England, and gamekeepers continue to exert a constant war on them in places. The days when estate abutted estate, or farmland came under the strict management of large numbers of full-time gamekeepers, has gone. Shooting continues to be popular, but on less and less available land, and game rearing is usually in the hands of part-time keepers or groups who share the work in syndicates.

Birds are mostly bought in from specialist game farms rather than reared in large numbers on site, and are kept in rearing pens where they grow before release. These release pens are maintained with high, fox-proof fences and electric wire in secluded parts of the woodland sections of the shoots. It is particularly in these areas that Fenn traps are set in tunnels to catch stoats and weasels. The electric fence strand keeps larger mammals away, but snares may also be set for foxes. All too often badgers and dogs may also be caught.

A common feature of such areas was the gibbet of dead 'vermin', usually carrion crows, magpies, grey squirrels, stoats and weasels, but these are less often seen nowadays.

They were intended to show the employer how well the employee was working at pest control. James Birdsall in *The Boys and the Butterflies* (1988) gives a detailed description of a gibbet near his childhood home of Walkern, near Stevenage. In 1941, he found a stoat caught in a gin trap which had eaten its own hind leg down to the bone in the attempt to escape. The local keeper's gibbet displayed:

*'Hung by their necks in forked twigs of the hazel bushes were the customary crows, jays and magpies, and skins of foxes, badgers and stoats were nailed to the sides of a wooden hut. But there were other corpses which struck horror into us. Tawny owls and barn owls and huge long-*

*eared owls rotted there, and sparrow hawks and even a green woodpecker. What possible threat to game could be held against the woodpecker, we could not conceive. We released a live red squirrel from a gin - not without considerable danger to ourselves as he naturally fought viciously as we tried to help him. Of course, we had no business to be there at all.'*

Rabbit control during the wheat harvest, near Hertford.

Modern keepers and their employers are aware of the laws to conserve non-game species and know that they have a very positive role in protecting their areas of land from all manner of callous, destructive people typified by those criminals who occasionally come to court and are convicted of badger digging or killing protected species of wildlife.

To overcome the criticisms of shooting and game-rearing, it would be ideal if shotgun licences could include a test on wildlife species identification, the wildlife and countryside legislation and other aspects of safe, legal use of firearms. Guns are essential to the humane management of all our wildlife, but must be used by informed and safe people. (Deer herds, for example, increase by a third annually, unless managed as they have no predators. It is now essential to cull so that the deer do not die of starvation when the herds get too big or do intolerable damage to farm crops and gardens.)

Gamekeepers, full or part-time, should be rewarded with a wildlife sponsorship subsidy for every predatory bird or mammal shown to have been present or bred on their land each year. This would be funded from nature conservation sources and greater use should be made of public hides, possibly with entry by purchased tokens, overlooking areas where buzzards and deer, for example, can be seen. The funding would compensate for proven losses to the game. The basic problem has always been that game is concentrated in unnaturally high numbers to give the maximum sport to those participating.

Predators will always be attracted to coverts where game has been reared. Wildcats, pine martens and polecats were lost directly because of game preservation. If pine martens were reintroduced successfully, their love of eggs and chickens would have to be taken into account despite their value in squirrel control. Again, electric fence protection and compensation where damage is shown would be a small price to pay for this beautiful indigenous mammal to return to its old Hertfordshire haunts after 150 years.

A portrait of how humans have influenced the countryside in Hertfordshire can be found in Richard Mabey's *Home County* chapter, first published as *Richard Mabey's Hertfordshire* in *Illustrated London News* March 1982, republished in his collected essays *In a Green Shade* (1983). Best known for his *Food for Free* (1972) and *Flora Britannica* (1996), this Hertfordshire author describes the county with wit and affection.

The traditional public houses, such as this one near Much Hadham, are less and less easy to find. A revised combination of pub, shop and post office is more viable and legislation is needed. John Card (right, and below out rough shooting) used to warden HCC land near his home. As well as protecting foxes, badgers and other species present, he was a keen photographer and recorded the grass snake laying eggs featured on p245.

Sheep skull, probably *Ovis aries palustris,* from River Lea under about 5m of alluvium (after Millais, 1906) from the collection of Dr.Frank Corner. Millais described this sheep as the 'turf of peat sheep'; probably the earliest domesticated variety.

Skull of *Bos frontosus* from the Thames alluvium, shown in Millais (1906) with one from the River Lea. He decribed it as a larger ox than *Bos longifrons*, previously thought to be the only one present when the Romans invaded Britain.

# Extinct species and early practices

Lydekker observed in 1902 that Hertfordshire was *'singularly deficient in interest so far as the palaeontology of vertebrate animals is concerned'.* However, Oakley (*Trans* **22**, 5: 239-246, 1947) gave a detailed summary of the material available (see Appendix 1). These includes moose, bison, aurochs (wild cattle), roe deer, red deer, giant deer *Megaceros*, mammoth, horse, hippopotamus, badger, reindeer, wild boar, cave bear, elk, bison, mammoth, woolly rhinoceros, straight-tusked elephant, hyena, fallow deer, water vole, hare, mole and fox.

It may seem eccentric to imagine a scene as we look out from our modern Hertfordshire homes where a hippo trots past, but the fossil record shows that we are only part of a very long story of mammals, amphibians and reptiles in the county and need not be too smug about our own presence. Two references add to the background of Oakley's excellent work in the *Trans:* Harting's *British Animals extinct within Historic Times* (1880) and the account of the Mammal Society's joint symposium with the Linnean Society (1989): *British Mammals: Past, Present and Future*.

Harting, like Lydekker, lived in Hertfordshire and he provides well-researched chapters on bear, beaver, reindeer, wild boar, wolf and white cattle on a national scale. He estimated the brown bear (still surviving in very small numbers in remote parts of Europe) became extinct here in the 10th century. They were caught for baiting and this later continued with imported bears.

Bulls and badgers were often baited at the same events. As many as 7 bears were exhibited at one: *'... each confined by a long rope or chain, and baited with 3 or 4 large and courageous dogs who rushed upon them with open jaws. The bears, ferocious and fretful with continued fighting, were of great strength, and not only defended themselves with their teeth, but hugged the dogs to death, or half-suffocated them before their masters could release them.'*

He describes a blind bear which broke loose and bit a man who died as a result of an infection from the wound. Rather like the acts of daring at bullfighting or bull running events still considered to be public entertainment in parts of Europe today, there were people who would run up and secure the chain of an escaped bear, disabled as the poor animal was by dogs. The noise of the bear garden, he concluded, must have been *'well nigh unendurable, what with the din of the men eager to bet on their favourites, and the loud shouts of the respective partisans of dog and bear'.*

Hine, in his *The History of Hitchin* (1929) records that when he first came to Hitchin in 1901, the stake and the ring for baiting bulls and bears still survived at The Bull public house in Bridge Street. The last reference to bull baiting in the county was 1776 when a chief constable put in a bill for expenses for *'suppressing a bull-baiting in Hertingfordbury'*. Hine notes that the 'sport' was not made illegal until Martin's 1822 Act.

John Carrington's Tewin diaries described an otter death already referred to (p182) and mentions in his inimitable way the death of a Ware man after a fight: *'They Quarreld about hunting the badger their (at Waterford Fair) as a Custom at this Holladay fair'* (1805). He also refers to fox-hunting (7th and 8th April 1804), mole catching, (5th May 1804), venison, rabbit and hare pie (consumed at meals) and the purchase of flint stones and eggs (June 1805). Coursing hares appears (March 1810) when his sons and friends were at The Rose and Crown *'who had Been a Courseing.'*

Rats were a constant worry due to their damage to stored crops: *'Catched 74 Ratts all Large ones, No Rat Catcher onley our Selves & Doggs'* (15th January 1810) and: *'Killed 70ty Ratts small & Great, it is a Great Loss to the Farmer to Stack Wheat abroad whear the Virmen can take it & in Barns if not soon Thrashed, my loss £10 in this'* (25th April 1809). Also in 1809 he recorded a fox caught in a hen house by a gin trap. He showed compassion for a poacher hanged in 1807: *'John Catheral Hanged at Hartford Fryday 20th for poarching or Snearing and for Resisting the Constable to Save him Self, which sentance too Bad.'*

Beavers had disappeared from Hertfordshire about 900 years ago but survived in Wales until around the end of the 12th century, from where most of the historical written evidence comes. There is plentiful sub-fossil material from the peat in The Fens and East Anglia generally. There are some beaver remains from Iron Age deposits near Baldock in the *North Herts Mus Colls.* but there is no evidence of place names connected with beavers from our small rivers in the county.

Reindeer would not have survived in the areas which became our county for long after the retreat of the ice about 12,000 years ago but lived in Britain before they finally became extinct, in Harting's estimation, by the 9th century.

Wild boar were commonly hunted and only finally became extinct in parks during the 17th century. Our modern breeds of pig are, however, unlikely to be the result of domestication of the local wild boars in the past. Harting gives an account from Derbyshire of the local reduction in adders due to predation by boars.

Rackham (1986) times the extinction of the wild boar in Essex as during the Saxon period. This timing might also apply to Hertfordshire although I am unable find any references to confirm this.

According to Rackham's records, wolves were exterminated about 1396 in England; 988 in Wales; 1621 in

**Wildcats** *Felis sylvestris* **disappeared from southern England and much of the Midlands before 1800. They probably vanished from Hertfordshire during the 16th century due to hunting and loss of habitats. Their decline after 1800 is well documented and illustrated in Derek Yalden's** *The history of British Mammals* **(1999). Like the big cats released into the wild in Britain over the past 30 years (see Appendix 4, p282), they do not leave claw marks, only pads, in their footprints.**

**The Lea Valley seems to produce all kinds of items whenever it is dredged, and the following deer and livestock bones from Stanstead Abbotts are based on the illustrations in Roberts & Roberts (1978).**

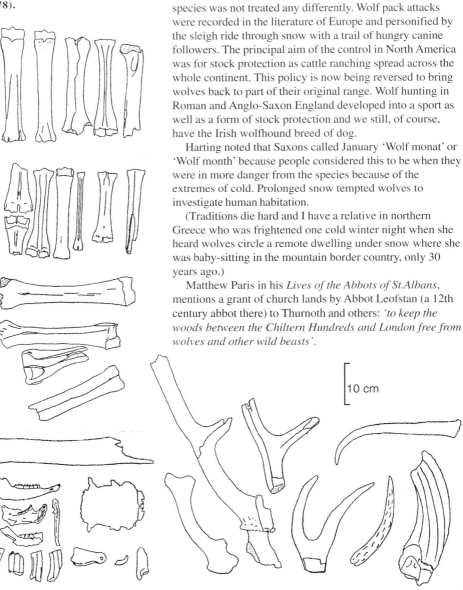

Scotland and 1710 in Ireland. Despite their rarity they still suffer persecution in the remote parts of Europe where small populations remain. Although there is no authentic account of wolf attack on humans in North America, Europeans took with them their traditional fear of wolves and persecuted the different sub-species unmercifully. Young's account in *The Wolves of North America* (1944) describes this persecution with many gruesome photographs.

There is evidence that the European race of wolf was more liable to attack humans, but the less dangerous American species was not treated any differently. Wolf pack attacks were recorded in the literature of Europe and personified by the sleigh ride through snow with a trail of hungry canine followers. The principal aim of the control in North America was for stock protection as cattle ranching spread across the whole continent. This policy is now being reversed to bring wolves back to part of their original range. Wolf hunting in Roman and Anglo-Saxon England developed into a sport as well as a form of stock protection and we still, of course, have the Irish wolfhound breed of dog.

Harting noted that Saxons called January 'Wolf monat' or 'Wolf month' because people considered this to be when they were in more danger from the species because of the extremes of cold. Prolonged snow tempted wolves to investigate human habitation.

(Traditions die hard and I have a relative in northern Greece who was frightened one cold winter night when she heard wolves circle a remote dwelling under snow where she was baby-sitting in the mountain border country, only 30 years ago.)

Matthew Paris in his *Lives of the Abbots of St.Albans*, mentions a grant of church lands by Abbot Leofstan (a 12th century abbot there) to Thurnoth and others: *'to keep the woods between the Chiltern Hundreds and London free from wolves and other wild beasts'.*

10 cm

There were 13th century references to paid 'pest controllers' who kept wolf-dogs in Finchingfield, Essex, and *'for hunting the wolf, fox and wildcat'* from Huntingdon, Northampton, Buckingham and Rutland.

The ancestors of our domestic cattle are thought to have died out in Britain in the Bronze Age, about 4,000 years ago, at a time characterised in Hertfordshire by round barrows, especially in the Royston area. This was when urn burials after cremation largely replaced inhumation.

In Europe, Urus (wild ox) became extinct in the 17th century, with the last animals recorded from the ancient Polish forests and Harting devoted a chapter to the wild white cattle of Britain. Several herds survive, all in parks, probably the best known of which is at the remote site of Chillingham in Northumberland.

Whitehead, both in 1953 and 1965, wrote on the origins of these cattle, which have been isolated for over 700 years in the single herd at Chillingham, but appear to have suffered little from this interbreeding. Records show that they have become smaller in stature due to this, but they have escaped the worst bovine disease epidemics so far, thanks to their isolation. These ancient breeds appear to have been introduced by the Romans and became feral in the forests during periods of social upheaval. Watching them, as I have found, gives one a great sense of history.

Matthews (1952) gives the diversity and numbers of mammals as having peaked 15 to 20 million years ago, since when the increasing dryness of climate, which produced deserts and the succession of glacations simultaneously, has been the main cause for a steady decline. This decline, he concludes, has been hastened by the activities of people in the last few centuries so that *'all the larger species will inevitably soon be extinct, except perhaps for a few that may be preserved in artificial sanctuaries.'*

During the preparation of this book, Derek Yalden's *The History of British Mammals* (1999) appeared and presents an exceptionally well documented and illustrated account which brings up-to-date Harting's and Matthews' work.

John Wallace (see also p38) is one of the few landowners to maintain coppice rotations in selected woods. If our wildlife is to survive in its present diverse form it is vital that pollarding, coppicing and open wood-pasture managements are carried out by more and more owners of woodland.

# Conservation and management

Our *HMWT* is the focus for organised conservation work in Hertfordshire and Middlesex, but the more humans there are to support mammal, amphibian and reptile survival wherever they live, the more likely this will happen. The Mammal Group, associated with the Mammal Society and the Hertfordshire Natural History Society, the Hertfordshire & Middlesex Badger Group, which is affiliated to the National Federation of Badger Groups and the Hertfordshire & Middlesex Bat Group are obvious groups to join.

By helping even in small ways, such as paying the

Graham White, *HMWT* Conservation Manager, who has monitored the recovery of otters in the county amongst his many other responsibilities.

membership subscription to keep informed of conservation work through newsletters and journals, *HMWT* members can encourage changes in public attitudes and improve the communication of good practices throughout the community.

Members can build bat boxes, construct ponds and act as guardians of badger setts. Records of observations of species are gratefully received by the different recorders in the *Herts Nat Hist Soc*, which has been the major naturalists' group in the county for over 125 years. All data thus passes to the central Hertfordshire Biological Records Centre at County Hall, Hertford. I urge membership of your local naturalists' group: Bishop's Stortford, Cheshunt, Letchworth and Welwyn, most of which are affiliated to the *HNHS*, and

**Top, the first *HNHS* Mammal Group Committee at a Digswell meeting, left to right: Martin Hicks, guest speaker Norma Chapman, Paul Smith, Jenny Jones, Steve Kourik (Chair) and Wayne Green.**
**Below, *HNHS* Recorders' Committee with the Hon. General Secretary John Scivyer, Raymond Uffen, Alan Outen, Trevor James, Pryce Buckle, John Baker and Graeme Smith.**

The Hertfordshire Geological Society and the Bird Club are sections within the Society itself.

The hide at Tewin Orchard, overlooking Hopkyns' Wood is an example of a co-ordinated effort by Badger Group and Trust members where visitors may watch mammals at dusk next to a local nature reserve. Bats, rabbits, muntjac deer, foxes and owls are typical subjects for observation as well as occasional mice and other animals.

## Recording what you see

However you record wildlife with whatever means, the importance is in the record and the use you make of it rather than the methods. Your records go towards the new survey and will be published in future Hertfordshire Naturalist's reports. The information will be invaluable to the Biological Records Centre data bank for planning and conservation advice. (See the example of a record sheet in Appendix 8.)

I devoted considerable space in *Mammal Watching* (1981) to 'Moments of time', covering still photography, sound recording and illustration in general. The developments in video had not then reached the ease of use of modern, tiny camcorders and I never imagined that I would go on to monitor wild mammals from my bedside with a continuous 24 hour video system. Steve Kourik and Dave Watson set up a video and telephone link which even enabled me to tape foxes mating on the wood edge (see p153 *et seq.*).

The fact that I have kept a daily diary for 40 years in which written, drawn and picture references are freely mixed puts me in the 'anorak' class of human (people who are sometimes told to 'get a life' or known as 'sad'). This diary has, however, been a data source for all my general book material and although I have carried a voice recorder and notebook in my pocket, more often than not an old envelope and a pen is still the starting point for day-to-day observations.

The *Herts Nat Hist Soc* has published papers on wildlife and the environment via its famous *Transactions* (now published as *The Hertfordshire Naturalist* with many colour plates) continuously since 1875. I have of course refered to this source throughout the book. Our long history of data gathering and publishing in Hertfordshire is an invaluable point of local reference for all research and knowlege in modern conservation issues.

The illustration from my earlier work, *Mammal Watching,* shows how a mammal record is collected and grid reference made to pinpoint the location for future reference. I would urge all naturalists to at least sketch from life because it can be so helpful in describing particular features if a record needs additional support. It is interesting that mammals appear to have been the oldest known subject matter for painters so far discovered.

Photography is a wonderful means of recording animals and I strongly recommend the new automatic focus and flash equipment such as the Canon EOS single-lens reflex still cameras and dedicated flash guns. If you can afford to venture into digital video work, the Canon system allows you to use the same lens with each format, which makes investment in the best crystal lens quality more justifiable.

Much of the guesswork in exposure and the problems of sharp focus have gone with this equipment, yet you are still able to override the settings as required. Most single frame pictures are spoilt by slight movement at the split second you take the picture or by unsteady camera handling in video pictures, so always use a tripod or rest the camera on a vacuum bean bag if stability is in doubt.

**By always having a camera at hand when coppicing and clearing scrub during his working life, John Card (see p239) was able to record many events, such as this female grass snake laying eggs in an old tree stump, near Much Hadham.**

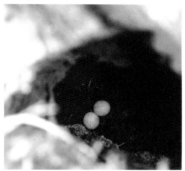

# Appendix 1

## Fossil and sub-fossil vertebrates

From K.P.Oakley's 1947 list (*Trans* **XXII**:5). The list of more abbreviations used by Oakley is given at the end of this appendix. Oakley's survey is the classic reference and to help future compilations I have reproduced it here.

### Tertiary Mammalia

***Coryphodon eocaenus*** Part of lower jaw. London Clay, Barnet (?). *A.Anderson Coll. N.H.M.* (M.12222).
***Hyracotherium leporinum*** Tooth. Basement Bed of London Clay, Watford Heath brick pit. *P.G.A.*, II (1871), 44; *T.W.N.H.S.*, I (1877), 170; *M.G.S*, London I (1899), p264. Specimen not traced.

### Quaternary Mammalia

#### (a) Pleistocene
***Alces machlis*** (elk or moose). Tibia. Gravels of Ponders End Stage, Low Terrace (Lea), Rikof's Pit, Broxbourne. *Mon. Pal. Soc.*, Alces (supplement), 1934, p8 *Warren Coll., N.H.M.*
***Bison priscus*** (i) Horn cores attached to part of skull, teeth, long bones. Late Pleistocene brickearth, c30m above OD, Cheshunt. *Q.J.G.S.*, LXVIII (1912), 228. *Warren Coll., N.H.M.*; (ii) Horn cores, bones, and teeth. Interglacial gravel, Waterhall Farm Pit, Hertford. *Emery Coll.*
***Bos primigenius*** (aurochs). (i) Bones and teeth (with Acheulian implements). Interglacial lake bed, Hitchin. *T.H.N.H.S.* X (1898) 18, footnote. *Arch.M.Camb.* (bones). (ii) Horn cores, bones, and teeth. Interglacial gravel, Waterhall Farm Pit, Hertford. *Emery Coll.*
***Bos*** (bison) (i) Teeth, lower jaw, horn cores, long bones. Interglacial gravel, Waterhall Farm Pit, Hertford. *Emery Coll.* (ii) Base of skull, astralagus molar, vertebra. Interglacial lake bed, Folly Pit, Hitchin. *Letch.M.* (iii) Metatarsal. Brickearth, Fisher's Green clay pit, Stevenage. *F.Ransom Coll.*,

**Mammoth** *Elaphus primogenius* **tooth.**

**Right: musk ox** *Ovibos moschatus* **jaw bone and red deer antler tools.**

**(Both from Hertford Museum, by kind permission.)**

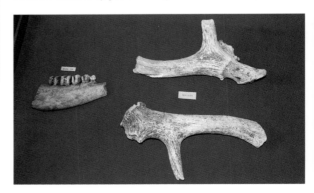

*Arch.M.Camb.* (iv) Fragmentary radius and horn core. Sandy loam, Wheathampstead. *Dr.R.T.Leiper Coll., St.A.M.*
**Capreolus sp.** (roe deer) Lower jaw. Interglacial lake bed, Folly Pit, Hitchin. *Hitchin M.*
**Cervus elaphus** (red deer) (i) Teeth, bones. 'Land-surface' above sands with erratics and below rubble drift, in trench, Bishop's Stortford. *T.H.N.S.*, XV (1915), 247. (ii) Gravels, Haileybury. *V.C.H.*, I (1902), 42. (iii) Antlers, bones. Interglacial lake bed, Folly Pit, Hitchin. *P.R.S.*, LXI (1897), 44 *Hitchin M.* (iv) Antler. Pleistocene deposit, Royston *N.H.M.*
**Cervus sp.** Bones and teeth not *C.elaphus*. Interglacial lake bed, Hitchin. *T.R.H.N.S.*, X (1898), 18, footnote.
**Elaphas antiquus** (i) Molars, tusk. Interglacial gravel, Waterhall Farm Pit, Hertford. *Letch.M., Emery Coll.* (ii) Molar. Interglacial lake bed, Folly Pit, Hitchin. *Hitchin M.*
**Elephas antiquus** (i) Tusk and molar. Terrace gravel, Croxley Green. *T.H.N.H.S.*, XIII (1908), 66, xxx. (ii) Tusk. Interglacial gravel, Brazier's Pit, Hertford. *Hertford M.*
**Elephas primigenius** (mammoth) (i) Potton Road, Biggleswade. one *Letch.M.* (ii) Tusk and molar. Bishop's Stortford. *V.C.H.*, III (1912), 292. (iii) Molars, scapula. Gravels of Ponders End Stage, Low Terrace (Lea), Rikof's Pit and adjoining excavations, Broxbourne. *N.H.M.*, Broxbourne School, *Hertford M.* (iv) Bones. Late Pleistocene brickearth, about 30m above OD, Cheshunt. *Q.J.G.S.*, LXVIII (1912), 228. *Warren Coll., N.H.M.* (v) Molar. Terrace gravel, Croxley Green. *N.H.M.* (vi) Midglacial gravel below brickearth, Camp's Hill, near Hertford. *T.H.N.H.S.*, I (1881), 105. (vii) Molar. Hoddesdon. *Hertford M.* (viii) Molar, brickfield near Hadham Mill, Much Hadham. Wigram Bequest, *St.A.M.* (ix) Tusk, molar. Terrace gravel, Mill End Pit, Rickmansworth. Specimens disintegrated. K.P.Oakley. (x) Molars, bones. Gravels of Ponders End Stage, Low Terrace (Lea), ballast pit by Eleanor Crossroads, Waltham Cross. *G.S.M.*
**Elephas primigenius** Molar, tusks, jaw. Interglacial gravels, Waterhall Farm Pit, Hertford. *Emery Coll.; Hertford M.*
**Elephas trogontheri** Molars, tusks, jaw. Interglacial lake bed,

**Prehistoric horse** *Equus sp.* **from Bishop's Stortford.**

**Detail from Millais' superb illustration in** *British Deer and their Horns* **(1897) of how the giant deer** *Magaceros sp.* **skulls and antlers were located in peat bogs. Found in Hertford (see text).**

Hitchin. *P.R.S.*, LX1 (1897), 44 (*E. primigenius*); *T.H.N.H.S.* XXII (1943), 5.

***Elephas sp.*** (i) Molar. Gade Valley gravels, Apsley End (south of Hemel Hempstead). *A.S.I.*, p597. (ii) Molar, tusk. Baldock. *Wiggs Coll.*, *Letch.M.* (iii) Humerus. Low-level gravel, Camp's Hill, near Hertford. *G.S.M.* (iv) Tusk. south of Hertford Station. *G.S.M.* (v) Tusk. Near Hitchin. *G.S.M.* (vi) Molar and tusk. Gravel below boulder clay, ballast pit south of railway line at end of Bricket Wood Cutting, Watford. *Geologist*, I (1858), 24I.

***Equus sp.*** (caballine). (i) Potton Road, Biggleswade, *Letch.M.* (ii) Bones and teeth (*E. caballus & E. robustus*). 'Land-surface' above sands with erratics and below rubble drift, in trench, Bishop's Stortford. *T.H.N.H.S.*, XV (1915), 18. (iii) Tooth. Gravel of Ponders End Stage, Low Terrace (Lea), Rikof's Pit, Broxbourne, *N.H.M.* (iv) Teeth. Late Pleistocene brickearth, c30m above OD, Cheshunt. *Q.J.G.S.*, LXV1II (1912), 228. *Warren Coll.*, *N.H.M.* (v) Metatarsal. Interglacial gravel, Waterhall Farm Pit, Hertford. *Emery Coll.* (vi) Femur, tibia, acetabulum. Hertford. *McKenny Hughes Coll.*, *G.S.M.* (vii) Tooth. Hertingfordbury *G.S.M.* (viii) Bones, ? teeth. Interglacial lake bed, Hitchin. *P.R.S.*, LXI, (1897), 44 (*E. caballus*). *Hitchin M.*, (metapodial). (ix) Tibia, metacarpal. Gravels of Ponders End Stage, Lower Terrace (Lea), ballast pit by Eleanor Crossroads, Waltham Cross. *G.S.M.* (x) Metapodials, tibia and teeth. Sandy loam, Wheathampstead. *Dr.Leiper Coll.*, *St.A.M.*

***Hippopotamus sp.*** (i) Tooth. Near railway tunnel, Bengeo. *Hertford M.* (ii) Tusks and bones. Interglacial gravel, Waterhall Farm Pit, Hertford. *Letch.M.*, *Emery Coll.* (iii) Tusk. Hertfordshire. *G.S.M.* (iv) Waterworn bone. Interglacial lake bed, Hitchin. *P.R.S.*, LXI (1897), 44; *T.H.N.H.S.*, XXII (1943), 5. (v) Tooth. Gravels, Hoddesdon. *Emery Coll.*

***Homo sp.*** See Appendix 2.

***Hyaena sp.*** Part of tibia (?). Interglacial gravel, Waterhall Farm Pit, Hertford, *Emery Coll.*

***Megaceros sp.*** (giant deer) Lower jaw. Interglacial gravel, Waterhall Farm Pit, Hertford. *Emery Coll.*

***Meles meles*** (badger) 2 teeth. Interglacial beds, in trench near Oughton Head Lane, Hitchin. *Wiggs Coll.*

***Microtines*** (voles). Various unidentified teeth. Interglacial gravel, Waterhall Farm Pit, Hertford. *Emery Coll.*

***Rangifer tarandus*** (reindeer) (i) Antler. Gravels of Ponders End Stage, Low Terrace (Lea), Rikof's Pit, Broxbourne. *Emery Coll.* (ii) Antlers and teeth. Gravel, Cheshunt. *Emery Coll.* (iii) Antlers and bones of barren ground variety of reindeer. Late Pleistocene brickearth, c30m above OD, Cheshunt. *Q.J.G.S.*, LXVIII (1912) 228 *Warren Coll.*, *N.H.M.* (iv) Midglacial sands below brickearth. Camps Hill, near Hertford, *T.H.N.H.S.*, I (1881), 105. (v) Antlers. Gravel & silt, Turnford. *Emery Coll1.*

**Rhinoceros antiquitatis** (woolly rhinoceros) (i) Potton Road, Biggleswade. *Letch.M.* (ii) Bones. Late Pleistocene brickearth, c30m above OD, Cheshunt. *Q.J.G.S.*, LXVIII (1912), 228. *Warren Coll.*, *N.H.M.* (iii) Midglacial sands below brickearth, Camp's Hill, near Hertford. *T.H.N.H.S.*, I (1881), 105.

**Rhinoceros hemitoechus.** Molars. Interglacial gravel, Waterhall Farm Pit, Hertford. *Emery Coll.*

**Rhinoceros sp.** (i) Femur. Charlton. *Hitchin M.* (ii) Pelvic bone. Hertford. *G.S.M.* (iii) Molars, bones. Interglacial lake bed, Folly Pit, Hitchin. *P.R.S.*, LXl (1897), 44; *V.C.H.*, I (1902), 42. *Hitchin M., G.S.M.*

**Sus scrofa** (wild boar). Part of skull. Gravels of Ponders End Stage, Low Terrace (Lea), Rikof's Pit, Broxbourne. *N.H.M.*

**Ursus ?spelacus** (cave bear). Molar, canine. Interglacial lake bed, Folly Pit, Hitchin. *T.H.N.H.S.*, X (1898), 18, footnote; *V.C.H.*, I (1902), 42. *Hitchin M.*

**Ursus sp?** Part of tibia. Late Pleistocene brickearth, c30m above OD. *Warren Coll., N.H.M.*

**Auroch** *Bos primigenius* **and skull.**

**(b) Holocene (sub-fossil)**
(Domesticated forms such as *Bos longifrons* are excluded)
**Arvicola sp.** (water vole) Teeth. Marl layer in valley gravel, 6m below surface, ballast pit, Kings Langley. *T.H.N.H.S.*, XXII (1943), 9.

**Bos primigenius** (aurochs) (i) Horn cores, lower jaw, thoracic vertebrae, fragment of radius, ribs. Peat over chalk, 4m below marsh surface, Chadwell Springs, near Ware Park. *Essex M.* (ii) Sacrum, lower jaw, molar, humeri. Peat over valley gravel, Canal Gravel Co. pit, Kings Langley. *T.H.N.H.S.*, XV11 (1929), xvii. (iii) Metatarsals. Peat and alluvium, Turnford. *Emery Coll.*

**Capreolus capreolus** (roe deer) (i) Peat over valley gravel, Canal Gravel Co. Pit, Kings Langley. *T.H.N.H.S.*, XVIII (1929) 216, xlvii. *St.A.M.* (ii) Refuse, filling well in Roman house, 2nd cent. AD, Verulamium. (iii) Post-Roman alluvium of Colne, Gas Works, Watford. *H.N.H.S.*, (1912), xlvi.

**Cervus elaphus** (red deer) (i) Lower jaw. Peat over chalk, 4m below marsh surface, Chadwell Springs, near Ware Park. *Essex M.* (ii) Antlers attached to skull bone. Peat over valley gravel, Canal Gravel Co. Pit, Kings Langley. *T.H.N.H.S.*, XVIII (1929), xvi. *St.A.M* (iii) Antler, shank bone. Roman villa, 4th cent filling, Park Street, near St.Albans. *Arch.J.*, Cll (1947), 100. (iv) Antlers, bones. Alluvium, Turnford. *Hitchin M.* (v) Refuse, filling well in Roman house, 2nd cent. AD Verulamium. *Ver.M.* (vi) Post-Roman alluvium of Colne, Gas Works, Watford. *T.H.N.H.S.*, XIV (1912), xlvi.

**Dama dama** (fallow deer). Shed antler. Roman Villa, 4th cent. filling, Park Street, near St.Albans. *Arch.J.*, Cll (1947), 100. *Ver.M.*

**Equus caballus** (wild horse). (i) Complete skeleton. ?Late

**Bison** *Bison sp.* **(see text for locations).**

**(All illustrations on this page from** *Die Säugetiere Deutchlands*, **Kurt Hennings, Leipzig.)**

prehistoric, in hillwash, about 1.5m below surface, associated with 'other bones and two shells', Bishop's Stortford. *E.N.*, XVI (1910), 132, 282. (ii) Alluvium, Turnford. *Emery Coll.*

***Lepus europaeus*** (hare) Refuse filling well in Roman house, 2nd cent. AD, Verulamium. *Ver.M.*

***Meles meles*** (badger) Mandibles, maxilla, femur. Roman Villa, ?4th cent. filling or debris, Park Street, near St.Albans. *Arch.J.*, CII (1947), 100-1. *Ver.M.*

***Talpa europaea*** (mole) Mandible, limb bones. Ibid.

***Vupes vulpes*** (fox) Mandible, limb bones, scapula. Ibid.

## Early humans in Hertfordshire

One of the displays in Mill Green Museum, which is on the River Lea between Welwyn Garden City and Hatfield. Like Redbournbury Mill near Harpenden, the visitor is reminded of how vital such sites were in human history.

Since Elaine Morgan's *The Descent of Woman* (1972) I have always supported her development of Alister Hardy's view of why we have bare skin and subcutaneous fat. The only other enthusiastic supporter I have ever spoken to about the theory is Prof. Simon Bearder, who went to the school I attended, Richard Hale, in Hertford. His brother Tim and I together teased out small mammal skeletons from barn owl pellets in Balls Park as schoolboys. He has written about Morgan's theories and how the flooding of the Rift Valley from the Red Sea may have isolated primates 6-9 million years ago in *Flood Brothers* (BBC Wildlife magazine, June 2000). These views are still resisted by the scientific establishment, but I recommend their consideration and the article is the best summary I have read of this view of anthropology.

K.P.Oakley's 1947 list of Paleolithic people (below) in the vertebrate list for Hertfordshire is here illustrated with Sir John Evans' outstanding plates which accompanied his anniversary address to *Herts Nat Hist Soc* in 1895.

The history of humans in the county has been very well documented in  histories such as Chauncy (about 1700), Cox (1720), Salmon (1728), Brayley (1801), Clutterbuck (1815) and Cussans (1881), but as Lloyd pointed out in 1947, none devotes any space to the wild fauna. Hine's Hitchin books include wildlife in the *Natural History* volume and modern county histories, the best of which is Tony Rook's *A History of Hertfordshire* (1984), which relates humans much more to the ecology of the county. Oakley, Evans and Ransom considered the study of early humans and their artefacts was very relevant to an understanding of the fauna of those times. Rook describes the oldest Stone-Age site in Hertfordshire as the Hill End, Rickmansworth, gravel pit, where hundreds of flint tools have been found. Although they were probably used by hunters who lived along the proto-Thames Valley about 350,000 years ago, more advanced flint work (which produced ovate axes) was found at higher locations in the same pit and at nearby Croxley Green.

The link with the mammals of that period, the people who

knapped the flints to make the tools and ourselves can be experienced vividly when you find and hold a hand tool which fits snugly into your palm. It concentrates the mind to realise that the original owner of the stone which I now grip with the same finger positions, was the last person to hold the tool, perhaps 6,000 years ago. I have found flint tools and fossils when looking for mammal tracks and inspecting (i.e. crawling about) badger setts and reference to them here seems appropriate.

Oakley wrote: '*Records of Lower & Middle Palaeolithic implements, as indicators of extinct species and sub-species of Homo, have a natural place in the survey of the fossil vertebrates of a county. They may serve as pointers to possible discoveries in the future. In the absence of any undoubted Upper Palaeolithic implements, finds of Mesolithic artifacts serve as records of the earliest undoubted works of Homo sapiens in the county.*

'*That there is a case for including detailed records of Neolithic artifacts in this list is less clear. Most of the stone tools used by Neolithic people (especially axes and scrapers) are indistinguishable from types used in the Bronze Age (particularly in the Early Bronze Age when metal was still a scarce commodity reserved for ornaments and special weapons). Logically if one included post-Mesolithic stone artifacts in the present list one should include also bronze implements, and if these why not relics of the Iron Age ? Thus it would seem wiser to limit the anthropological part of this survey to Palaeolithic and Mesolithic finds, and to leave distributional studies of the works of later prehistoric races to archaeologists.*

'*Nevertheless, the distribution of stone axes of the so-called Neolithic type is not without palaeo-ecological significance because they represent the equipment of the first people to begin clearing the woodlands for small-scale agriculture. Polished or finely chipped stone axes (celts) were probably used for felling trees, while the roughly chipped ones may have been used as hoes. A list follows of localities at which stone celts have been found, but it must be admitted that the list is far from complete, and many of these implements may date from the Bronze Age. Neolithic arrowheads are listed*'.

Hertford Museum; a treasure trove of exhibits. The dynamic use of lettering on the exterior, which breaks all the rules of typography, has a special appeal.

### (a) Palaeolithic people (*Homo sp.*)

Oakley's list covered the following sites (OD; Ordnance Datum, means sea level).

*Abbots Langley* (Gade Valley). Acheulian hand axe of Grays Inn Lane type from brickearth at head of coombe, c50m above River Gade, near Bedmond; small rough ovate from surface, Bedmond Hill. *Arch.*, XXXIX (1863), 73; *T.H.N.H.S.*, VIII (1896), pl.xi, fig.8; *A.S.I.*, pp.596-7); *Arch.*, LXVII (1916), 50. *Evans Coll.*, *A.M.*

*Amwell* (Lea Valley). Palaeoliths in gravels at c50m above

*For centuries the horse was the power on the land for cultivation as well as transport. George Soper, from his base at the studio in Harmer Green near Welwyn, drew and painted this relationship between people and horses in many parts of Hertfordshire early in the last century.*

**Robert Gilmore with a painting by George Soper of one of his typical horse-drawn ploughs. Robert, famous for his wildlife paintings and print-making, organised the sales of George, Eileen and Eva Soper's work in aid of the Artists' Benevolent Fund.**
**A detail of one of George Soper's most atmospheric scenes (below) illustrates this ancient link between horse and farm worker.**

*Winter Sun* **by George Soper (1870-1942). Wood engraving in author's collection.**

OD; rare. *M.P.S.*, p185.

**Ayot St.Peter** (Lea Valley). Large Palaeolithic flake from upper drift, brick field near station. *M.P.S.*, p184.

**Bayford** (c100m above OD, south of Lea Valley). Fine Palaeolithic implement (presumably hand axe) in *Pitt-Rivers Coll., A.S.I.*, p602.

**Bedmond** See Abbots Langley.

**Bengeo** See Hertford.

**Bishop's Stortford** (Stort Valley). Acheulian hand axe of Hoxne type, from brickearth close to river one mile north of town, found by W.H.Penning, of Geological Survey. *A.S.I.* pp602-3.

**Broxbourne** (Lea Valley). A late Levalloisian flake implement was recorded by Mr.S.H.Warren from gravels of the Ponders End stage in Rikof's Pit, east of the railway station. *P.P.S.*, IV (1938), 328 fig.1, No.3. *Warren Coll.*

**Bushey** (Colne Valley). Palaeoliths, including flake tool of High Lodge type (Clactonio-Acheulian), from gravels 40ft. above River Colne, near Bushey Park. *A.S.I.*, p597. *Evans Coll., A.M.*

**Caddington** (between Ver and Lea Valleys). The famous Acheulian 'floor' is mainly in Bedfordshire. See notes under Gaddesden Row and Markyate. *M.P.S.* pp60 ff. *W.G.Smith Coll., B.M.*

**Cheshunt** (Lea Valley). Acheulian hand axes and cores and flakes of unspecified types, from gravels at about 120ft. above OD (c55ft. above river) at Flamstead End, one mile west of the town. *M.P.S.* pp185-6, fig.130; *A.S.I.*, p. 603; *E.N.*, XV (1908), 258. *Evans Coll., A.M.*; *W.G.Smith Coll., B.M.* (? Palaeolithic 'pick'). A number of flakes, apparently of various dates, from gravels at 120-130ft. above OD, about Churchgate and Flamstead End. *Warren Coll.*

**Chorleywood.** (300-350ft. above OD). Several small triangular and cordate hand axes with white patina, found on surface of fields west and southwest of Heronsgate. *F.Lofts Coll.*

**Codicote** (Mimram Valley). Palaeolith in *Letch.M.*

**Colney Street** (Colne Valley). Acheulian hand axe found in gravel 200yd. northeast of Old Parkbury Farm in September, 1946 (teste Mrs.Audrey Williams, *Ver.M.*).

**Croxley Green** (Gade Valley). Numerous palaeoliths have been found in terrace gravels on the west side of the valley; thickish, long-ovate hand axes of Lower and Early Middle Acheulian types predominate but flake tools of Clactonian and Clactonio-Acheulian types also occur. Most of the implements show some degree of abrasion. The gravels abut against glacial gravels from which they are inseparable lithologically; they rest on an irregularly channelled shelf of chalk at about 195ft. above OD (c40ft. above the River Gade). In 1915 the section in the Long Valley Wood Pit (from which most of the implements have been obtained) showed in descending sequence: soil, 1ft.; loam with gravel trail, 3-5 ft.;

mottled clay, 1-2ft.; fluviatile sands and gravels, 11ft.; coarse
unstratified gravel with erratic boulders, 7ft. The basal gravel
is probably a periglacial deposit (in a test excavation it yielded
only flake tools, apparently Clactonian). The fluviatile sands
and gravels were probably deposited late in the penultimate
interglacial period. *T.H.N.H.S.*, XIII (1907-8), 65, xxx, pls.
ii, iii, vii; *Arch.*, LXVI (1915), 195-224; *M.G.S.*, 255,
Beaconsfield (1922), p43. *Fox Coll.*, *Arch.M.Camb.*; *B.M.*;
*G.S.M.*; *Letch.M.*; *St.A.M.*

*Gaddesden Row* (between Gade and Ver Valleys). An
implement floor, apparently representing a marsh-side
occupation site of Acheulian Man, was discovered here in
about 1906 by Worthington Smith. The floor occurred 20ft.
below the surface (544ft. above OD, 184ft. above River
Gade) in stratified brickearths in Butterfield's Pit, 500yd.
west of Widmore Farm (the pit is now overgrown and
disused). The brickearths, which are up to 45ft. thick, consist
of resorted Reading Beds they rest on a layer of chalk-and-
flints (coombe rock?) and are overlain by trail. The
brickearths probably represent a combination of wind-blown
and rain-washed material accumulated on a high-level marsh
(impeded drainage) early in the last interglacial period or
during an interstadial of the penultimate glaciation. The
implements from the floor include finely chipped, pointed
hand axes of an advanced Acheulian type, together with flake
tools similar to those of High Lodge. The industry is now
regarded as early Upper Acheulian influenced by Clactonian.
Apart from a few trimmed flakes of sarsen stone, the
implements are of flint and show an ivory or pale brown
patina. Scattered implements were found below the floor,
particularly at 30ft. and 35ft. below the surface. Those from
the main floor were accompanied by waste flakes, some of
which fitted together, showing that they were manufactured
on the site. A similar Palaeolithic workshop floor was
discovered by Worthington Smith in brickearths at
Caddington (about 550ft. above OD), on the county border,
mainly in Bedfordshire; it yielded hundreds of replaceable
flakes and numerous finished implements (perhaps
representing a slightly more primitive stage of the Acheulian
industry than at Gaddesden Row); *M.P.S.*, 60ff.
(Caddington); *Q.J.G.S.*, LXIV (1908) 2, fig. 1, *T.H.N.H.S.*,
XIV (1909), 1 pl. 1; *Arch.*, LXVII (1916), 49-62, figs. 8-25;
*M.G.S.*, 239, Hemel Hempstead (1922), 43; *S.A.G.*, 49, figs.
40-41. *W.G.Smith Coll.*, *B.M.*; *St.A.M.*; *Evans Coll.*, *A.M.*

*Harpenden* (Lea Valley). A few ochreous Palaeolithic flakes
from gravels at 286ft. above OD (i.e. a few feet above
present river level). *M.P.S.*, p180.

*Hastoe* (700ft. above OD). Small, thin, finely worked
triangular hand axe with white patina, found on surface at
intersection of Grim's Dyke and the Cholesbury-Hastoe road.
*F. Lofts Coll.*

*Hatfield* (Lea Valley). A few palaeoliths from gravel pit in

Tony Rook is the best known local
historian and his *A History of
Hertfordshire* (**1984 & 1997**) is the
most popular text on the subject.
It makes an ideal companion to the
*HNHS* natural history books on the
county.

Hertford road. *H.G.O.Kendall Coll., B.M.*

**Hemel Hempstead** (Gade Valley). Two flattish Acheulian (or Levalloisio-Acheulian) ovates found in 1868 in gravel apparently dredged from River Gade between Nash Mills and Apsley. *A.S.I.* p597. *Evans Coll., A.M.*

**Hertingfordbury** (Lea Valley). A few doubtful palaeoliths recorded from gravels at base of 'glacial drift'. *P.P.S.E.A.*, II (1915), 137. *H.G.O.Kendall Coll., B.M.*

**Hertford** (Lea Valley). Palaeoliths, including heavily rolled pointed hand axes and flakes, found (i) in gravel pits in Ware Road; (ii) in pits close to River Lea (north side), on both sides of the River Beane and (iii) in pit at Bengeo between Hertford and Ware (130-140ft. above OD). *J.R.A.I.*, VIII (1879), 278, *M.P.S.*, pp184-5, *A.S.I.* p602; *P.P.S.E.A.*, II (1915), 137. *Evans Coll., A M.* (massive pointed hand axe from Hertford gravels); *H.G.O.Kendall Coll., B.M.* (two palaeoliths). Pieces of bone and ivory apparently worked by man were recently found by Mr.J.N.Emery in interglacial gravel in Waterhall Farm Pit, south of Hertford (unpublished).

**Highbury** See Hitchin.

**Hitchin** (floor of gap in Chiltern Escarpment). An extensive series of finely made Acheulian implements have come from lower part of obscurely stratified brickearth formerly exposed in pits and excavations at Hitchin. The majority were obtained between 1880 and 1900, from Ransom's brickfield, south of Hitchin Cemetery, and from Jeeve's brickyard at the Folly (Highbury), just over half a mile southwest of the station. Special borings and excavations were conducted by Clement Reid for the Royal Society and British Association in 1896 to prove the relation of the Palaeolithic brickearth to the glacial beds of the area. The following sequence was established in part of Ransom's pit (surface 270ft. OD): (soil about 1ft.), brown brickearth with palaeoliths 30ft., stratified alluvial loams with freshwater shells 24ft., glacial loams, gravels, and sands 14ft. In Jeeve's pit (surface 246ft. OD) the sequence was: soil, 1ft., brickearth with implements, 10ft., Chara marl with freshwater shells and mammalian bones, 8ft., alluvial loams and gravel, with plant remains (including mosses), fish bones, insects and freshwater shells,

ELLINGHAMS
PIT
LEVERSTOCK GRN
HEMEL HEMPSTEAD
W.G.SMITH 1907

Hand axes are always shown pointing upwards, but this one is reproduced actual size and in the position the flint was used (Leverstock Green, near Hemel Hempstead, 1907). More commonly found are flint scrapers for general uses including cleaning fat from the skins of deer or domestic stock.

254

20ft. A few implements were subsequently found in the bone-bearing bed (*T.H.N.H.S.*, X (1898), 18, footnote). The evidence of the test bores combined with that of well-sections in the district showed that the Palaeolithic brickearth and alluvial beds overlie the glacial beds (including chalky boulder clay) which occupy a north-south channel cut to a depth of 68ft. below sea level (= 0D). The fauna of the alluvial beds is of temperate type (as is the flora) and indicates correlation with the Middle Barnfield stage of the 100ft. terrace of the Thames. The beds were evidently laid down by a stream which became ponded (they are commonly called Hitchin Lake Beds). The brickearth, which contains stony seams near the top, is partly wind-blown, partly rain-washed material laid down on a marshy surface, probably just before, or during a mild interval within, the period of the penultimate glaciation. Implementiferous brickearth occurs patchily over a wide area in the Hitchin Gap. It was worked between Windmill Hill and Maydencroft Lane, half a mile south-southwest of Jeeve's yard. One implement was recovered from near Thistly Farm, half a mile south. (For occurrences on the north side of Hitchin see under Ickleford.) The main series of implements from the Hitchin brickearth comprises many thin, triangular to sub-ovate hand axes of Hoxne type, a few cordate and ovate hand axes, several cleavers, a fair number of flake tools of High Lodge type, and various forms including a cylindrical flint nodule used as a hammerstone (*A.S.I.*, p536). Most of the implements are in mint condition; a few are unpatinated, but the majority have a brown or buff patina. The industry is now classed as late Middle or early Upper Acheulian influenced by Clactonian. Refs.: *T.W.N.H.S.*, I (1877), lxi; *Arch.*, LIII (1893), 244; *T.H.N.H.S.*, VIII (1896), pl. xi, figs. 2 7, pl. xii, figs. 2-7; *P.G.A.*, XIV (1896), 415; *P.R.S.*, LXI (i897), 44; *A.S.I.*, pp536-7, fig. 418a; *T.H.N.H.S.*, X (1898), 14; *Q.J.G.S.*, LXIV (1908), 8-24 (geology of Hitchin gap); *P.G.A.*, XXIII (1912), 221, pl. xxxi (map); *S.A.G.*, p59; *S.C.*, pp104-7, figs. 415-22; *N.H.H.R.*, p38, 237, frontispiece, pls. opp. p38, 242; *T.H.N.H.S.*, XXII (1943), 5, *P.P.S.*, XI (1945), 18. Material: *H.Christy, H.G.O.Kendall, W.Ransom, and others Colls., B.M., St.A.M.; Hitchin M.; Francis Ransom Coll. (Arch.M.Camb.), Letch.M.* (palaeoliths, mostly hand axes, from Folly Pit, Highbury, Brand Street, Crow Furlong, the Cemetery, Weston Dane and Brampton Park Road); *Evans Coll., A.M.; Wiggs Coll.*

**Hoddesdon** (Lea Valley). Mr.S.H.Warren has contributed this note: '*Brickyard west of main road, worked about 1895, showed loamy hill-wash (stratified at a steep angle downhill) of Pleistocene date with an Acheulian hand axe in mint condition, a flake in similar condition that would be at home at Clacton, an ochreous flake blade that would not seem out of place in the Upper Palaeolithic, the butt end of a very clumsy hand axe in abraded condition probably from a thin*

**Bronze axe head found near Tewin (Hertford Museum). Although the implement is much more refined than the hand axe shown opposite, the work it was put to was much the same.**

Entrances to a badger sett and (opposite) the same sett after the extreme wet weather of 2000 showing tunnels which have fallen in and new entrances dug by the badgers.

*overlying bed of gravel, etc.' A.S.I.*, p603. *Warren Coll.*

***Ickleford*** (Hiz Valley, Hitchin Gap). Ovate and small cordate Acheulian hand axes, associated with Clactonoid flake tools, have been found in brickearth about 1½ miles north of Hitchin. Palaeoliths, including early Acheulian hand axes, have been found in gravels here, but these are mostly rolled. An acutely pointed hand axe is on record from Bearton Green nearby. *T.N.N.H.S.*, VIII (1896), pl. xi, figs. 2, 6; *A.S.I.*, p536; *Arch.*, LXVII (1915), 31-3, figs. 4-8; *S.C.*, p124. *F.Ransom Coll., Arch.M.Camb.; W.Ransom* and *Sturge Colls., B.M.; Evans Coll., A.M.; F.Sadler Coll.* (whereabouts unknown).

***Ippollitts*** (Hitchin Gap). Palaeoliths collected here by Mr.T.Ransom. *Arch.*, LIII (1893), 257.

***Kings Langley*** (Gade Valley). Palaeoliths recorded here (in gravel ?). *P.S.A.*, 2, V (1871), 165. *Evans Coll., A.M.*

***Knebworth*** (Stevenage Valley). Pointed and ovate Acheulian hand axes were recovered from gravels exposed in railway cutting in 1887. *Arch.*, LIII (1893), 257; *T.H.N.H.S.*, VIII (1896), pl. xi, fig. 5; *A.S.I.*, p602; *Evans Coll., A.M.; F.Ransom Coll., Arch.M.Camb.* Two small Acheulian ovates were found on surface (c300ft. above OD on floor of dry valley) at Langley, northwest of Knebworth. *S.C.*, p106, figs. 423-4 *Sturge Coll., B.M.*

***Langley*** See Abbots Langley and Knebworth.

***Letchworth*** (Hitchin Gap). Thick, shuttle-shaped Acheulian ovate, creamy-grey, found on surface in 1906. *W.Ransom Coll., B.M.*

***Leverstock Green*** (between Ver and Gade Valleys). A number of finely made late Middle or Upper Acheulian hand axes have been found in brickearth at 460ft. above OD (170ft. above River Gade). They show ochreous or ivory patina. One from Ellingham's Pit, northeast of the Saracen's Head, has been figured by Evans, *Q.J.G.S.*, LXIV (1908), 2, fig. 2; *T.H.N.H.S.*, XIV (1909), 1, fig. 1. *W.G.Smith Coll., St.A.M.*

***Markyate*** (near head of Ver Valley). A rough pyramidal core (Clactonian ?) consisting of a massive flake of puddingstone was found by Worthington Smith in 'contorted drift', Caddington Common, Markyate Street (cf. *M.P.S.*, map ante p1). *Arch.*, LXVII (1915), 53; *V.C.H. Beds*, I (1904), 158, fig. 37. *W.G.Smith Coll., B.M.* Five flint palaeoliths from Markyate Street are preserved in the *Sturge Coll., B.M.*

***Nomansland Common*** (coombe leading to Colne Valley). A few ochreous Palaeolithic flakes and hand axes in abraded condition have been found in dry valley gravel exposed in pits on Nomansland Common, south of Wheathampstead, at c293ft. above OD. The top layer of the gravel has yielded a series of implements with greyish-white patina, apparently Mesolithic or Neolithic, but including a chopping tool and a hand axe of early Palaeolithic form. *T.H.N.H.S.*, VIII (1896), pl. xi, fig.4; *M.P.S.*, pp180-3; *P.P.S.E.A.*, II (1916), 225,

fig.25e; *S.C.*, p124. *Evans Coll., A.M.*; *Sturge Coll., B.M.*
**North Mymms** (southeast of Colne Valley, about 300 ft.
above OD). At least one palaeolith has been recorded here.
*P.S.A.*, 2, V (1871), 165; *A.S.I.*, p602.
**Redbourn** (Ver Valley). Small pear-shaped hand axe of late
Middle or Upper Acheulian type, patinated white, found on
surface one mile northwest of Redbourn. *Evans Coll., A.M.*
**Rickmansworth** (Colne Valley). Gravel pits at Mill End have
yielded large numbers of palaeoliths. The pits show about
16ft. of stratified red gravel with sandy seams, resting on a
chalk bench at about 167ft. above OD (22ft. above present
river). The gravel was probably laid down under conditions
associated with the penultimate glaciation. Large hollows
occur in the gravel; these probably originated through the
inclusion of blocks of river ice in the deposit. The
predominant implements from the gravel are blunt pointed
hand axes with thick butts, probably Lower Acheulian; a few
Middle Acheulian types occur. Flake tools of Clactonio-
Acheulian type and flakes of Clactonian and early
Levalloisian types have also been found. Most of the
implements show some degree of abrasion. The gravels and
their implements were systematically investigated in 1914 by
Reginald Smith and Henry Dewey. *Arch.*, LXVI (1915),
195-224; *M.G.S.*, 255, Beaconsfield (1922), p44.
*Arch.M.Camb.*; *G.S.M.*; *B.M.*

Badger sett entrances are always worth checking for flints and other items brought to the surface and left in the spoil heap. The industrious occupants also provide excellent soil samples through their digging.

**St.Albans.** The *Evans Coll., A.M.* includes a small pear-
shaped hand axe, identified by Prof.D.A.E.Garrod as of
'Chellean' type (? Lower Acheulian), heavily rolled, patinated
brown, found at unspecified site at St.Albans; and two flake
tools (one identified by Prof. Garrod as of Upper Acheulian
type, with ochreous patina; the other unclassifiable, patinated
white) from Barnard's Heath Brickfield, found by P.Norman
Evans in 1870.
**Sandridge** (coombe tributary to Colne Valley). Small, rough
late-Middle or Upper Acheulian hand axes have been found
on the surface. *St.A.M.*
**Stevenage** (valley leading from Hitchin Gap). Acheulian
hand axes have been found in brickearths hereabouts. There
is a pointed hand axe from Fisher's Green in the *Evans Coll.,
A.M.*, another in the *W.Ransom Coll., B.M.*, and two more in
the *F.Ransom Coll., Arch.M.Camb.* Evans records a rough
ovate made from a broad flake found in brickearths south of
the town. *T.H.N.H.S.*, VIII (1896), pl. xi, fig. 3; *A.S.I.*, p602.
A twisted ovate of late Middle Acheulian type, in mint
condition, from brickearth, Stevenage, is in the *F.Ransom
Coll., Arch.M.Camb.*
**Stocking Pelham** (c400ft. above OD, between Ash and Stort
valleys). A water-worn ovate hand axe was found here by
W.H.Penning of the Geological Survey in 1872. *Arch.*, LIII
(1893), 258; *A.S.I.*, p603.
**Turnford** (Lea Valley). Greatly abraded tortoise core
(Levalloisian) from gravel below loam in Turnford brickyard,

Roe antlers from a complete skeleton found in Northaw Great Wood by John Castle, September 1959 (see p210).

Hare country between Wallington and Ashwell, north Hertfordshire.

about 90ft. above OD. *Warren Coll.*

**Waltham Cross** (Lea Valley). Mr.S.H.Warren has contributed this note: '*A pit 250 yards south of Bullscross Farm (Theobalds), indicated by stippling on the 6-in. map of 1882, about 118 OD, has yielded a number of palaeoliths. Most of the hand axes are pointed, but one or two are more ovate. The best closely resembles the Gray's Inn Lane implement, another is axe-edged (cleaver) with transverse sharpening flake, a rough scraper is of typical Clacton form. One pointed implement with untrimmed butt appears to be an Early Acheulian derivative. A trimmed flake implement apparently came from overlying loam and may be Late Acheulian, but is not typical of the High Lodge industry.*' A.S.I., p603. *Warren Coll.*

**Ware** (Lea Valley). Palaeoliths recorded from gravels about one mile northwest of town. *M.P.S.*, p185; *A.S.I.*, p602; *Evans Coll., A.M.*; *W.G.Smith Coll., B.M.* (specimen from road-side gravel Tottenham ex Ware). See also under Amwell and Bayford.

**Watford** See Bushey.

**Welwyn** (Mimram Valley). A few palaeoliths, including flake tools were found in Workhouse Gravel Pit, New Road, about 1914. *P.P.S.E.A.*, II (1915), 135-9; *H.G.O.Kendall Coll., B.M.* A small pointed Acheulian hand axe was found in clay filling of a solution pipe during cutting of Welwyn Tunnel. *A.S.I.*, p602; *Evans Coll., A.M.*

**West Hyde** (Colne Valley). Rolled hand axe of Lower Acheulian type found in terrace gravel at 200ft. above OD, west of West Hyde Church. *F.Lofts Coll.*

**Weston** (plateau south of Baldock). Palaeolith in *Letch.M.*

**Wheathampstead** (Lea Valley). Palaeolithic flakes and implements reported from here, for example in gravels at 290ft. OD (26ft. above river) in pit near railway station. *M.P.S.*, p180; *S.C.*, p124, *B.M.* (See also under Nomansland Common.)

**Wigginton** (head of Bulbourne Valley). A few surface palaeoliths recorded from here. *A.S.I.*, p597.

**(b) Mesolithic people** *(Homo sapiens)*

**Broxbourne.** An extensive Mesolithic industry, representing a squatting site where flints were knapped and fires lit, was found in Rikof's Pit on the Lea Marshes, east of Broxbourne Station, in about 1933. The artifacts, including core axes, buries, micro-buries, scrapers, hammerstones, cores, core dressings and other waste flakes, occurred in a sandy layer which lapped over a buried bank in the Holocene alluvial series of the Flood-plain Terrace, and which was covered by peat dated by pollen analysis to the Boreal period (±6000 BC). This Broxbourne industry has been taken as the type of the Mesolithic Forest Culture 'A' in Britain: a culture of Baltic origin. *J.R.A.I.*, LXIV (1934), 181ff. *Warren Coll.*; *B.M.*; *Broxbourne School.*

**Royston.** A bone 'harpoon' of Kunda type (Mesolithic Forest Culture 'A'), said to have been found at Royston, but probably from a drained mere about three miles to the northeast of the town, ie near Fowlmere, Cambridgeshire. J.G.D.Clark, *The Mesolithic Age in Britain* (1932), p18, fig.2, no.5. *Fenton Coll., B.M.*

**Turnford.** Mr.S.H.Warren has contributed these notes on worked flints found in a brickyard *'situated between the High Road at the 14th milestone from London and the New River, and near the deep well and pumping station'*. He says that the *'flint industry is found in loam'* and that the material he has recovered comprises *'several axes with tranchet edge, several gravers, numerous small scrapers, large numbers of fluted cores, flakes, etc.'* He says *'There is only one microlith, which is of the form that is commonest at Broxbourne, but the collection was made fifty years ago when I was inexperienced. The industry agrees closely with the Early Mesolithic of Broxbourne, although some of the flints are Neolithic or later (chip of polished axe, a triangular arrowhead with hollow base, several pointed flake arrowheads, etc.). The site also yielded a fine series of Iron Age 'A' pottery, with which some of the flints are doubtless contemporary.'* Specimens in *Warren Coll.*

**Wheathampstead.** The surface layer of dry valley gravel on Nomansland Common (c293ft. above OD) yields whitish-grey patinated flint artifacts (scrapers, cores, ? core axes and flakes) which are possibly Mesolithic. The underlying gravel yields derived ochreous palaeoliths, while the overlying soil yields unpatinated glossy black flint artifacts of Neolithic or Bronze Age types. *M.P.S.*, pp180-3, figs. 125-9; *P.P.S.E.A.*, II (1916), 222-9, figs. 25a; *S.C.*, p124; *W.G.Smith Coll., B.M.*; *A.E.Peake Coll.*

### (c) Neolithic people *(Homo sapiens)*

**Chipped axes** (celts) have been recorded from: Abbots Langley and Bedmond (*T.H.N.H.S.*, VIII, 1896, pl. xi, fig. 1; *Evans Coll., A.M.*); Aldbury (*Essex M.*); Berkhamsted Common (*T.H.N.H.S.*, XII, 1905, 157; *Evans Coll., A.M.*); Chaplefoot, near Hitchin (*Warren Coll.*); Curmingham Hill (*St.A.M.*); Digswell (*St.A.M.*); Hertford Heath (*St.A.M.*); Sens (*St.A.M.*); Wheathampstead (*M.P.S.*, 180; *Sturge Coll., B.M.*).

**Polished or partly ground axes** (cells). Albury, Bishop's Stortford (*A.S.I.*, p100); Abbots Langley (*A.S.I.*, pp87,139); Ashwell (*N.H.H.R.*, p239); one, of which there is a cast in *Letch. M.*, in *W.H.Lane Coll.*; another specimen in *Francis Ransom Coll., Arch.M.Camb.*; Buntingford (*St.A.M.*); Burymead, near Hitchin (*B.M.*); Chorleywood (*F.Lofts Coll.*); Duckland (*N.H.H.R.*, p239); Kelshall (*St.A.M.*); Panshanger (*P.S.A.*, 2, IX, 1881, 71; *A.S.I.*, p101); Hitchin, near Pirton (*A.S.I.*, p114; *N.H.H.R.*, p239); Sawbridgeworth (*Essex M.*, No.12111); Shephall (property of G.W.Cooke,

**Combine harvester in action below Queen Hoo, August 1976. Bramfield Forest fills the background.**

| | Per annum |
|---|---|
| Countryside Stewardship Scheme ......... | £51m |
| Environmentally Sensitive Areas Scheme ................. | £48.3m |
| Organic Farming Scheme ... | £18m |
| Farm Woodland Premium Scheme ................. | £9m |
| Hill Farm Allowance .......... | £40.9m |
| Woodland Grant Scheme (run by Forestry Commission) ....................... | £16m |

The Eco-grants available to farmers were listed in *The Sunday Times* on 7th January 2001.

The Natural History Museum, South Kensington. Part of the British Museum, it also provides the administration of The Walter Rothschild Zoological Museum, Tring, and was the main source of historic records for this book.

THE
WALTER ROTHSCHILD
ZOOLOGICAL MUSEUM
TRING

Rothamsted); The Camp, three-quarters of a mile west-southwest of Hill End Station, St.Albans (*St.A.M.*); Turnford brickyard (with Neolithic arrowheads) *Warren Coll.*; Welwyn (*St.A.M.*); Weston (*N.H.H.R.*, p239); Wormley Hill (*St.A.M.*). **Arrowheads.** Leaf-shaped flint arrowheads, characteristic of British Neolithic culture, have been found at Ashwell (*St.A.M.*), Hitchin (*St.A.M.*) and Letchworth (*Letch.M.*). Other types, possibly Neolithic, have been found at Turnford (for details see above under Mesolithic people). Barbed and tanged flint arrowheads, characteristic of the Bronze Age, are slightly more numerous and widespread in the county, but are considered outside the scope of this survey.

**Abbreviated references to literature used in Appendix 1**

| | |
|---|---|
| *A.M.N.H.* | Annals and Magazine of Natural History |
| *Arch.* | Archaeologia |
| *Arch.J.* | Archaeological Journal |
| *A.S.I.* | Ancient Stone Implements (J.Evans), 2nd edition 1897 |
| *C.R.B.* | Cretaceous Rocks of Britain (A.J.Jukes-Browne and W.Hill) Vol. III, 1904, Memoir of Geological Survey |
| *E.N.* | Essex Naturalist |
| *G.M.* | Geological Magazine |
| *J.R.A.I.* | Journal of Royal Anthropological Institute |
| *M.G.S.* | Memoir of Geological Survey |
| *Mon.Pal.Soc.* | Monograph of Palaeontographical Society |
| *M.P.S.* | Man the Primeval Savage (Worthington G. Smith) 1894 |
| *N.H.H.R.* | Natural History of the Hitchin Region (Hine, Bloom & others) 1934 |
| *P.G.A.* | Proceedings of Geologists' Association |
| *P.P.S.* | Proceedings of Prehistoric Society |
| *P.P.S.E.A.* | Proceedings of Prehistoric Society of East Anglia |
| *P.R.S.* | Proceedings of Royal Society |
| *P.S.A.* | Proceedings of Society of Antiquaries of London |
| *Q.J.G.S.* | Quarterly Journal of Geological Society of London |
| *S.A.G.* | Stone Age Guide, British Museum 1926 |
| *S.C.* | The Sturge Collection (Britain), British Museum publication 1931 |
| *T.H.N.H.S.* | Transactions of Hertfordshire Natural History Society |
| *T.W.N.H.S.* | Transactions of Watford Natural History Society |
| *V.C.H.* | Victoria County History (Hertfordshire, unless otherwise stated). |
| *V.F.E.E.* | Vertebrate Faunas of the English Eocene, (E.I.White), British Museum (Natural History) Catalogue 1931 |

## Abbreviated references to collections, with notes

| | |
|---|---|
| *Arch.M.* *Camb.* | Museum of Archaeology and Ethnology, Cambridge |
| *A.M.* | Ashmolean Museum, Oxford. The Evans Collection of stone implements is here. |
| *B.M.* | British Museum, Bloomsbury (Dept. of British Antiquities) |
| *Broxbourne* *School* | Broxbourne Voluntary Secondary Modern School |
| *Emery Coll.* | Private collection of Mr.J.N.Emery, partly at Wormley Lodge, Broxbourne, partly deposited in Geology Dept., British Museum (Natural History), London SW7 |
| *Essex M.* | Essex Museum of Natural History, Stratford, London E15 |
| *Fordham* *Coll.* | Fossils from Cambridge Greensand at Ashwell (and Morden) collected by Mr.H.G.Fordham were presented to the St.Albans Museum while these lists were in the press |
| *G.S.M.* | Geological Survey Museum, London SW7 |
| *Letch.M.* | Letchworth Museum |
| *Lofts Coll.* | Private collection of Mr.F.Lofts, 'Beverley', Heronsgate Lane, Chorleywood |
| *M.* | Museum |
| *N.H.M.* | British Museum (Natural History), Geology Dept. |
| *St.A.M.* | Hertfordshire County Museum, St.Albans |
| *Sedgw.M.* | Sedgwick Museum, Cambridge |
| *Ver.M.* | Verulamium Museum, St.Albans |
| *Warren Coll.* | S.H.Warren Coll. Palaeontological part now in Geology Dept., British Museum (Natural Hististory); archaeological material at 'Sherwood', Loughton, Essex, unless otherwise stated |
| *Wiggs Coll.* | Private collection of Mr.R.J.Wiggs, 70 Lytton Avenue, Letchworth |

Oakley also acknowledged help from the following: E.M.Alexander *(British Museum)*, A.C.T.Atkinson *(Ashmolean Museum)*, D.M.A.Bate *(British Museum, Natural History)*, A.G.Brighton *(Sedgwick Museum)*, M.C.Burkitt *(Cambridge University)*, A.T.Clarke *(Letchworth Museum)*, J.N.Emery, Prof.C.F.C.Hawkes *(when at British Museum)*, S.W.Hester *(Geological Survey)*, F.Lofts, A.Poulton *(St.Albans Museum)*, P.Thompson *(Essex Museum)*, H.Toombs *(British Museum, Natural History)*, S.Warren & Dr.E.White *(British Museum, Natural History)*.

**The Tring bypass road cut through the original park where Walter, Lord Rothschild kept many varieties of animals early in the last century. Volunteers helped secure the badger-proof fencing at Tring.**

**The first diversion of badgers was carried out at Hoddesdon on the A10 bypass. Roger and Lyn Favell (right) are shown amongst helpers covering the wire mesh with soil.**

# Appendix 2

## Annotated index of related items from the Transactions of the Hertfordshire Natural History Society

Philip Kingsbury compiled an index from his set ot the entire bound volumes of *HNHS Trans* 1875-1990 and I have extracted the following which relate to this book. More recent items have also been added. The bold figures refer to the volume and are followed by the page numbers. The *Transactions* are now published as *The Hertfordshire Naturalist*.

### Amphibians and reptiles

***Adder***. Possible at Therfield Heath 1962 - W.H.Fordham, **26**,211.

***Amphibians and reptiles*** in Vertebrate List of Herts - B.Lloyd, **22**,170-172.

***Common lizard***. Flourishing in Baldock/Royston colony in 1938 - W.H.Fordham, **21**,123. At Wareside in 1956 - T.Lloyd-Evans, **24**,237.

***Crested newt***. At Park Street in 1945 - **22**, xlii.

***Fossil Reptilia***. Ichthyosaurus at Tottenhoe - **6**, lxiv. Ichthyosaurus from Ashwell. Iguanodon from Hitchin, some pterodactyl-like material from Ashwell forming holotype of Ornithocheirus machaerorhynchus Seeley, Polyptychodon, all from the Cretaceous; also some turtle bones from the basement bed of the London Clay at Watford Heath - K.P.Oakley, in the Vertebrate List, **22**, 241-242.

***Frog***. Presence of cilia on tadpoles - R.B.Croft, **1**,264. Retarded development - C.Oldham, **19**,211. Blastopore of egg in relation to the hypoblast, with plate - J.Russell, **9**,85-100.

***Grass snake***. At Aldenham in 1886 - A.Stradling, **4**,119. At Shenley in 1918 - **17**, xxxviii. Many records, plus a colour plate, including Grove Mill in 1933, Rye House in 1936, Shenley in 1936, Barnet/Shenley in 1913 and 1926. Bentley Priory 1936, Bricket Wood 1937, Hilfield 1937, Rushden in 1937, Rickmansworth and Elstree in 1938; B.Lloyd - **21**,64-66. Pendley in 1912, Tring in 1928, London Colney in 1940, Bishop's Stortford in 1938 - B.Lloyd, **21**,277. Eggs in a crate at Ashwell Brewery, of uncertain provenance - W.H.Fordham, **26**,210. More earlier records collected by B.Lloyd with notes on habits - **20**,30-40. Bushey in 1931 - **19**, xxxv. Hertford Heath 1947 - **23**, xxiv.

***Hertfordshire distribution maps for amphibia and reptiles*** by M.Clark in 1973 - **27**, 270: in 1977 - **28**, 9-16; in 1986- **29**, 382-389.

***Natterjack toad***. A Berkhamsted record appearing in books

Philip Kingsbury was a past president and secretary to the *HNHS* for 18 years until his retirement with his wife Sylvia to Shropshire in 1988. He first joined the Society in 1949 as a young veterinary surgeon. He was also a member of the Deer Society and a founder member of the East Anglian branch, of which he was treasurer from 1967 to 1970.

Pond conservation by the Tewin Society volunteers in 1976. Further work was undertaken in 1996. The results of this work are shown on p31.

was in error - B.Lloyd, **21**, 345.

*Palmate newt*, Berkhamsted area, with other spp. in 1914 - Chas.Oldham, **15**, 207-208. More records from same area - **14**, xli and **19**, xxx and **19**, 209. Scarce or absent in the Hertford area - E.S.Brown, **23**, 73.

*St.Albans district* Amphibians and Reptiles in the area c1909 - **14**, 238-240.

*Slowworm*. Watford, Dr.Brett's meadow in 1886 - A.Stradling, **4**, 119. Hertford area - E.S.Brown, **23**, 73. Fairly common in Northaw Great Wood - B.L.Sage c1954, **24**, 78. Barnet area in 1954 - G.M.Fenner & P.D.Hager, **24**, 161. Hoddesdon in 1956 - T.Lloyd-Evans, **24**, 237. Heavier mowing of Sandon churchyard in the 1960s caused a decrease there - Col.Faure-Walker *per* M.Clark, **27**,164.

*Smooth snake*. Two shown at a meeting in 1893 (not from Hertfordshire) and said to be getting commoner - **7**, xliv.

*Toad*. Many seen on Berkhamsted Common during dawn chorus walk in 1949 - **23**, liv. Toad lifts became significant in the 1970s as cars killed still more: at Stevenage, Titmore Green Pond and Redcoats Green Pond 932 were saved and 239 run over in 1975; at Hampermill, Bushey 1,573 (incl. some frogs) were saved and 300 run over, whilst at Pixie's Mere, Bourne End 2,227 were saved and 130 killed - N.Gammon *per* M.Clark, **27**, 329-330.

# Archaeology

*Ancient man*. L.P.Shadbolt - **19**, 149-160.

*Berkhamsted Castle* - D.Montgomerie, **13**, 195-198 (2 plates). A piece of castle wall fell down in April 1915 - **16**, xx. Neolithic celt at Manor End - Sir J.Evans - **12**, 157- 158. Romano-British pottery from Northchurch Common - **17**, xxxix.

*Bronze Age*. Sir J.Evans - **8**, 1-12.

*Broxbourne*. About 200 Mesolithic or ? Neolithic flint artefacts from gravels at Church of England School - F.R.Sanger, **20**, 131-132. Mesolithic flint flake and core implements on boreal floor land surface found in 1933/34 - **23**, xxiii-xxiv.

*Coins*. Ancient British coins with plate showing their evolution; a stand-in Presidential Address in 1884 by Sir John Evans - **3**, xxii-xxxiv. On an ancient British coin found near Watford - Sir J.Evans, **9**, 133-134. Natural history objects on ancient Greek and Etruscan coins include field and house mice, prawns, horses, dogs, swans, butterflies, bees, wasps, echinoderms, laurel, olives - **9**, xli-xlii.

*Hamper Mill*. Perhaps an old Colne ford; Celtic and Roman pottery 1946 - **23**, x.

*Hitchin*. Palaeolithic implements - **Wl**, lxi. British and Roman remains (including Astwick, Danes Field, Great Wymondley, Pegsdon Common and others, with plan of villa and lists of coins) - W.Ransom, **4**, 39-48 (4 plates). Palaeoliths in clay

Celebrity opening of mammal hide by Kim Wilde, shown here with Steve Kourik, Badger Group Chairman (1991).

Badger Group tent at the annual Apple Day celebrations on the *HNWT* reserve at Tewin Orchard.

The magazine of the Hertfordshire and Middlesex Badger Group has maintained a very high standard over many years with Lesley and Jim Harmer and then Maureen Cullin as editors. Above is the first issue produced by the new editor, Sally Taylor.

Bryan Sage, author of books on the county and elsewhere and joint author with Tom Gladwin of *The Birds of Hertfordshire*, contributed information on mammals, reptiles and amphibia during the survey, especially from Northaw Great Wood

pits on Hitchin Hill site of old lake bed - **8**, xxxvii. Further notes by C.Reid devoted to trial borings to establish stratification of gravels and boulder clay - **10**, 14-22, and suggesting that attention be given to beetles in the deposits - **11**, 64.

*Mesolithic flint implements*. At Broxbourne Church of England School - F.R.Sanger, **20**, 131-132.

*Palaeolithic implements*. Sir John Evans' Presidential Address in 1877 gave a general view of implements recovered from caves and river gravels in England and France - **Wl**,187-200. Note that Evans' *Ancient Stone Implements of Great Britain,* 2nd ed. 1897 lists over 40 Hertfordshire localities and figures Hitchin (p537) and Wheathampstead (p601) specimens - **10**, 114. An idea of the size of the author's collections appears in **5**, xxxviii (1889). Then more recent discoveries in Hertfordshire/Bedfordshire eg at Caddington, Gaddesden Row, Ellingham's Pit, Leverstock Green, Kensworth, Whipsnade Heath - Sir J.Evans, **14**, 1-4 reprinted from Quart. J. Geol. Soc. **44** (1908) and drawing attention to Caddington comment in Worthington-Smith's *Man the Primaeval Savage* (1894). Grove Road and Back Lane, Bushey, also Rickmansworth, with 2 plates of locality about 1904 - Sir J.Evans, **13**, 65-66. Croxley Green and Mill End pits - **14**, xli.

*Prehistoric man in Britain* H.Hicks - **5**, 147-154

*Roman coins*. Hoard of 432 denarii at Brickendonbury - Sir J.Evans, **9**, 169-174 (plate).

*Southwest Herts.* Prehistoric artefacts from Bushey and Croxley Green - R.W.Innocent, **22**, 110.

*Spindle whorls of late Celtic period*. In Hertfordshire - **17**, xviii (lecture, no details).

*Stone Age in Hertfordshire.* Sir J.Evans - **8**, 169-187 (6 plates).

*Stotfold*. A visit to see Bronze and Iron Age finds on Mr.Howitt's fruit farm near the Ivel in 1948 (no details given) - **23**, xlii.

*Tertiary man*. A few words on, by Sir J.Evans - **1**, 145-150.

*Watford*. Supposed prehistoric hearth in Rousebarn Lane seen in 1917 (no details) - **17**, xvii.

## Geology - Hertfordshire general

*Before further quoting Philip Kingsbury's index summary, it is worth noting a few additional points. The geology and landscape of the county are well described in 'The Birds of Hertfordshire' (1986) by Gladwin & Sage and 'The Butterflies of Hertfordshire' (1987) by Sawford. Catt in 'Quaternary History of the Hertfordshire Area' (1978) and Dony in 'Flora of Hertfordshire' (1967) also give excellent accounts.*

*Roberts & Roberts (1978) listed the mammals found in post-glacial deposits at Stanstead Abbotts in a key paper in*

*'The London Naturalist' No 57, with illustrations. They are recorded at TL 400 106:*

|  | Clay | Peat | Gravel |
|---|---|---|---|
| *Arvicola* - water vole | 0 | 1 | 0 |
| *Bos* - ox or *Bison* - bison | 0 | 2 | 9 |
| *Capreolus* - roe deer | 0 | 1 | 0 |
| *Castor* - beaver | 0 | 3 | 0 |
| *Cervus* - red deer | 0 | 1 | 10 |
| *Equus* - horse | 0 | 1 | 7 |
| *Ovis* - sheep | 1 | 0 | 0 |
| *Rangifer* - reindeer | 0 | 0 | 1 |
| *Sus* - pig or wild boar | 1 | 2 | 0 |
| Bird sp. | 0 | 1 | 0 |

David Hosking (right) photographed many of the Hertfordshire bats in flight as they were released at Hoddesdon after being measured during our survey work. His father, Eric, the famous bird photographer, was described in Eileen Soper's *Harmer Green Diary* as visiting her wildlife garden in the 1950s to photograph the bird life. David's mother, Dorothy, is in the centre of the picture.

Our most distinctive feature is the chalk escarpment which runs along the west and north boundaries as part of the Chiltern Hills. The highest point at Hastoe, Tring of 245m (804ft) above sea level drops to about 160m (525ft) at Royston. There is a particular gap in the ridge from the Hitchin region, southeast through Stevenage into the lower London clay in the southern and eastern districts where the woodland (mostly oak and hornbeam) predominated and still does in parts, despite conifer plantations. Melting glaciers in the Ice Age have left a mixture of sands, gravels and clays in the more central areas between the chalk ridge and the clay regions.

Of the mammals, badgers are the most geologically aware, a preoccupation reflected in their selection of places to dig their setts in the most easily-worked soils available. Many of their underground workings appear to develop from preliminary, more superficial sampling by rabbits which leave a fine tilth of material outside their burrows. Frequently these are taken over by both badgers and foxes, having inspected the soil and ease of working. Their new diggings are typified by larger debris. In the mixed glacial soils of the central region, sand, clayey-sand and chalk appear in sett spoils in otherwise clay-dominated sites, indicating that the more easily worked, drier and best drained material is chosen. In the section on badgers this is examined in more detail with reference to the Chilterns.

The difficulty of working clay and large flints by Hertfordshire farmers has historic significance to mammal distribution because far less woodland would have survived in the southern region if the soil had been easier to plough.

Woodland gives the greatest diversity of species, and it is interesting to find that some of our best hedgerows and lush field boundaries are also in southeast and southwest Hertfordshire.

Thus, indirectly as well as directly, the geology of a county and especially its soil types can influence the distribution of mammals, amphibians and reptiles due to farming activities, drainage, cover and the availability of foods.

The glacial mix near Welwyn results in sand on the left-hand badger sett entrance and chalk on the right.

The same sett two weeks later. As the wild garlic has grown, chalk now appears on the left-hand spoil and sand covers the chalk on the right following further excavations by the occupants.

*The Kingsbury index continues:*

**Agricultural geology**. Approximate acreages are loamy clay (chalky boulder clay) - 133,000; clay, sand and gravel derived from lower Tertiary drift plus some clay-with-flints lying between Bovingdon and St.Albans - 66,000; clay-with-flints 58,000; glacial sands and gravels and alluvial gravels in the Lea Valley from Harpenden to Hoddesdon - 35,000; chalk, mainly between Hitchin and Royston - 33,000; tenacious London clay in the Elstee/Barnet area - 20,000; badlands of stones from clay-with-flints and glacial materials (southwest of Stevenage) between the rivers Mimram and Beane - 14,550; blue pebbles and clay from Reading beds southeast of Hatfield - 5,851; yellow London clay west of Hoddesdon and Cheshunt - 5,365; peat in the lower Lea Valley - 3,000. Coprolite beds (remains of gault) worked at Lilley Hoo and from Hitchin to Cambridgeshire. Note that the southern slope of the county was enough for streams to drive mills. In the east the valleys cut through the chalky boulder clay to expose glacial sands and gravels - J.Vincent Elsdon, **2**, 145-163.
**Boulders and boulder clay of north Hertfordshire**. The boulders are 75% sandstones and grits, 12% basalts, 10% limestones and 4% granites. Notable are boulders at Claybush Hill at Ashwell, at Kelshall, and the Royston Stone. Also see under Hertingfordbury pit - H.G.Fordham, **3**, 33-46.
**Chalk of Hertfordshire.** H.Kidner, **14**, 5-14.
**Chalk rock**. Notes on forming outline of Chilterns, Micraster fossils, calcium carbonate crystals, shallow water sponges and gastropods; lists about 70 fossils - J.Morison, **5**, 199-202. The best fossil section is in the Luton/Chiltern Green cutting. Dr.Morison left a valuable collection of chalk fossils to the County Museum at St.Albans in 1912 - **l5**, xxix. Abstract of a paper on molluscs by H.Woods in Quart. J. Geol. Soc. - **52**, 68-98 and **53**, 377-404; **10**, 112-114.
**Chilterns**. A geological model by P.Evans and J.F.Osborne given to the City Museum, St.Albans, around 1950 - **23**, xxii.
**Earthquakes in Hertfordshire**. April 1185, 1246, 1248, 1275, 1382, 19th March 1750, Great Lisbon Nov 1st 1755 (early ones based on inference for Hertfordshire); paper deals with the Great Essex Earthquake of April 22nd 1884 which in that county damaged 1,213 buildings, 20 churches and 11 chapels, mostly between Wivenhoe and Peldon: map given - R.Meldola, **4**, 23-32. 1896 earthquake - **9**,183.
**Fossil mammals**. See entries under Mammals.
**Gravels of Hertfordshire**. A useful paper, with references - A.E.Salter, **12**, 137- 144. For High Level Gravels see Proc. Geol. Assoc., 1896 - **14**, 389-512.
**Gravels, sands, clays and loams of west Hertfordshire**. Map and 10 sections, including Bricket Wood, Gubblecote, Long Marston, Champneys, Bernard's Heath - T.E.Lones, **10**, 153-164.

*Hertfordshire papers on geology*. 58 papers from 1756-1873, several related to water supply - W.Whitaker: **Wl**, 78-82. List for 1873-1883 gives 78 papers plus 18 additions for earlier period - J.Hopkinson, **3**, 165-172. A further list for 1884-1900 adds 176 papers, plus 40 overlooked for previous years - J.Hopkinson, **11**, 87-104. More information for 1890-1899 in Presidential Address by W.Whitaker in 1899 - **10**, 105-118.

*Ice and its work*. Includes Hertfordshire material - J.Morison, **7**, 147-156.

*Puddingstone* site near Radlett recommended for conservation - P.Evans, **22**, 83. An occurrence of puddingstone in Reading beds at St.Albans, showing process of incorporation into overlying drift - J.A.Catt & A.J.Moffatt, **28**, (3), 1216. (The 7th Day Adventist Church site in St.Peter's Street.)

*Quaternary history of the Hertfordshire area*. A summarising paper - J.A.Catt, **28**, (4), 27-54 (available as a separate offprint).

*River systems of west Hertfordshire*. Theories in 1905 - A.Sutton, **13**, 1-4.

*Sarsens and other boulders in Hertfordshire*. Gives specific localities all over the county and 23 references - A.E.Salter, **14**, 135-142.

*Soils of Hertfordshire*. With coloured map - A.J.Thomasson & B.W.Avery, **25**, 247-263. Errata in **26**, 46.

**Gravel extraction in Hertfordshire - a picture from the 1980s near Cole Green; it shows 'sand at 55 feet down to 75 feet'.**

*The following may be of interest in future surveys of holes sunk in the ground for bat roosts and hibernaculae:*

**Well sections**. There are 41 Hertfordshire well sections mentioned in Geol. Survey Memoirs, **Vol.IV**, 447-456 and another 16 in sheet 47 Memoir pp82-83. This paper, by W.Whitaker, includes Albury. Aldenham House, Barnet Waterworks, Bishop's Stortford Sanatorium, Broxbourne New River Co., Cheshunt New River Co., Essendon Place, Home Farm Little Hadham, Green Tye public well, Ponsbourne Park Hatfield, Sawbridgeworth H. & E. Waterworks, Chandlers Green and North End, Waltham Cross - Theobalds Square, Ware New River Co., Ware - Little Fanhams Hall, Watford - London Orphan Asylum - **3**, 173-180.

More well sections, mostly in southeast Herts, abstracted from Whitaker's geology of the London Basin part 1, 447-456 by J.L.Lobley include Amwell End, East Barnet - Lions Down. New Barnet Station, several at Bishop's Stortford, Broxbourne, Bushey L. & N.W. Railway, several at Cheshunt, Chorleywood Parsonage, Elstree, Hadham - Berry Green, Harefield Park, Haileybury College, Hitchin Brewery, Hoddesdon Brewery, Waltham Cross, Watford L. & N.W. Railway, Wormley West End - **Wl**, 170-171.

Whitaker gives more well sections (with dates of sinkings)

*HNHS* **members at Gobions Wood Well where a new grille for bats has been fitted.**

in **6**, 53-64, *viz* Amwell, Aston, Berkhamsted, Bishop's Stortford, Braughing, Cottered, Datchworth, Flamstead, Furneaux Pelham, Gaddesden, Great Offley, Harpenden. Hatfield, Hemel Hempstead, Hertford, Hinxworth, Hitchin, Hunsdon, Little Hadham, Much Hadham, Northchurch, Norton, Puckeridge, Puttenham, Radwell, Redbourn, Rye Common, St.Albans, St.Margarets, Sawbridgeworth, Shenley, Shephall, Thorley, Walkern, Waltham Cross, Ware, Watton.

## Mammals - miscellaneous and review papers

*Aldenham Reservoir*. Mammals - B.Lloyd, **22**, x-xi.
*Brocket Park*. Minor notes in 1893 - **7**, xliv.
*Eyes of mammals*. Structural variation in relation to function; F.Maule-Campbell's Presidential Address in 1889 - **5**, 107-128.
*Fossil and extinct mammals*. Fossil and sub-fossil vertebrates of Hertfordshire include *Coryphodon*, *Hyracotherium*, badger, bear, bison, boar, deer (including *Megaceros*), elephants, horses, hippopotamus, hyaena, mammoth, moose, reindeer, rhinoceros, voles (and many spp. of Cretaceous and Tertiary fish and a few Cretaceous and Tertiary reptiles) - paper in Vertebrate List by K.P.Oakley - **22**, 239-246. Hitchin Hill clay pits had bear, elephant, rhinoceros etc - **8**, xxxvii. Palaeolithic deposit at Hitchin with bear, hippopotamus, red deer, rhinoceros, *Elephas primigenius*, also fish - C.Reid, **10**, 14-22. Long Valley Wood gravel pit at Rickmansworth had molar of *Elephas antiques* 20 feet down - **13**, xxx. Ox, horse and pig in post-Tertiary beds at Watford gas works - **12**, 17- 20. Historically extinct animals in Britain include bear, beaver, boar, deer and wolf - J.E.Harting, **1**, 5-24.
*Hertfordshire mammals*. Notes by T.V.Roberts in 1893 include some useful old records - **7**, 169-174. More information in paper surveying Society's work from 1875-1925 - T.E.Lones, **18**, 136-149. Mammals in Vertebrate List - B.Lloyd, **22**, 227-238. M.Clark has given more recent information in a series of articles in volumes **27** onwards:

*1970*. Note of remains of 20 otters nailed to a Hertfordshire trapper's door in the 1930s - **27**, 37-38.
*1971*. More harvest mice being found - **27**, 85-88.
*1972*. Warfarin poisoning of grey squirrels legalised - **27**, 161-164.
*1972/73*. Map of badger persecution in last decade in Hertfordshire - **27**, 237-238.
*1974*. Tetrad mapping progress - **27**, 265-270.
*1975*. First county records for Brandt's bat (Wilstone). Red deer herd well established at Knebworth. Roe buck confirmed present in Hertfordshire - **27**, 325-330.
*1976/77*. Including notes on 115 bat visits during 1975-77 which showed 449 pipistrelles, 70 long-eared,

**Skull of wild boar (from Millais 1906).**

25 Daubenton's, 29 serotines, 24 Natterer's, 17 noctule, 16 Leisler's, 6 whiskered and 3 Brandt's. Roe deer again - **28**, (2), 9-16.

*1976*. A sad note was loss to agriculture of the famous badger sett at Cuffley School Camp - **28**, (1), 28.

*1978*. First record for Nathusius' pipistrelle bat and a report of five otters - **28**, (3), 910.

*1979-82*. Notes on various spp. - **29**, (1), 11-14.

*1987*. Set of tetrad maps - **29**, 382-389.

**Mammal watching**. Review of Michael Clark's book - **28**, (6), 12.

***Ruminating animal***. Presidential Address by P.A.Kingsbury in 1970 - **27**, 34-36.

**St.Albans area mammals** - situation about 1910 - C.Oldham, **14**, 238-245.

***Symonshyde***. Minor notes on mammals in 1893 - **7**, xliv.

***Terrestrial British quadrupeds*** existing wild at the present day (1891) - T.V.Roberts, **7**, 41-52.

***Vermin payments*** by Berkhamsted church wardens 1639-1820 were notably for polecats, hedgehogs. stoats and weasels - C.Oldham, **18**, 45-50. Various payments by Hertfordshire churchwardens include Aldbury (about 30 polecats a year in the 1730s); Aldenham (also polecats in the 1730s); Chipping Barnet up to 1,805 (polecats, stoats, weasels, hedgehogs and mad dogs); Bushey (up to 60 hedgehogs per annum and a few polecats); Codicote (mainly sparrows); Elstree (polecats and hedgehogs); Gaddesdens (foxes, hedgehogs, polecats and sparrows); Harpenden, Rickmansworth, Ridge, St.Albans and Sandridge follow the same pattern. Welwyn included 2 otters in 1706. Also Buckinghamshire information for Drayton Beauchamp, Ivinghoe, Marsworth and Pitstone - C.Oldham, **19**, 79-112.

## Mammals - species information

**Badgers**. Sold for baiting about 1840 - **W1**, 236. Notes on Badger in Hertfordshire - A.T.Brett, **W1**, 236-237. Shot by an Earl of Essex's keeper at Watford in 1878, the first seen here for 36 years - **W2**, xxv. Not uncommon in Rib area near Buntingford - **W2**, xxvi. Rare at Odsey in 1883 - **2**, liv. Frequent at Westmill and Braughing, also in Plashes Wood in 1882 - **2**, 128 and 131. Scarce at Watford: present in Panshanger, A.T.Brett (1886) - **4**, 119-120. At Ashlyns in 1893 where sett then known for at least 100 years - **7**, 169. Setts at Dancer's End - **23**, lvii and Pancake Wood, Berkhamstead - **23**, lx. Badgers in west Hertfordshire and Buckinghamshire - Presidential Address by Phyllis Hager in 1956 - **24**, 201-208. Conservation in Hertfordshire - M.Clark, **27**, 39-47. Pet badgers released near Ashwell in 1971 - W.H.Fordham, **27**, 210.

**Bats**. Associating with birds - S.B.Hodgson, **24**, 78. Barbastelle at Willian in 1920, previously at Frithsden in

Harry Bott (right) who farms at Benington has given generous help throughout the survey. He is seen here with Phil Collins, *HNHS* recorder for *Hemiptera*, at a hornet nest in a pollarded oak.

As well as helping with the survey over many years, Jim Sutton (right) has constructed ponds for wildlife at Ramerwick Farm, and Duncan Cree (left) monitors the river and wetland habitats there.

The survey benefits from annual lists of records from naturalists like Mike Russell (see p41) who has also contributed interesting summaries of exotic animals introduced here.

Alison Burton helping to measure a serotine bat at Stanstead Abbotts. She has supported all kinds of survey work (see p79) and done much for the youth membership of the Mammal Society. She regularly organises group visits to the mammal hide at Tewin for the People's Trust for Endangered Species.

1908/09 - C.Oldham, **17**, 295. Brandt's bat at Tring - M.Clark, **27**, 325. Daubenton's bat at Abbots Langley with parasite *Nycteribia pedicularia* - **14**, 1xvii. Several Daubenton's localities given - **14**, 300. Nathusius' pipistrelle. second British record: caught in flight in Hertfordshire - C.Banks, M.Clark & R.Newton, **29**, 15-18. Natterer's bat from Tring Park in 1898 plus east Buckinghamshire records - **21**, 316, also from Tring in 1943 - A.H.Bishop, **22**, 53. Pipistrelles - summer roosts in Hertfordshire 1975-1980; 51 roosts visited were mostly in modern houses favouring south and southwest sides 5 to 6 metres up, especially associated with cavity walls and hung tiles; usually 10-30 per roost, but up to 100 encountered - **28**, (6), 59-62. Serotine at Sawbridgeworth - C.Oldham, **18**, 194. Observations on unusual mixed roost of serotines and noctules in east Hertfordshire - C.Banks, M.Clark & R.Newton, **28**, (3), 20-26. A ten year study of this roost - R.Newton, **29**, 348-360. For relative frequency of bat species see Hertfordshire Mammals Report for 1976-77 quoted in the previous section. Hibernation in an ice house at Wormleybury 1978-88. Observations on Natterer's, Daubenton's and long-eared bats - R.Newton, **30**, 245-250.

***Beaver***. An 1882 paper gives notes on reintroduction to Britain and visit to Lord Bute's colony at Rothesay, which grew from 7 or 8 in 1875 to 30 animals - A.Hawks, **2**, 223-228.

***Brown rat and house mouse***. Seasonal population movements in east Hertfolrdshire - M.Clark & Susan Summers, **28**, (3), 17-19 (also see under 'Rat').

***Deer***. Red and fallow mixing freely at Ashridge for several years about 1881 - **2**, xii. Feral deer at Ashridge: 200 fallow, 100 red and 20 sika in 1928, then substantial numbers of fallow up to 1937 - C.Oldham, **20**, 305-306. Cassiobury Park said to have had about 700-800 deer in 1815 but only half that by 1880s - **2**, x-xii. In 1821 a quarter of the 600 Cassiobury deer died and in 1887-88 about 120 of 300 died of a 'nervous disease' - A.T.Brett, **W2**, iii and 162. North Hertfordshire, fallow prospering in 1937 - M.E.Berry, **20**, (3), 7-308. Odd fallow in Sandon area 1966 and first muntjac at Odsey in 1962 - W.H.Fordham, **26**, 21.

***Deer fossils***. Kings Langley gravel pit; red deer antlers found in peat 4 metres below ground - **18**, xvi-xvii. Fossil roe here too in 1927 - C.Oldham, **18**, 216. Walkern; a large quantity of antlers found when moats dredged, probably 1860s - **2**, x-xii. Watford; excavations for new retort house at the gas-works in 1910 revealed, probably post-Roman, roe and red remains - **14**, xlvi. Deer, probably red, in section at Watford Fields sewage farm in 1886 - A.T.Brett, **4**, 117.

***Deer parks***. Existing in 1881 were Ashridge, Cassiobury, Gorhambury, Grove Park, Hatfield, Knebworth, Moor Park, Putteridge, Rickmansworth and Woodhall (omits Tring). List of 34 previous parks given - J.E.Harting, **2**, 97-111.

***Dormouse***. St.Albans - A.E.Gibbs, **12**, 135. Codicote in 1959 - **25**, 168.

***Fox***. An eulogy in *Bats and some other beasts* - G.Rooper, **7**, 37-40. In Pancake and Hockeridge Woods, Berkhamsted - P.D.Hager, **23**, 236-237.

***Hare***. Overran the zoo area in Regents Park in 1828 - A.Stradling, **6**, xlvi- xlviii.

***Harvest mouse***. Hertford area - E.S.Brown, **23**, 73.

***Horse***. Early Iron Age mare found in lily pond at Maple Avenue, Bishop's Stortford, and several more horses later (1909) - Rev.A.Irving, **15**, 177. Prehistoric horse remains in Kings Langley gravel pit - **18**, xvii.

***Mammoth***. Remains in gravel below boulder clay at Bricket Wood (about 1857) - **7**, xxxiii.

***Man***. Prehistoric man in Britain - H.Hicks (1889), **5**, 147-154. A wonderful animal doomed to extinction by having too big a brain - Presidential Address by A.Stradling in 1894 - **9**, 85-100. Early Man in Hertfordshire - summary by K.P.Oakley in Vertebrate List, with gazetteer of records for about 50 Palaeolithic sites, with Acheulian artefacts prominent in many of them, four Mesolithic sites including an important one at Broxbourne (Type of Mesolithic Forest Culture 'A' in Britain) and some 30 Neolithic finds - **22**, 247-257. (An essential source paper.)

***Marten***. An 1872 record taken from the Zoologist in 1879 - **7**, 46.

***Mole***. Thirty white moles taken in half an acre of oats in 1883 - **2**, liv. White moles in 1891 - **7**, 41. Albinos in Hertford area, especially Cole Green and Panshanger (1906) and other places in the county - A.E.Gibbs, **12**, 135 and **13**, 14.

***Mouse***. A musical mouse exhibited in 1884; it sang! - **3**, xxxviii. Mouse seasonal movements in east Hertfordshire; see under 'brown rat' above.

***Otter***. Notes - A.J.Brett, **Wl**, 236-237. Izaak Walton described a hunt at Amwell and still a few in the Lea - R.B.Croft (1881), **2**, 9-16. Otter killed at Munden, exhibited in 1875 - **Wl**, lxi. Old records given by A.T.Brett - Piccotts End about 1815, Tolpits about 1855, Watford/Munden 1875 - **Wl**, 236. Iver Moor in 1878 - **W2**, xxv. Seen twice at Cassiobury in 1883 - **2**, liv (also see under Hertfordshire Mammal Reports).

***Ox***. *Bos primigenius* from Kings Langley gravel pit - **18**, xvii and xliv.

***Pig***. Skulls of wild boars from Roman level of St.Albans have tooth wear suggesting they were used in harness with bits - G.E.Bullen, **16**, 49-50 (a stretch of the archaeologist's imagination? - More likely worn on bars, *[M.C.]*).

***Pygmy shrew***. Berkhamsted area - C.Oldham, **17**, 261. Hertford area - E.S.Brown, **23**, 73. Northeast Hertfordshire - W.H.Fordham, **24**, 199. Redbourn - **25**,168.

***Polecat***. See under 'Vermin payments' above. Killed on Earl of Essex's estate about 1886 - **7**, xi and 41.

**Andrew Martin during survey work on badgers along the route of the M25 motorway through Hertfordshire. He edited vintage issues of** *Bat News* **for the local group.**

**Professor Stephen Harris at Royal Holloway College during his research on the red fox. Chairman of the Mammal Society and editor with Gordon Corbet of the** *Handbook of British Mammals***, Stephen first visited Hertfordshire to help survey harvest mouse sites on 8th August 1970.**

The Mammal Group are able to view black rats at close quarters thanks to the unusual display at the British Wildlife Centre in Surrey. In the middle is David Mills, Centre Director, who takes visitors round following an introductory talk.

Bernard White with one of his orphan roe deer which took part in a breeding project in Hertfordshire.

*Rabbit*. Colony of black rabbits at Wiggenhall - A.T.Brett, **W2**, 112. Dog trapped following rabbit into a tree - Lord Ebury, **4**, 223. Scarce at Odsey until after 1860 - W.H.Fordham, **20**, 352.

*Rat*. Known for 1,000 rats to be killed in one day at Watford in past years; 1883 note by A.T.Brett - **2**, 1iv. Brown rats used to be sold to pubs for 3 shillings a dozen for matches with dogs but this is now (1891) prohibited; black rats used to be very numerous in Whitbread's brewery (town not given) - T.V.Roberts, **7**, 49. Black rats at Ware in 1951-1956, probably there at least since early in the century - R.A.Davis & L.Lloyd-Evans, **25**, 4-6. Seasonal movements in east Hertfordshire - see under brown rats above.

*Squirrel*. Watford had an outstanding red squirrel year in 1876 - A.T.Brett, **Wl**, xlv. Very numerous at Cassiobury in 1883 - **2**, 1iv. Grey squirrel invasion still in Chess Valley and not on the tops in 1932 - Presidential Address by L.P.Shadbolt on *The Invasion of the Grey Squirrel* - **19**, 163-170. Grey squirrel eating sycamore seeds and yew fruits - C.Oldham, **20**, 86. Melanic greys at Berkhamsted in 1936 - C.Oldham, **20**, 153, also at Ashwell, some partly black - W.H.Fordham (1945), **22**, 160. More notes on melanic greys - W.H.Fordham & B.Lloyd, **22**, 53. Again from Ashwell (W.H.F.) and Berkhamsted - P.D.Hager in 1954-55 - **24**,198 (these seem to have disappeared at least from the Ashlyns area soon after and I saw none there up to the late 1980s). Red squirrel; 6 records from the Whitwell/Hitchin area in 1939-44 - A.H.Foster, **22**, 52. and one shot at Northaw in 1953 - B.L.Sage, **24**, 78.

*Stoat*. White stoat at Hoddesdon - F.M.Campbell, **6**, 76. Also at Hitchin - A.H.Foster, **22**, 160. Caught in underground mole trap - W.Lewis; **6**, 196. Unusual voice and behaviour (play?) - B.R.Sawford, **27**, 27.

*Vole*. Albino *Microtus agrestis* at St.Albans in 1920 - **17**, 1v.

*Water shrew*. Tring town - R.B.Benson, **22**, xxxvii and 108, and at Marsworth Reservoir in 1975 - P.D.Hager, **24**, 199, and Redbourn in 1960 - G.Dangerfield, **25**, 168.

*Water vole*. Common in Grand Union Canal and Colne in 1891 - T.V.Roberts, **7**, 41.

*[Whales]* The 'Save the whales' campaigns were prominent in the 1980s but Arthur Earland alerted the Society back in 1918 - **17**, xxxix. In 1893 whalebone from Atlantic right whales was worth £3,000/ton - **8**, x.

*Yellow-necked field mouse*. Hitchin - A.H.Foster, **22**, 139. North Hertfordshire records from W.H.Fordham - **24**, 199 and **26**, 210. Associated with fruit stores at St Ippollitts - Lord Cranbrook, **24**, 199. Cuffley Great Wood in 1954 (and several references) - B.L.Sage, **24**, 161.

# Miscellaneous papers

The main interest of these is an insight into the state of knowledge at the time and historical curiosity.

***Animals, mutual aid amongst***. Prince Kropotkin (standing in to give the Presidential Address for Henry Seebohm in 1895) - **9**, 1-13.
***Bacon, Francis*** (buried at St.Michaels, St.Albans) - J.Hopkinson, **7**, 1-36.
***Colours of animals*** in relation to their habits - F.Maule Campbell, **2**, xxix-xxx.
***Darwin, Charles***, an Hon. Member of *HNHS* - J.Hopkinson, **7**, 101-136.
***Field sports***, their bearing on the national character - Earl of Clarendon, **6**, 1-15.
***Hertfordshire maps***, a series of papers by Sir H.G.Fordham - 1579 to 1673 in **11**, 1-32; 1673 to 1794 in **11**, 173-212; 1790 to 1842 in **12**, 169-208. Supplement - **15**, 73-104.
***Hertfordshire, natural history of*** - F.W.Jane (1946) gives the best summary of work done in the county to that time - **22**, 142-159. This was done before by T.E.Lones for the first 50 years (1875 to 1925) - **18**, 136-149; and again by W.J.Cox - **19**, 231-242.
***Horse, the***. Earl of Clarendon - **6**, 103-113.
***Library of HNHS***. Notes the most valuable works - R.B.Freeman, **27**, 348-352.
***Mimicry and protective resemblance***. Walter, Lord Rothschild - **15**, 105-120. Of the vast number of papers written by Lord Rothschild, this long, erudite study is the only one I can trace that was actually read to the *HNHS*, delivered at the anniversary meeting in Watford on 26th February 1913 *'by the President, the Hon L. Walter Rothschild, PhD, FRS, FLS, FZS'*. It was illustrated by lantern slides. He was President of the Society between 1911 and 1913, the customary 2 year term *(MC)*.
***Products of Hertfordshire*** (includes some history of the watercress industry) - J.C.Clutterbuck, **W2**, 41-48.
***Roads and travel before railways*** in Hertfordshire and elsewhere - Sir H.G.Fordham, **16**, 1-36(11 plates).
***Watford place and field names*** (in the parish of) - P.Manning, **10**, 193-212.

Caged out of Whipsnade on the farm side: Brian Barton, past president of *HNHS*, with Clive Herbert and Phoebe Killey heading a group of members on a New Year's Day visit to watch the Chinese water deer rut.

Bernard Nau devised the first tetrad system for the survey on a MAC OS.

# Personalities

I have selected those with particular links to the mammal, amphibian and reptile recording in the county, based on Philip Kingsbury's lists.

***E.H.(Ted) Cunningham*** (d.1970, after collapsing in a snowstorm on his way home from work) always seemed to be cheerful and worked in the printing trade. He and his wife,

Peggy Cunningham.

W.H.Fordham.

Phyllis Hager, by kind
permission of Katherine
Broadbent, née Hager.

*Peggy Cunningham*, *HNHS* President 1986-88, with the
financial support of a local dentist, Victor Bascombe,
produced some excellent colour films and sound recordings
of mammals and other wildlife which were widely used in
support of the conservation movement - **27**, 29.

*C.Double* (1878-1946), not a *HNHS* member but very well
known as one of the family of keepers at Tring Reservoirs.
His son Bernard succeeded him - **22**, 113.

*Essex, 7th Earl* of (d.1916 aged 58).

*Percy Evans* (1892-1974) was chief geologist with Burmah
Oil. In retirement he took much interest in the Pleistocene
period just before there was an explosion of new ideas and
knowledge about it arising from modern techniques. The
Herts Geological Society instituted an annual lecture in his
memory. His father took many of the sepia landscape photos
which used to adorn railway carriages; many of them
included Percy and his sister as children for scale and human
interest. Most who took part in rambles with him will
remember him standing on some eminence declaiming the
geology of the landscape with a slight stammer. He did much
service for all the bodies with which he was connected,
including the Society - **27**, 253-254.

*Sir H.G.Fordham* (d.1929) was the leading figure in the
Society in the north of the county. He took great interest in
local geology, especially erratics, and published a definitive
list of Hertfordshire maps spread over several papers in the
*Trans*. Obituary in *The Times* on 22nd February 1929.

*W.H.Fordham* (d.1976 - aged 92). A tall, thin, likeable
gentleman who had worked in the petroleum industry in his
youth and then managed the family brewing business and
estate around Ashwell; always a very active observer and
recorder with a particular interest in mammals, for which he
was recorder, 1945 - 1949. Well known for his almost annual
bonfire teas at Odsey. He is pictured in Dr.Dony's *Flora*
handing over the deeds of Fox Covert to the Herts & Middx
Wildlife Trust.

*A.H.Foster* (d.1946) was a medical man in Hitchin; he was a
major contibutor to Hine's *Natural History of the Hitchin
Region*, covering birds, fishes, reptiles, amphibians and
mammals - **27**, 321-322.

*Phyllis D.Hager* (d.1987, aged about 80) worked in the
personnel department of the Berkhamsted firm of Coopers.
Without any pretensions to science she had a genius for
interesting ordinary folk in natural history; this was grounded
in her immense sincerity. Many active members were first
recruited by her enthusiasm for field signs of wildlife, most
of which she had picked up from an old local poacher turned
gamekeeper, Jimmy Bunn. She kept copious notes on
mammal subjects, invited the author to be Mammal Recorder
in 1968, and lived with her batchelor brother, Osborne (**27**,
254), who was our auditor for many years - **30**, 183.

*John Hopkinson* (1844 - 5th July 1919) worked in the
family piano-making business; moved from Yorkshire to
London. He was a busy, immensely energetic man who was
*de facto* the Society for its first 44 years, during which time
he was active in other scientific bodies and secretary of the
Ray Society, 1902-1919. In his younger days he was expert
on graptolites. The only task which defeated him was trying
to write up Pryor's *Flora*, which he abandoned at the end of
*Cruciferae* and then others took over. He married
Miss K.Willshin in 1877 (given an elegant dining room clock
and side ornaments by the Society - **W2**, x), who survived
him until 1938. He had two unmarried daughters - **17**, 250-
259 (with photo).

John Hopkinson, founder of *HNHS*.

*Bertram Lloyd*, 'Wolf' to his intimates, (1881-1944). He
started work in insurance and was then self-employed. A
leading figure in the League Against Cruel Sports, he was
anti modern inventions, an expert on Elizabethan drama, and
always kept his clock one hour and ten minutes fast. He did
not marry until 1938. He spent the first 20 years of his death
as ashes in a dirty brown paper parcel tied up with string,
first under his wife's bed, then under his sister-in-law's bed
alongside his wife's ashes, before both were offered back to
the Society; the offer was politely declined - **22**, 57-59 (with
plate which one hopes does not do him justice).

Bertram Lloyd.

*Chas.Oldham* (1868-1942) worked in insurance and became
one of the leading naturalists of his time with special
expertise in mammals, molluscs and birds. Tribute on his
70th birthday - **21**, 1-2. Obituary - **21**, 319-321(with photo).
Mrs.Dorothy Oldham survived until 1961 and was
frequently at meetings in Berkhamsted, and a niece,
Dr.Ruth Kemp, was a Life Member of the Society. (In the
1980s Philip Kingsbury passed to the author a bound volume
of papers on bats collected by Oldham, *Bats 1*, from which
the pictures of him here are taken. These were added to the
book by Betram Lloyd in the 1940s when it was passed to
him as Society Recorder. As well as his own papers, there are
the works of various authors bound inside the book,
including several by T.A.Coward with his handwritten
compliments to Oldham and his signature. He went to school
with Coward.)

Chas Oldham.

*Wm.Ransom* (d.1914, aged 88) became an expert on flint
implements and also excavated a Roman villa near his home
in Hitchin - **16**, xiii-xiv.

*Sir E.J.Salisbury FRS* (1886-1978). Teddy to the intimates
of his youth, he was a pleasant, busy man who made a career
in botany, became Director of Kew, and was scientifically
active into his 90s; 28,(3).2. His nephew, Gerald Salisbury, is
another excellent botanist and member of the Society who has
contributed mammal records from the under-researched
southwest of the county.

Gerald Salisbury.

'Am having a lovely time' wrote Rose to a Mr. and Mrs.G.Leonard on this postcard sent from Tring on 15th May 1928 to Princes Risborough.

**Walter, Lord Rothschild FRS** (1868-1937). When I first went to survey the collections in the Natural History Museum at South Kensington for this book it soon became obvious that a large proportion of the mammal specimens had labels of *'Roth, Tring'* origin. Although since my childhood I had visited the Walter Rothschild Zoological Museum at Tring many times, it was only by noticing the many labels at the Natural History Museum that I began to realise how fortunate Hertfordshire is, not only to have had such a remarkable zoologist living in it, but one who recorded its natural history so well that the material represents the national types too.

Furthermore, Lord Rothschild gave his collections to the nation and his unique museum at Tring means that we have a treasured part of the British Museum in our county. Someone pointed out to me how the Duke of Bedford gave the land to create the out-of-town zoo at Whipsnade as part of the London Zoo, but has been given precious little credit for this. Much the same can be said of the treatment given to Lord Rothschild.

Fortunately, the wonderful collections remain and I strongly recommend visits to both the museum at Tring and the British Museum (Natural History) in London to further the study of mammals, amphibians and reptiles.

**Walter Rothschild with one of his zebras.**

Miriam Rothschild, in her fascinating biography of her uncle, Walter Rothschild, *Dear Lord Rothschild* (1983) wrote:
*'The paragraph concerning Walter in the Encyclopaedia Britannica is remarkably straightforward. The second Lord Rothschild did not marry; was a zoologist who made the greatest collection of Natural History objects assembled by one man; the Balfour Declaration was addressed to him; his collections, including his library, were the largest single gift ever received by the British Museum. But this simple paragraph is deceptive, for Walter was an enigmatical man of colossal contradictions.*

*Thus he worked at N.M. Rothschild & Sons in the partners' room for eighteen years, yet only one business letter out of the thousands he wrote from the Bank (New Court) and not one of those addressed to him in return has survived. There is no record anywhere of what he did or said during the hours he spent in the partners' room. On the other hand something like 80,000 letters and papers written to him and his museum curators and relating to his collections, are now stored in the British Museum.*

*Walter never at any moment took anyone into his confidence - except perhaps his mother when he was a small boy. Paralysing shyness afflicted him all his adult life and he lived in a shell of silence, shattered at intervals by cracks of thunder. As I have indicated, it is impossible to write a conventional biography of Walter. All that one can do is to portray the people in the landscape in which he moved, and hope that the strange enigmatical figure, about which everything yet nothing is known, will somehow emerge out of his entourage.'*

She sums up his contribution to zoology: *'...he amassed the greatest collection of animals ever assembled by one man, ranging from starfish to gorillas. It included 2¼ million set butterflies and moths, 300,000 bird skins, 144 giant tortoises, 200,000 birds' eggs and 30,000 relevant scientific books. He, and the two collaborators he had selected as assistants, described between them 5,000 new species and published over 1,200 books and papers based on the collections. A century later over 100,000 people visit his museum every year.'*

Miriam Rothschild's account (and I consider her to be one of the great writers of the last hundred years) helps explain how on the one hand their careful European banking family shunned the relative who spent so much of the family fortune on his love of natural history and on the other hand how we as a nation tend to quickly forget our heroes. (The same neglect has been shown to the memory of Thomas Rivers; perhaps the greatest name in fruit growing in the world who developed so many important cultivars and invented the garden greenhouse, all in Hertfordshire.) Her book should be in the national curriculum, and it is such a brilliant mixture of science, natural history, adventure, crime, modern history and family life that it puts the *Forsyte Saga* in the shade.

The giant tortoise at Tring was well able to carry Walter, who did so much to save these remarkable reptiles from extinction.

# Recorders

### Amphibians and Reptiles

| | |
|---|---|
| 1881-84 | G.Turner (amphibians only to 1889) |
| 1884-99 | A.Stradling (reptiles only until 1889) |
| 1899-02 | A.F.Crossman |
| 1912-21 | G.E.Bullen |
| 1935-45 | B.Lloyd |
| | *Subsequently with mammals, q.v.* |

### Mammals

| | |
|---|---|
| 1882-91 | A.T.Brett |
| 1891-00 | T.V.Roberts |
| 1900-02 | A.F.Crossman |
| 1903-12 | A.E.Gibbs |
| 1912-19 | G.E.Bullen |
| 1919-35 | Miss M.E.Gibbs |
| 1935-45 | B.Lloyd |
| 1945-49 | W.H.Fordham |
| 1949-53 | A.H.Bishop |
| 1953-68 | P.D.Hager |
| 1968-00 | M.Clark |
| 2000- | J.Jones |

Phyllis Hager, County Recorder until 1968 (see pp109, 111-113, 124, 146, and 274). She was always keen to share her knowledge of wildlife with *HNHS* members on rambles, and she prepared the Ashridge Nature Trail.

# Appendix 3

## Death tolls on roads

To illustrate the death toll suffered by mammals when coming into contact with vehicles, Steve Kourik has kindly allowed me to reproduce the dates and localities of badgers killed on the roads in the county from the Hertfordshire Police and Hertfordshire Badger Group records for a recent complete year (1998). This can only give a hint of the numbers of animals which escape injured or which die out of sight, having attempted to return to their setts, and these are only the notified RTAs (Road Traffic Accidents).

With this under-estimation in mind and assuming that the following 102 listed are typical of most years, I have estimated a total annual death toll for all wild mammals in the county (taking into account their relative abundance) as 13,450.

If amphibians and reptiles were added to this figure, an estimate of 22,600 is reached for our roads alone, quite apart from natural predation and victims of cats and dogs.

The smallest loss of badgers is found during December and this indicates the reduced activity of badgers during this month.

### Dead badger report for 1998

Dead mink (left) and polecat. Two easily confused road casualties, especially when badly damaged by vehicles. It is vital for an accurate survey that they are distinuished. The best guide to the mink is the white chin. Any pattern on the face and light under-fur indicates polecat.

*January 1998*

| | |
|---|---|
| 6th | Bedmond Road by old Horlicks building |
| 11th | **A41** Tring Bypass |
| 20th | **M11** 5 miles south of Junction 8 |
| 22nd | The Green, Sarratt |
| 23rd | **A602**, Watton to Tonwell Road by Dane End turning |
| 26th | Great Hadham Road, Bishop's Stortford at junction with Wentworth Drive |

*February 1998*

| | |
|---|---|
| 1st | Stevenage Road, Knebworth by railway bridge |
| 6th | High Wych Lane by school |
| 7th | **A1(M)** northbound by Junction 6 (Welwyn) |
| 9th | Stortford Lane junction with **A120**, Braughing |
| 11th | **M1** southbound by Junction 8 |
| 20th | Sandpit Lane, St.Albans **TL 183 085** |

*March 1998*

| | |
|---|---|
| 8th | **M10** southbound between Junctions 1 and 2 |
| 8th | **A1(M)** northbound by Junction 6 (Welwyn) |
| 9th | Watton Road, Stapleford **TL 312 180** |
| 14th | Rushton to Royston road 2 miles from Rushton |
| 19th | **A10** Ware Bypass |
| 20th | Between Cromer and Walkern **TL 293 274** |
| 20th | **A10** Buntingford **TL 372 278** |

| 22nd | **A4251** Tring between Cow Lane and Twist Roundabout |
| 23rd | Wadesmill Road, Chapmore End |
| 24th | **A602** Little Wymondely bypass |

### April 1998
| 4th | **A602** Watton at Stone **TL 323 191** |
| 6th | St.Albans Road, Hemel Hempstead 500yds from the 'magic roundabout' |
| 10th | Box Lane, Hemel Hempstead |
| 11th | Ringshall Road, Dagnall, Berkhamsted |
| 11th | **A414** Hatfield Road, Cole Green |
| 11th | Widbury Hill, Ware |
| 11th | **A4251** Cow Roast, Tring |
| 14th | Bell Lane, London Colney by Salisbury Hall |
| 14th | High Wych Lane between High Wych and Gilston |
| 20th | **A505** Royston Road, Baldock |
| 26th | **A10** Westmill, Buntingford |
| 30th | **A1(M)** southbound between Junctions 8 and 7 |

As well as road casualties, bottles left by motorists in lay-bys produced mammal records. In the 1970s, before glass recycling was well established, bottle dumps like this one near Widford would be responsible for the deaths of thousands of small mammals.

### May 1998
| 3rd | **A4251** Tring |
| 4th | **A5** Watling Street, Friars Wash |
| 5th | **A41** Berkhamsted Bypass by Chesham Road |
| 5th | Watford Road, Hunton Bridge |
| 5th | Wadesmill Road between the two Chapmore End turns |
| 7th | Radlett Road, Colney Street one mile north of Radlett |
| 7th | Brickenden Lane, Hertford 200 yards east of Clements Farm |
| 11th | outside 16 Gallows Hill, Abbots Langley |
| 13th | Gresley Way, Stevenage |
| 17th | Wadesmill Road, Westmill, Ware |
| 17th | **A10** Westmill **TL 373 273** |
| 19th | **A505** Royston between Little Chef and Tesco's roundabouts |
| 20th | **A414** Stanstead Abbotts by Roydon fly-over |
| 25th | Smug Oak Lane by Moor Mill |
| 28th | High Trees, Pains End, Anstey |
| 30th | Chorleywood Common by the Cricket Club |
| 31st | **A10** northern end of Puckeridge bypass |

The fatal angle of a discarded milk bottle is shown. Investigating shrews, mice and voles enter only to slip on the glass when they try to exit. The species present in an area can be identified by emptying the bottle contents onto newspaper and the dentition in the skulls will show the type of victim. The skulls can be kept for reference in plastic bags (see pp71, 72 & 74).

### June 1998
| 2nd | **A1(M)** northbound between Junctions 9 and 10 |
| 5th | Thieves Lane, Hertford |
| 12th | **A411** Hempstead Road junction Bridge Lane |
| 14th | Bulbourne Road, Berkhamsted |
| 18th | **A505** between Baldock and Royston by Sandon turn |

A road casualty weasel is noted with location and date.

The site of the casualty is fixed on an Ordnance Survey map. In this case the grid reference is TL 214 192

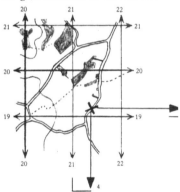

| 26th | Cambridge Road, Sawbridgeworth between London Road and Parsonage Lane |

### July 1998

| 9th | Park Street, St.Albans |
| 13th | Watton to Datchworth Road |
| 13th | **A1(M)** Junction 6 at Welwyn |
| 18th | Bennetts End Road, Bennetts Ends by path to Three Corners |
| 20th | Ayres End Lane, Harpenden |
| 25th | **A416** Kingshill Way, Berkhamsted |

### August 1998

| 3rd | Springfield Road, Berkhamsted |
| 3rd | **A505** Slip End, Baldock |
| 4th | Bedmond Road, Pimlico, near Hyde Lane |
| 5th | Station Road, Albury, Tring |
| 12th | **A1(M)** between Junctions 4 and 5 |
| 17th | **A5183** Dunstable Road, Redbourne |
| 22nd | Brickenden Lane, Brickendenbury **TL 326 106** |
| 23rd | Icknield Way, Tring between Industrial Estate and Crows Nest |
| 23rd | Mundells Roundabout, Welwyn Garden City **TL 250 135** |

### September 1998

| 6th | Wiggley Lane, Little Tring |
| 10th | **A505** Beech Hill, Lilley |
| 10th | **A41** Bourne End, Hemel Hempstead |
| 14th | Wadesmill Road, Chapmore End |
| 15th | **A41** Tring Bypass by Tring turn |
| 17th | **A41** Bypass, Hemel Hempstead |
| 27th | **A41** Bypass, Hemel Hempstead |
| 28th | **M25** clockwise between Junctions 19 and 20 |
| 30th | Gresley Way, Stevenage near Six Hills Way |
| 30th | Bedmond Road between Hemel Hempstead and Leverstock Green |

### October 1998

| 4th | **A1(M)** southbound at Junction 6 at Welwyn |
| 19th | **A10** Westmill, **TL 372 278** |
| 21st | Stapleford **TL 310 160** |
| 24th | Breakspear Way, Hemel Hempstead 500 yds from **M1** |
| 26th | Cory Wright Way, Wheathamstead, by Sheepcote Lane |

### November 1998

| 1st | Lower Luton Road, Harpenden between Bower Heath Lane and Hydemill Farm |
| 9th | Redbourne Road, Hemel Hempstead by kennels |

280

| | |
|---|---|
| 14th | Lower Luton Road, Harpenden between Bower Heath Lane and Farrs Lane |
| 16th | Digswell Hill, Welwyn |
| 18th | Cromer to Rushden Road |
| 20th | Tonwell TL332177 |
| 21st | Watton to Datchworth Road **TL 285 186** |
| 23rd | Welwyn **TL 236 166** |
| 24th | Hempstead Lane, Potten End |
| 25th | Nettledon Road, Little Gaddesden |
| 26th | Toms Lane junction with Primrose Hill, Kings Langley |
| 30th | **A411** Hempstead Road, Watford |

*December 1998*

| | |
|---|---|
| 3rd | Watton at Stone, Heathmount School **TL 316 192** |
| 20th | by Digswell Water **TL 243 150** |
| 29th | **A1(M)** southbound at Junction 6 (Welwyn) |

*If road casualties or other dead specimens are measured, disposable gloves should always be used. Instruments must be cleaned after use and the body disposed of safely.*

## How to take standard measurements for mammals

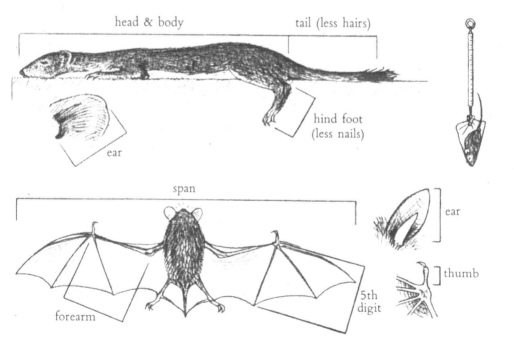

# Appendix 4

# Table of large cat sightings

**The President of the *HNHS*, Brian Sawford, with Quentin Rose when the Society conference featured alien species established in Britain. Quentin considers that unless action is taken now to catch big cats bred from those released in the 1970s, there will eventually be a dramatic increase in their numbers.**

**Any paw prints twice the size of this, or larger, *without* claw marks, are worthy of plaster casts. Robert Martin at the Cat Survival Trust is willing to check them at:**
**The Centre,**
**Codicote Road,**
**Welwyn,**
**Hertfordshire.**

Prepared by Inspector Steve Kourik, the Wildlife Liaison Officer of Hertfordshire Police and a past Chairman of the Hertfordshire Mammal Group

It should be noted that all these descriptions are as given by witnesses. There have been no incidents where independent confirmation has been forthcoming except the report of 6th November 1995. There are clusters of reports which may be significant (as is the report by Terry Moore of The Cat Survival Trust, who keeps most types of cat species, 12th October 1998).

I am most grateful to Steve Kourik for making this material available in the hope of learning more about feral big cats. Peter James, who owns an exceptional private collection of 13 big cats in central Hertfordshire, tells me that puma *Felis concolor* and black panther *Panthera pardus* are the two species of exotic large cats mostly sighted loose in the wild, both in Hertfordshire and nationally.

Up to 1974 many dangerous species of carnivore were kept in little more than kennels and chicken runs in gardens. New legislation in that year meant that many owners, to avoid prosecution, offered their 'pets' to zoos. When the zoos became saturated with big cats and could absorb no more, many people released them to the wild. Only now have a few owned up to this: the BBC National News (28th January 2000) showed two men who released big cats near Sheffield in the 1970s. One was styled 'The Black Country Lion King' and he admitted releasing a panther on the Pennines, followed two days later by a cougar.

With so many released, breeding has clearly taken place and Hertfordshire alone now produces many sightings each year, as Steve Kourik's list shows. Peter James' collection is subject to strict licencing and inspection. At the time of writing he has African leopard *Panthera pardus*, black panther (the black-coated form of the leopard), puma *Felis concolor*, snow leopard *P. unicia*, Persian leopard *P. saxicolor*, and clouded leopards *Neofelis nebulosa*.

When looking at possible large cat kills such as deer, pull back the skin and check the claw marks. If five claw marks are present a badger may have eaten from the victim after its death. In this country only a badger will leave 5 claw marks in a row (elsewhere it could be a bear).

The list of sightings in Hertfordshire follows.

**2nd January 1995** Digswell Hill. Welwyn - *Black 'panther' '2 inch paw prints' found*

**12th January 1995** Gubblecote, Tring - *'2ft tall, Leopard markings'*

**14th April 1995** Nup End, Knebworth - *Large black 'panther'*

**25th April 1995** Harpenden - *Black 'puma'*

**8th May 1995** Harpenden - *Tawney coloured lion, 2ft high, 4ft long*

**19th July 1995** Tring - *Grey speckled with stripes from cranium to jaw. 'Gregorys Safari Cat'*

**20th October 1995** Rickmansworth - *'Larger than guard dog'* Seen by 3 people over 2 nights

**6th November 1995** Potters Heath - *Snow leopard -Peter James'*

**21st December 1995** Rickmansworth - *'Black panther'*

**10th January 1996** Rickmansworth, Moor Park - *'Very large black cat'*

**11th January 1996** Rickmansworth, Moor Park - *'Very large black cat'*

**16th June 1996** Berkhamsted Golf Course 95?10? - *'Cream coloured with black. Saw it several times whilst camping'*

**27th June 1996** Welwyn TL 225 214 - *'3ft high cat'*

**5th July 1996** Bayford, nr. Hertford TL 310 097 - *'Panther like cat'- sheep killed*

**3rd August 1996** Rickmansworth ? ?04? 99? - *'2ft 6ins at shoulder; 4ft long'*

**20th August 1996** Tring - *'Lion'* Numerous calls

**1st September 1996** Knebworth Park TL 230 208 - *'Dark fur; long tail, thick neck, small head, feline ,*

**9th November 1996** Digswell Hill, Welwyn TL 22? 15? - *'3ft tall cat'*

**12th March 1997** Letchworth TL 202 323 - *'Huge, heavy. Jumped on parked cars'*

**10th July 1997** Letchworth TL 209 323 - *'Twice size of domestic cat'*

**10th August 1997** Furneaux Pelham TL 453 267 - *'Large, pale coloured cat. From book -looked like a puma'*

**11th August 1997** Stevenage TL 256 268 - *'Size of Alsation with very long tail, ran low on ground, dark orange'*

**31st October 1997** Harpenden TL 127 161 - *'Large black puma/panther'*

**19th January 1998** Stanstead Abbotts TL 386 120 - *'Large light coloured cat'*

Peter James (see p282) with tiger cub and visitors to Paradise Park Zoo near Broxbourne.

Familiarity with hand-reared adult tigers appears to be safe until these big cats are about two years old.

No tigers *Panthera tigris* or cheetahs *Acinonyx jubatus* are known to have been released into the wild in Britain. Of the big cats, only a cheetah leaves claw marks in its tracks. If a very large paw print has any kind of claw marks, it has been made by a dog like a great Dane or other very large breed.

Domestic cat.

A big cat in silhouette.
Where they are concerned it is difficult to produce a risk assessment for humans in the countryside. Nobody should be put off enjoying outdoor walks, but never behave like a victim. If you see one, stand still and stare; never turn and run. If a big cat has stalked you and starts its final run you have about three seconds to take evasive action. The danger from big cats (which are more likely to be watching you from a tree as you walk past below) may be linked to the time of day, your behaviour and if you have a prey item with you, such as a small dog.

Leopard.

**17th January 1998** Kings Langley ?? ?52 003 - *Nothing seen 'Goat ripped apart'*

**10th February 1998** Hemel Hempstead ?? 03? 02? - *'Large puma cat'*

**2nd March 1998** Anstey. Buntingford TL 40? 32? - *No specific sightings reported. Various rumours of large cat*

**22nd April 1998** Rickmansworth area ?? 041 939 - *Large black cat*

**24th April 1998** Rickmansworth ?? 041 939 - *'Large black cat puma/panther'*

**20th May 1998** Hoddesdon TL 367 078 - *Large cat with tufts on ears. Numerous reports*

**22nd June 1998** Sawbridgeworth TL 476 152 - *'Very large, large head, dark or black, thinner/longer than Labrador'*

**30th June 1998** Sawbridgeworth TL 482 154 - *'Large cat in tree, weight bent the branches'*

**3rd August 1998** Stapleford TL 297 172 - *'Large cat, 50% bigger than fox, grey brown'*. Seen by police officers

**3rd August 1998** Braughing TL 393 252 - *'Loud growling heard, deep scratch marks on wall'*

**17th August 1998** Essendon TL 276 076 - *'4 huge paw prints in bunker of golf course'*

**18th August 1998** Furneux Pelham TL 436 276 - *'Sandy coloured'*

**29th August 1998** Bishop's Stortford TL 486 216 - *'Lioness, long tail'*

**14th September 1998** Rickmansworth ?? 02? 94? - *'Black panther'*

**20th September 1998** St.Albans TL 183 072 - *'Dark brown or black long tail. Jumped 5ft gate'*

**27th September 1998** South Mimms ?? 148 150 - Call from police.

**27th September 1998** Harpenden - *'Sighting, three weeks old'*

**27th September 1998** Tadlow, Royston - *'Large cat, alsation-sized, liver brown, long tail touching ground'*

**28th September 1998** Hatfield - *'Heard growling outside house'*

**28th September 1998** St.Albans TL 156 053 - *'Light brown with darker markings' Two witnesses; cat had rabbit in mouth*

**29th September 1998** Flamstead ?? 081 152 - *'Claw marks on shed'*

**29th September 1998** Sawbridgeworth TL 480 150 - *'Huge black cat, 4ft tall'*

**29th September 1998** Welham Green TL 229 058 - *'Fawn, large, splash ofwhite. Bounding gait'*

**30th September 1998** St.Albans TL 243 109 - *'Black shape'*

**1st October 1998** Stanstead Abbotts TL 38? 11? - *'Large, light coloured, white patch under chin. Stalking by river'*

**3rd October 1998** North Mymms Park TL 21? 04? - *'Big cat, pale brown, very long tail, low to ground'*

**5th October 1998** Brookmans Park TL 255 034 - *'Puma, size of greyhound, biscuit coloured'*

**12th October 1998** Welwyn TL 227 165 - *'Black cat, size of Labrador'*

**12th October 1998** Sacombe TL 337 197 - *Female puma. Seen by an expert: T.Moore (Cat Survival Trust)*

**20th October 1998** Watford ?? 118 963 - *'Puma, light brown, mountain lion'*

**7th November 1998** Rickmansworth TQ 025 945 - *'Black cat: puma'*

Dave Watson with a snow leopard cub at Peter James' collection in central Hertfordshire.

**11th November 1998** Hertford Heath TL 348 105 - *'Lynx, collie-size, light tan, grey tints'*

**21st November 1998** Bishop's Stortford TL 502 215 - *'6 ft nose to tail, dusky brown'*

**23rd November 1998** Stevenage TL 256 238 - *'Black, short-haired, size of medium dog, long whiskers, pointed ears'*

**6th December 1998** Hemel Hempstead ?? 07? 07? - *Nothing seen but high pitched wail heard'. Fox?*

**6th December 1998** Felden Lane. Hemel Hempstead ?? 04? 05? - *'Big black cat'*

**4th January 1999** Whitehill Golf Course, Dane End TL 34? 20? - *'Very large golden animal' (see 12th October 1998)*

**20th January 1999** Welham Green TL 23? 04? - *'Large black animal like a panther' - see next report*

**24th January 1999** Hatfield TL 227 098 - *'Large dun brown cat-like animal, 4ft long 20ins high travelling at 20mph' (see above)*

Dead muntjac with bite marks on its neck. Collected by Mark Allen, *HMWT* Wildlife Ranger, from the Potters Bar area where sheep were also killed. One or more large dogs are usually to blame for these attacks.

**25th January 1999** Bishop's Stortford *'Large dark animal, may be a panther'*

**6th January 1999** A41 Tring bypass ?? 908 109 - *'Very large black cat' On footbridge*

**28th March 1999** Aynsworth Ave., Bishop's Stortford TL 493 226 - *'Black puma'. In a tree*

**28th April 1999** Northchurch Common ?? 975 098 - *'Large tiger'. Stalking deer*

**20th May 1999** High Wych Road, Sawbridgeworth TL 467 147 - *Heard cat killing something in bushes*

The distinguished botanist David Bellamy frequently helps promote conservation in the county. Here he is speaking to Elizabeth Maughan, past *HMWT* Council member, with Kathy Kourik in the background.

**26th May 1999** Shoplands, Welwyn Garden City TL 239 145 - *Black doberman - chased informant*

**27th May 1999** High Wych Road., Sawbridgeworth TL 467 147 - *Size of Labrador*

**13th July 1999** Aldbury, Tring ?? 97? 13? - *'Black panther'*

**19th July 1999** Bedmond Road, Hemel Hempstead ?? 08? 06? - *'2ft long, 15ins tall short tail, brown stocky'*. Erythristic badger?

**21st July 1999** Jacks Hill, Graveley TL 23? 29? - *'Ocelot' black/brown*

**1st August 1999** West Road, Sawbridgeworth TL 47? 15? - *'Large dark coloured'*

**9th August 1999** Waterhouse Street, Hemel Hempstead - *'Cat with bob tail seen on CCTV'*. Moggy with half a tail?

**19th August 1999** Church Lane, Stapleford TL 31? 16? - *'Size of Labrador; black, long tail, fast'*

**5th September 1999** Hemel Hempstead TL 060 073 - *'Large black cat with very long tail'*

**15th September 1999** Watford ?? 135 967 - *'Very large black cat with red eyes, 3 times size of a fox'*. In cemetry

**5th October 1999** Stevenage TL 270 260 - *'Black, twice size of Staffordshire bull terrier'*. In Box Wood

**6th October 1999** Watton at Stone TL 297 197 - *'Sandy coloured, lithe'*. On the Lammas

**6th October 1999** Hertford TL 328 127 - *'Black, larger than domestic cat'*. In church graveyard

**22nd November 1999** Cottered TL 320 293 - *'Half grown puma'*

**19th December 1999** Tile Kiln Fm, Much Hadham - *'Large black animal'*. Caught in fox trap, smashed its way out

**3rd February 2000** Long Marston, Tring ? ?90 ?15 - *'Black, size of Alsation dog'*. Was up tree, bounded away.

**16th March 2000** Kimpton TL 165 183 - *'Panther sized'*. Dog paw prints found

**28th March 2000** Weston TL 25? 30? - *'2½ft tall, tufted ears'*

**4th September 2000** Batford TL 14? 15? - *'Black, shiny coat, 3ft long, long tail'*. Bounding very fast

**5th September 2000** Kings Langley 08? 00? - *'Stripey ginger/brown, tufted ears, size of Labrador.'* Dug lawn up

David Attenborough (right) giving his time freely to promote local conservation at the Old Palace, Hatfield House, with *HNHS* President Brian Sawford and Terri Sawford.

# The Victoria County History for Hertfordshire

# Appendix 5

Named after Queen Victoria, the *Victoria County Histories* were begun in 1899. The text has been edited but the common and Latin names are left in their original form, though many of them have since been changed. Numerous wildlife books refer to records from these County Histories and it seemed worthwhile to include this difficult-to-source reference to compare with the current status of animals. The following is A.H.Cocks' entry for mammals for the 1905 edition (copied to county recorders by Gillie Sargent, the Look Out for Mammals Development Officer of the *Mamm Soc*, autumn 1999). Cocks also wrote the Buckinghamshire entry.

*'It is unfortunately the case that until a few years ago the mammals of Hertfordshire had received but little attention from local naturalists.*

*'The chief sources from which I have procured information are the Transactions of the Watford Natural History Society and the Transactions of the Herfordshire Natural History Society; I have also found some interesting records in Mr.Harting's articles on British Mammals which have appeared from time to time in the Zoologist.*

*'Of the several branches the Chiroptera have received the least amount of attention. Only four species of bats have up to the present been identified, and it is reasonable to suppose that when more time and trouble have been given to them, several species which are found in other counties will be added to the list.*

*'The distribution of the various mammals has by no means been thoroughly worked out, so that there is little of special interest that can be said about the majority, as they are common throughout the county, but to such animals as the badger (Meles meles), the polecat (Putorius putorius), the pine marten (Mustela martes) and the otter (Lutra lutra), especial interest is attached owing to their declining numbers and rare occurrence at the present day.*

*'At the end of the list will be found the mention of two animals, the red deer (Cervus elaphus) and the fallow deer (Cervus dama), which appear in the county at the present day only in a semi-domesticated state in parks, and are not feral naturally.'*

### *'CHEIROPTERA*

*1* **Lesser horseshoe bat** *(Rhinolophus hipposiderus) The Rev.H.A.Macpherson in the Zoologist for 1887, p152, states that a fresh example of this species, which had been obtained in Hertfordshire, was sent in the summer of 1886 to Spalding of Notting Hill.*

**Practical conservation always needs helpers. David Laming, Chair of *HMWT* local group for Welwyn and Hatfield, during scrub clearance by volunteers at Dawley Woods, Tewin. Les Borg, who helped to illustrate this book, is in the centre background.**

**Ponds need management and Mike Ainger is shown carrying out winter work at Tewin.**

Visits to city farms and other places such as Standalone Farm at Letchworth, encourage an interest in animal life generally. It is vital to introduce young people to the natural world whenever possible as in the survey of moths below.

2  *Long-eared bat* (*Plecotus auritus*)
The long-eared bat is generally distributed throughout the county.
3  *Great or White's bat* (*Pipistrellus noctula*)
This bat is found in all parts of Hertfordshire.
4  *Pipistrelle* (*Pipistrellus pipistrellus*)
This is an abundant species everywhere in the county.

'*INSECTIVORA*
5  *Hedgehog* (*Erinaceus europæus*)
This animal is common in Hertfordshire, though many are destroyed in various ways. A female hedgehog in my possession in July of this year (1900) devoured one of the young ones which I found with it.
6  *Mole* (*Talpa europæus*)
The mole is very abundant, though apparently it is more plentiful during some years than others. In the winter of 1879-80 it seems to have been unusually numerous throughout the county. This species is subject rather often to variations in colour, for in the Trans of the Herts Nat Hist Soc for 1883 the late Dr.Brett recorded the finding of thirty moles of a white or cream colour in about half an acre of a field of oats. Some albino moles also, caught in a hedgerow at Ley Farm on the St.Albans Road, Watford, were exhibited by Mr.T.Vaughan Roberts at a meeting of the Society in December 1891.
7  *Common shrew* (*Sorex araneus*)
This animal is found throughout the county, but of its congener (*S. pygmæus*) I can find no record. In August or September 1893, Mr.Henry Lewis of St.Albans obtained from a clover-field near that place two specimens of the common shrew which were albinos; this is a most unusual occurrence, as albinism is seldom found in this species.
8  *Water shrew* (*Neomys fodiens*)
This species is to be found in many parts of Hertfordshire where the locality is suitable. There are, I believe, several specimens in the national collection which are labelled as having been obtained at Tring.

'*CARNIVORA*
9  *Fox* (*Vulpes vulpes*)
So long as fox-hunting lasts in this country will the fox remain with us, but when the evil day comes that the noble sport is given up in England then will this species soon become extinct. In many districts in Hertfordshire the fox is by no means so plentiful as can be desired. This is chiefly due to the fact that so much of the county is given up to shooting rather than hunting. It is however most strictly preserved by many owners in the county.
10  *Pine marten* (*Mustela martes*)
The pine marten has unfortunately been so long extinct in Hertfordshire that I am unable to find more than one record

*of it. This is in Mr.Harting's article on the British marten which appeared in the Zoologist for 1891, p456, where it is stated that a specimen was obtained in Oxhey Wood near Watford on December 26th 1872, which animal is, I believe, now preserved at Bushey.*

**11  Polecat** *(Putorius putorius)*

*The species is nearly, if not quite, extinct as a Hertfordshire mammal, although at one time not an uncommon resident. In the neighbouring county of Buckingham polecats are still to be found and may still travel into Hertfordshire.*

*Mr.T.Vaughan Roberts has informed me that Seymour of Hertford, who was at one time keeper at Ware Park, trapped one there about 1885. Mr.Roberts also stated that a polecat was obtained some years ago near Hitchin. These are the only specific records I can find of this animal in Hertfordshire.*

**12  Stoat** *(Putorius erminius)*

*This is a common inhabitant of the county although it suffers a great deal at the hands of gamekeepers. This species occasionally frequents mole-runs, as is evidenced by one being caught in a mole-trap at Knightlands Farm, Barnet, in February 1891. Albino specimens have from time to time been procured in Hertfordshire.*

**13  Weasel** *(Putorius nivalis)*

*The weasel is also common throughout the county, though its numbers, as in the case of the last species, are well kept down by gamekeepers. The extreme fearlessness of this animal is wonderful and is shown by the fact that Lord Aldenham's keeper once killed one with his foot when it approached him in the grass, while he was feeding young pheasants.*

**14  Badger** *(Meles meles)*

*Although perhaps not so plentiful as formerly, the badger is still far from being extinct in Hertfordshire and breeds in large earths in many parts of the county. In 1886 a badger weighing 25lb was caught in Lord Cowper's park at Panshanger about the middle of February, while in the Society's Trans for 1892 Mr.T.Vaughan Roberts mentioned Odsey as an additional locality for this species. In the following year, he gave a very interesting account of a large earth at Ashlyns which had existed there for many years.*

**15  Otter** *(Lutra lutra)*

*This animal cannot be considered common although it has occurred on a good many occasions in Hertfordshire. Seymour showed Mr.Vaughan Roberts two others, one of which was trapped in Ware Park about 1888, while the other was shot about a mile and a half from Hertford in 1892.*

**'RODENTIA**

**16  Squirrel** *(Sciurus leucourus)*

*This is a fairly plentiful resident in most parts of the county.*

**An unusually close view of a bat as it is measured at Wormleybury (by kind permission of Trevor James).**

*Brett's Trans of the Watford Nat Hist Soc (1877) is quoted in the section on the badger at p173 et seq.*

When mammal records are based only on field signs it is vital to be certain the correct species is identified. These swan mussel shells were found in large numbers on the side of the River Rib near Ware. To see if they were mink or otter feeding remains they were passed to Pryce Buckle, who in turn checked them with Dr. David Aldridge at Cambridge. He was able to establish that they were eaten by brown rats which have a particular way of biting open the shell.

The section of the River Rib where the swan mussel shells were found.

17 **Dormouse** (*Muscardinus avellanarius*)
*This small animal is certainly plentiful in many parts of the county, being often caught in the autumn and kept as a pet. In the Zoologist for 1885, p204, it is stated, on the authority of the Rev.H.A.Macpherson, that it was found commonly in Hertfordshire.*

18 **Brown rat** (*Mus decumanus*)
*This is another very common resident which often does a vast amount of damage. In January 1892 a specimen of the dark variety, which is sometimes known as Mus hibernicus, was obtained at Wheathampstead and was preserved by Cane of Luton.*

19 **House mouse** (*Mus musculus*)
*The common mouse is ubiquitous.*

20 **Wood mouse or long-tailed field mouse**
(*Mus sylvaticus*)
*This animal is found commonly throughout the county.*

21 **Harvest mouse** (*Mus minutus*)
*In a paper by Mr.Harting on the harvest mouse, which appeared in the Zoologist for 1895, p421, Hertfordshire is mentioned on the authority of the late Frederick Bond as being a county in which this species has occurred. It is recorded in the Fauna and Flora of Haileybury (1888) as having been found in that neighbourhood. I have found it in the county: in 1900 I came across the nest and young and saw the parent in the neighbourhood of Berkhamsted.*

22 **Water vole** (*Microtus amphibius*)
*The water-rat, as it is usually called, is generally distributed throughout Hertfordshire wherever the conditions are suitable.*

23 **Field vole** (*Microtus agrestis*)
*An extremely common species throughout Hertfordshire.*

24 **Bank vole** (*Evotomys glareolus*)
*In the Zoologist for 1887, p365, Mr.Harting stated, on the authority of Yarrell, that this species had occurred in the county, while on p425 of the same journal the late Frederick Bond included Hertfordshire in the list of counties in which he had taken the bank vole. In March 1893, Mr.T.Vaughan Roberts had some of these animals sent to him from near Berkhamsted, where they had been found in a nest in a heap of marigolds. He had a cage made for them, and some of them eventually bred in confinement, but after there had been two broods he thought it time to get rid of them. He was accustomed to feed them on corn, bread, apples, carrots and gooseberries, and he gave them plenty of water. In the Trans Herts Nat Hist Soc (1893), p173, and the Zoologist (1892), p329, may be found very interesting accounts by Mr.Roberts of his experience with these creatures.*

25 **Common hare** (*Lepus europæus*)
*This animal is found in most parts of the county, though its numbers vary considerably in different districts and in different years. In some places it is very common, while in*

others only one or two can be found in a day. It is most interesting to observe how the colour of this species varies according to the soil of the district in which it is found.

**26  Rabbit** (Lepus cuniculus)
This species is very abundant in nearly every part of the county, though no doubt more plentiful in some places than others. Dr.Brett in the Trans Watford Nat Hist Soc (1878), p112, gave some interesting notes on some coloured varieties of this species. He mentioned that a Mr.King of Wiggenhall had a wild grey rabbit which about twenty years before had produced three black young ones. These he had preserved, and, at the time that Dr.Brett wrote, Mr.King had a large colony of black rabbits. In fact in 1878 they outnumbered the grey animals. He also stated that pied varieties never occurred, and that, although the black and the grey inter-bred, the offspring were always all black or all grey.

The Beane Valley provides a background to this demonstration of horse-drawn ploughing at a farm open day at Aston, near Stevenage.

**'UNGULATA**

**27  Red deer** (Cervus elaphus)
Although neither this nor the following species occurs in a wild state in Hertfordshire at the present day, a paper on the mammals of the county is hardly complete without some mention of them. In the Trans Watford Nat Hist Soc (1878), p32, there is mention made of the discovery, in the peat in Panshanger Park, of a fine pair of antlers and fifteen vertebrae which were referred to this species. The antlers were in a good state of preservation and measured 3 feet in length, 21ins in spread and 7ins in circumference, just above the place where they joined the skull. Whether these remains belonged to the indigenous red deer of Hertfordshire or to the former enclosed animals is uncertain, but I should rather think to the former category.

In contrast, the modern approach to ploughing: a reversible plough at Dawley, Tewin.

There is however the possibility of their belonging to enclosed animals as formerly there were deer in this park, although I believe there are none there at the present day. In the Trans of the Herts Nat Hist Soc (1883), p97, Mr.Harting supplies a very interesting paper on Hertfordshire deer parks, from which it would appear that at that time this species was only kept in one park in the county, viz. Ashridge Park, the seat of Earl Brownlow. There are still red deer there, some of which occasionally bear fine heads. During the present year I saw a stag there with a fine head of nineteen points. I believe that at the present time there are from 100 to 150 red deer there.

**28  Fallow deer** (Cervus dama)
Though now only to be found in parks in this county, no doubt the fallow deer, which still exists in a practically wild state in Epping Forest in the adjoining county of Essex, was also found wild here. Those days however have unfortunately long since passed away.'

# Appendix 6

# The London Natural History Society mammal records for Hertfordshire *by Paul Moxey*

**Paul Moxey.**

*Paul Moxey has kindly prepared a summary for me of the LNHS mammal records for 1961-1979. Because the LNHS covers part of Hertfordshire I felt it important to publish extracts from his summary here and the references for the Society's journal, London Naturalist, to help with future research.*

The *LNHS* recording area covers a circle with a radius of 20miles from St.Paul's Cathedral, which extends into southern Hertfordshire. The *London Naturalist* was first published in 1920, but there seems to have been no systematic mammal recording until about 1960. The first mammal report appeared in 1962; detailed reports and species studies continued until 1969, the main author being 'Bunny' Teagle, but there were also significant contributions from Ian Beames, John Burton and Pat Morris. Ken Gold revived the regular reports in the 1970s but commented that the number of active recorders was declining and the last report was by Jeremy Cotton in 1980. However, the Roberts' 1978 paper on the fossil fauna at Stanstead Abbotts belongs to this period.

There have been no mammal reports for 20 years, but there have been designated mammal recorders who collate sightings as a report. The current recorder is Clive Herbert.

Hertfordshire has always been under-recorded by the *LNHS* because their most active mammal enthusiasts did not live near the county. I have summarised all the published Hertfordshire records (apart from grey squirrels) since 1961. Some, such as the water vole, suggest significant differences from today.

*Teagle W.G. (1962)* **Mammal recording in 1961** *LN41 88-89.* Muntjac - Cuffley Great Wood and in woodland in the Lea Valley - referred to as 'outstanding records'.

*Teagle W.G. (1963)* **Mammals in the London area** *LN42 42-58.* Brown hare - 3 at Old Parkbury, 28th June 1958, one at Shenley 1st February1959. Wood mouse - total of 62 trapped in Gobions Wood, Brookmans Park, October to December 1960; yellow-necked mouse - 2 in traps; bank vole - 6 in traps; field vole - 1 in trap.

*Teagle W.G. (1964)* **The harvest mouse in the London area** *LN43 136-149.* Said to be particularly abundant on waste ground at Rye Meads (Tom Gladwin). Records from 1962, 1963 and 1964 - in open community of docks, goosefoot and polygonum on dried-out sludge; assumed they were collecting seed. Harvest mice appeared to be recovering in the London area generally and moving into new habitats. The first record of the species at a sewage works was in 1959.

*Teagle W.G. (1965)* **Mammals in the London area 1962** *LN44 43-57.* Noctule caught in mist net at Rye Meads, 2nd June 1996; pipistrelle - 7 caught in mist nets, July-September 1962. Brown hare - 'greatly increased' at Essendon.

*Burton J.A. (1966)* **The distribution of weasel, stoat, common shrew, roe deer, water shrew and mole in the London area** *LN45 35-42.* Weasel - map gives 6 records, but not place names; one appears to be Rye Meads (covers 1960-64). Stoat only 1 site, Rye Meads - 3 records? (1960-64). Mole about 15 sites (1960-65). Common shrew - 7 sites, one of which is Rye Meads (1960-64). Water shrew - 3 records, 2 at Rye Meads, one just south of Rickmansworth (1960-65).

*Morris P. (1966)* **The hedgehog in London** *LN45 43-49.* Records for 1956-64: 'It is unfortunate that most of the more assiduous observers live south of the Thames so that the hedgehog's distribution ... is very poorly known in Hertfordshire and Essex'. Map shows 7 sites, with 9 records of which 2 from Rye Meads.

*Burton J.A. (1967)* **Notes on mammals in the London area** *LN46 40-43.* Brown hare - map showing 7 sites, two records from Rye Meads area.

*Teagle W.G. (1967)* **The fox in the London suburbs** *LN 46 44-68.* Unfortunately this benchmark paper does not cover Hertfordshire although there is a reference to foxes scavenging from dustbins at Broxbourne in June 1964. This appears to have been a new development.

*Beames I.R. (1968)* **Mammals in the London area 1966** *LN47 25-37.* Hedgehog - Barnet, Brookmans Park, Colney Heath, East Barnet, Northaw, Potters Bar, Whetstone. Mole - Croxley Moor, Leggatts Wood, London Colney, Moor Park, North Mymms, Otterspool, Water Hill. Fox - over 40 sightings in Potters Bar area. Bank vole - one in Longworth, London Colney, 2nd October. Water vole - Maple Cross about 10 on 15th October; West Hyde - 3 on 18th April; 3 on 15th October.

*Beames I.R. (1968)* **Bats in the London area** *LN47 38-49.* Serotine - 3 caught in flight, May 1963, and in mist nets on several dates in 1964; all at Rye Meads. Noctule - one in mist net, Rye Meads, June 1962; about 20 in mist nets during May 1963. One shot at Broxbourne, 14th November 1964. Pipistrelle - in mist nets at Rye Meads on several dates in

Without numerous volunteers who help on various conservation projects and send in records for the surveys, little of this work would be possible. Here Janine Tyler and Joyce Smith construct bat boxes at a North Hertfordshire College workshop. They organised the *HNHS* programme of meetings to great effect for many years.

293

June Crew helping at the annual Apple Day at Tewin Orchard. June's organisation of toad lifts is referred to on pp37, 39 and 42. She has long served as Hon. Secretary to Cheshunt Natural History Society founded in 1968, and sings with Hertford Choral Society.

Jim Harmer and his family worked on the mammal hide and the enclosures for polecats and pine martens at Tewin Orchard. Although animals are no longer kept at Tewin, Jim and Lesley continue with polecat breeding and are expert on ferrets and ferret welfare.

1962 and 1964. Long-eared bat - one caught in flight at Rye Meads, May 1963.

*Beames I.R. (1969)* **Mammals in the London area 1969** *LN48 40-47.* Weasel - Old Parkbury, 1st January. Muntjac - 'woods around Potters Bar' appear to have provided several records.

*Teagle W.G. (1969)* **The badger in the London area** *LN48 48-75.* This dated but still important paper included the records from the Hertfordshire survey.

*Gold K.A.J. (1974)* **Mammals in the London Area 1972-1973** *LN53 100-104.* Hedgehog - Brickendon, Hertford, Hertingfordbury, Potters Bar. Fox - Broxbourne Woods, Hoddesdon. Stoat - Eastwick, 1972. Weasel - Brickendon, Essendon. Muntjac - Broxbourne. Rabbit - Bayford, Berkhamsted, Broxbourne, Cuffley, Eastwick, Essendon, Hatfield, Hunsdon, Letty Green, Panshanger, Stanstead Abbotts. Water vole - River Rib.

*Gold K.A.J. (1975)* **Mammals in the London area 1974** *LN 54 66-68.* Hedgehog - Cheshunt, Colney Heath, Cuffley, Goff's Oak, London Colney, Potters Bar, Sarratt. Common shrew - Cheshunt, Cuffley. Noctule bat - Barnet. Long-eared bat - Broxbourne, Cheshunt Gravel Pits. Fox - Barnet, Cuffley, Radlett. Stoat - Cassiobury Park. Badger - Turnford. Fallow deer - Broxbourne Woods. Muntjac - Wormley. 'Deer' - Queenswood (North Mymms). Hare - Childwickbury (near Hemel Hempstead), Redbournbury. Rabbit - Cheshunt Gravel Pit, Essendon, Goffs Oak, Hatfield, London Colney, Northaw, Panshanger, Turnford, Wormley. Wood Mouse - Cheshunt. Bank Vole - Cheshunt. Water Vole - Cheshunt and gravel pit, Kings Langley. Field vole -Radlett.

*Gold K.A.J. (1976)* **Mammals in the London area 1975** *LN55 58-61.* Hedgehog - Radlett. Mole - Bricket Wood, Cassiobury Park. Weasel - Water End. 'Deer' - Chiswell Green. Hare - Essendon. Rabbit - Colney Heath, Essendon, North Mymms, Ridge. Water vole - Cheshunt.

*Roberts K.A. & Roberts P.L.E. (1978)* **Post-glacial deposits at Stanstead Abbotts** *LN S7 6-10.* Describes material from gravel working including some plant remains and range of animal bones. Unfortunately the stratigraphy was destroyed but comparison between material adhering to bones and the layers of peat and other soil exposed in the side of the pit suggests a transition from open to wooded conditions, perhaps Mesolithic. A useful insight into the early Hertfordshire mammal fauna.

*Hall D.G. (1978)* **Mammals in the London area 1976** *LN57*
*92-95.* Hedgehog - Rickmansworth. Mole - Pond Wood
Nature Reserve (then Middlesex but now Hertfordshire).
Common shrew - Cheshunt. Weasel - Cheshunt. Muntjac -
Broxbourne Woods. Fallow deer - droppings observed in
Pond Wood Nature Reserve. Rabbit - Broad Colney,
Essendon, Hadley Wood, Hatfield, How Green, Lee Gravel
Pit, Northaw, North Mymms, Panshanger. Water vole - River
Colne, Colney Heath. Field vole - Pond Wood Nature
Reserve.

*Hall D.G. (1978)* **Mammals in the London area 1977** *LN57*
*96-97.* Hedgehog - London Colney, Newgate Street. Weasel -
Cuffley. Muntjac - Broxbourne. Rabbit - Letty Green,
Northaw Great Wood.

*Cotton J. (1979)* **Mammals in the London area 1978** *LN58*
*71-73.* Hedgehog - Cuffley. Muntjac - Broxbourne Woods.
Rabbit - Cuffley

*Cotton J. (1980)* **Mammals in the London area 1979** *LN59*
*84-86.* Hedgehog - London Colney, Rickmansworth. Mole -
Croxley Green, Rickmansworth. Otter - Cheshunt (I later
found this to be false, *MC*). Rabbit - Rickmansworth. Water
vole - Bricket Wood, Broad Colney, Croxley Green,
Rickmansworth, St.Albans, Hertford.

**This old stable on the** *HMWT* **reserve at Tewin Orchard was converted into a hide to watch**
**mammals in twilight by the Badger Group in 1991. Animals are attracted to the illuminated area in**
**front of the hide by bait left throughout the year. The hide can be booked between May and**
**October and details are on the Group's website or via** *HMWT.*

# Appendix 7

## Biodiversity Action Plan and Red Data Book for Hertfordshire

![Amphibian deflectors in place]

**Amphibian deflectors in place, see p42.**

The *HMWT*'s *Biodiversity Action Plan* is part of a national initiative to structure and co-ordinate conservation of the environment and includes sections on the great crested newt, Natterer's bat, water vole, common dormouse and otter. The plan was commissioned by the Hertfordshire Environmental Forum and a range of organisations have contributed to the *HMWT*'s *Fifty Year Vision*. I am most grateful to the Trust's Graham White; *HMBG*; The Bat Conservation Trust; and the *HMG* for making copies available to me. Although there is not space to reproduce all the documents for each related subject, the *Vision* document is an essential reference for all involved with the study of natural history and conservation in the county. It should be used in conjunction with the *Red Data Book* which is still in preparation (see opposite).

As part of the research for the Plan, a very well researched and fully illustrated report has been published by the Trust: *The River Mimram water vole, otter and crayfish survey*. Such a well prepared document reflects the very active approach being demonstrated by the Trust to conserve our native species and gives hopes for future progress in this vital work. See Pearce H., Baker M. & White G. (2000).

**The Bat Group taking a break during ice house restoration work near Hitchin.**

296

# Relevant Societies

# Appendix 8

As you become interested in wildlife a great deal of help and encouragement can come from the local societies concerned with natural history.

## Hertfordshire Natural History Society
*Registered Charity No.218418*

Readers who are not already members of the Society are strongly recommended to join. The Society was one of the earliest natural history groups formed and was founded in 1875 as the Watford Natural History Society before achieving full county status in 1880. The specialist sections include the Hertfordshire Mammal Group (*HMG*), affiliated to The Mammal Society.

The Society arranges conferences each year and surveys are carried out, the records of which are forwarded to the *HBRC*. The Society also publishes newsletters and programmes of field meetings being held around the county.

The published papers referred to in this book (abbreviated as *Trans* for Transactions) are now available for public sale as *The Hertfordshire Naturalist*, as is the *Hertfordshire Bird Report*. Both are published annually and include colour plates.

Recorders for the various fields of study meet regularly and publish reports on their work annually. All are preparing material for the *Hertfordshire Red Data Book* on species where numbers are dangerously low. It is anticipated that it will be updated and reissued every few years. The species relevant to this volume are: smooth newt *Triturus vulgaris*; palmate newt *Triturus helveticus*; great crested newt *Triturus cristatus*; common lizard *Lacerta vivpara*; slowworm *Anguis fragilis*; grass snake *Natrix natrix*; adder *Vipera berus*; hedgehog *Erinaceus europaeus*; common shrew *Sorex araneus*; pygmy shrew *Sorex minutus*; water shrew *Neomys fodiens*; whiskered bat *Myotis mystacinus*; Brandt's bat *Myotis brandtii*; Natterer's bat *Myotis nattereri*; serotine bat *Eptesicus serotinus*; noctule bat *Nyctalus noctula*; Leisler's bat *Nyctalus leisleri*; pipistrelle bat *Pipistrellus pipistrellus*; Nathusius' pipistrelle bat *Pipistrellus nathusii*; barbastelle bat *Barbastella barbastellus*; brown long-eared bat *Plecotus auritus*; stoat *Mustela erminea*; weasel *Mustela nivalis*; polecat *Mustela putorius*; badger *Meles meles*; red deer *Cervus elaphus*; fallow deer *Dama dama*; roe deer *Capreolus capreolus*.

The following national organisations I strongly recommend; they will network your local knowledge and records with the rest of the country (and thus to the world) through their contacts.

The *HNHS* logo.

New members are always welcomed to the *HNHS* and the *HMWT*. Everyone who has any concern for their environment and lives in the county should join both organisations.

In the late 1990s, past President of the *HNHS* Ken Smith introduced many changes that gave new direction to the Society.

Emma Cooper is the present Secretary to the *HNHS* and the Mammal Group. She is also a full-time member of staff at *HMWT*.

Keith Seaman (right) chairs the Mammal Group. He is shown during a survey of fieldfares with Barry Trevis (left) and Mike Reed.

Barry Peck with a ferret. As well as being the *HNHS* examiner, Barry has been instrumental in reviving the publishing activities of the Society in association with Training Publications.

## The Herpetological Conservation Trust *and* The Mammal Society

Both give full details on very attractively presented web sites and list their regular publications, including *The Herpetological Journal*, *Mammal Review* and newsletters for general and young members. Membership is the ideal way to increase knowledge of a subject and contact like-minded people.

## Other environmental organisations

Members of Wildlife and Countryside Link

Bat Conservation Trust
British Association of Nature Conservationists
British Ecological Society
British Mountaineering Council
British Naturalists' Association
British Trust for Conservation Volunteers
Butterfly Conservation
Council for British Archaeology
Council for National Parks
Council for the Preservation of Rural England
Earthkind
Environmental Investigation Agency
Fauna & Flora International
Friends of the Earth
Greenpeace
International Fund for Animal Welfare
Marine Conservation Society
National Trust
Open Spaces Society
People's Trust for Endangered Species
Plantlife
Ramblers' Association
Royal Society for the Prevention of Cruelty to Animals
Royal Society for the Protection of Birds
The Shark Trust
Universities Federation for Animal Welfare
Whale & Dolphin Conservation Society
The Wildfowl & Wetlands Trust
The Wildlife Trusts
Woodland Trust
World Conservation Monitoring
World Fund For Nature-UK
Young People's Trust for the Environment
         & Nature Conservation
Youth Hostels Association (England & Wales)
Zoological Society of London.

I also commend the *BBC Wildlife* magazine because it has established, under the editorship of Rosalind Kidman Cox, a rare combination of scientific accuracy and attractive reading combined with a very high standards of illustration. World-wide entries are attracted to its wildlife photography competitions. The resulting exhibitions are toured round museums after an annual launch at the Natural History Museum. *BBC Wildlife*, together with the equally carefully produced *British Wildlife*, keep their readers informed of the recent developments in research.

I have not given contact addresses or telephone numbers for the above because they so quickly go out of date. It is now easy to search on the internet for this information or visit that invaluable institution, your local library, where they have all the details. Hertfordshire Archives and Local Studies are based at County Hall.

Our museums and their staff are always helpful, and contain a treasure trove of material carefully catalogued and stored for reference. The Walter Rothschild Zoological Museum at Tring and the Natural History Museum at South Kensington, London, are both part of the British Museum and details are listed for both on the same web site. We are fortunate to have eighteen exceptional museums distributed across the county, some of which are combined with libraries and art galleries:

The Walter Rothschild Zoological Museum, Tring
Watford Museum
St.Albans City Museum
Verulamium Museum
Mosquito Aircraft Museum, near Shenley
Lowewood Museum, Hoddesdon
Hertford Museum
Ware Museum
Rhodes Memorial Museum, Bishop's Stortford
Bishop's Stortford Museum
Old Mill House Museum, Welwyn Garden City
Welwyn Roman Bath House
Stevenage Museum
Hitchin Museum & Art Gallery
First Garden City Heritage Museum, Letchworth
Letchworth Museum & Art Gallery
Ashwell Village Museum
Royston Museum.

**Ros Kidman Cox, editor of the** *BBC Wildlife* **magazine, soon after the editorial offices moved from London to Bristol in 1983. The magazine informs and entertains, and has influenced public opinion on wildlife matters. The use of photography is outstanding and the annual photographic competition, which tours the country, is remarkable.**

**Members of the** *HNHS* **test a footpath seat at Bolt Head, south Devon, during a field study stay.**

# Appendix 9

## Sending in your records

You can send in the details of your observations to the appropriate recorder either in your own format or using one of the pre-printed record forms available from the various organisations. The following is a guide to the information required.

### Essential information
Date of observation:
Location: *(be as precise as possible)*
Species:
Number: *(how many? Estimate if not possible to count)*
Confidence: *(how confident are you that your identification is correct?)*

Your name:
Your address/telephone No.:

### Desirable/optional information as appropriate
OS grid reference: *(In the standard format, ie TL 123 456)*

Weather conditions
- temperature: *(eg freezing; warm; deg.C)*
- wet or dry: *(eg heav rain; drizzle; dry)*
- cloud cover: *(eg overcast; % cloud cover)*
- wind strength: *(eg light breeze; gale; still air)*
Time of day: *(use 24 hour clock, eg 16:45)*
Description of habitat:
Other species present:
Tracks:
Droppings:
Feeding residues:
Remarks: *(other relevant information, eg dead or alive; what was it doing?)*

**An *HNHS* 'ramble'**

# Bibliography:

*references and further reading*

Abbott W. (1892) *The section exposed in the foundations of the new Admiralty offices,* Proc Geol Ass **12**: 346-56

Ager N. (1991) *The Hertfordshire farmer in the age of the industrial revolution,* Hertfordshire in history, Ed Doris Jones-Baker, Hertford: The Hertfordshire Local History Council

Alderton D. (1993) *Turtles & tortoises of the world,* London: Blandford

Alibhai S.K. & Gipps J.H.W. (1991) *The bank vole,* in Corbet G.B. & Harris S. (eds)

Anderson D. (1985) *Distribution of Bedfordshire mammal species 1971-1985,* Bedford: Bedfordshire Naturalist

Arnold E.N., Burton J.A. & Ovenden D.W.A. (1978) *A field guide to the reptiles and amphibians of Britain and Europe,* London: Collins

Arnold H.R. (1995) *Atlas of amphibians and reptiles in Britain,* London: HMSO

Arnold H.R. (1993) *Atlas of mammals in Britain,* London: HMSO

Ashby M. (1991) *Forster country,* Stevenage: Flaunden

Arnott A. & Beckett C. (eds.) (1993) *The Herpetofauna worker's guide,* Herpetofauna conservation international (see Gibb & Foster for current edition)

Ashley Cooper A. (1986) *A harvest of Hexton,* Hexton

Baker S. (1990) *Escaped exotic mammals in Britain,* Mammal Review **20**: 75-96

Balharry D. (1993) *Social organisation in martens: an inflexible system?* London: Symp Zool Soc **65**: 321-345

Bang P. & Dahlstrom P. (1974) *Animal tracks and signs,* London: Collins

Banks C., Clark M. & Newton R. (1980) *Observations on an unusual mixed root of serotine and noctule bats in east Hertfordshire,* Trans Herts Nat Hist Soc **28**: 3, 20-22

Banks C., Clark M. & Newton R. (1983) *A second Nathusius' pipistrelle* Pipistrellus nathusii *in Britain,* Trans Herts Nat His Soc **29**: 15-18

Barlow K & Jones G. (1996) *Pipistrellus nathusii* (Chiroptera: Vespertionidae) *in Britain in the mating season,* London: Journal of Zoology **240**: 767-773

Barnes R.F.W. & Tapper S.C. (1986) *Consequences of the myxomatosis epidemic in Britain's rabbit* (Oryctolagus cuniculus) *population on the number of brown hares* (Lepus europaeus), Mammal Review **16**: 111 - 114

Barratt E., Deauville R., Burland T.M., Bruford M.W., Jones G., Racey P.A. & Wayne R.K. (1997) *DNA answers the call of pipistrelle bat species,* Nature **387**: 138-139

Barret-Hamilton G.E.H. and Hinton M.A.C. (1910-1921) *A History of British mammals,* Gurney & Jackson

Bateman J.A. (1971) *Animal traps and trapping,* Newton Abbot: David & Charles

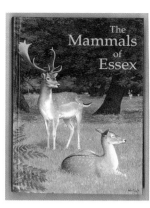

John Dobson's very well illustrated study (1999). There are references to Hertfordshire and it has distribution maps throughout.

Batten H.M. (1923) *The Badger afield and underground,* London: Witherby

BBC Wildlife (1984 to date) *Magazine articles, news items,* reports Bristol: BBC

Beames I.R. (1968) *Mammals in the London area, 1966,* London: The London Naturalist **47**: 25-37

Beames I.R. (1969) *Mammals in the London area, 1969,* London: The London Naturalist **48**: 40-47

Beames I.R. (1968) *Bats in the London area,* London: The London Naturalist **47**: 38-49

Bearder S. (2000) *Flood brothers,* Bristol: BBC Wildlife June 2000 issue, **18**: 6, 64-68

Bedford J., Duke of (1959) *A silver-plated spoon,* London: Cassell

Beebee T. (1985) *Frogs & toads,* London: Whittet

Beebee T. (1992) *Pond life,* London: Whittet

Bell T. (1874) *A history of British quadrupeds,* London

Bell T. (1889) *A history of British reptiles,* London: Vorst

Bentley E.W. (1959) *The distribution and status of* Rattus rattus *in the United Kingdom in 1951 and 1956,* Journal of Animal Ecology **28**: 299-308

Benton M.J.B. (1991) *The Rise of the mammals,* London: Quarto Publishing Ltd.

Berry R.J. (1991) *The ecology of an island population of the house mouse,* Journal of Animal Ecology **37**: 445-470

Berry R.J. (1991) *The house mouse* in Corbet G.B. & Harris S. (eds.)

BHS *Surveying for amphibians, garden ponds as amphibian sanctuaries and Being kind to snakes,* advisory leaflets issued by BHS Conservation Committee

Birks J.D.S. & Dunstone N. (1991) *The mink* in Corbet G.B. & Harris S. (eds.)

Birks J.D.S. & Kitchener A.C. (1999) *The distribution & status of the polecat* Mustela putorius *in Britain in the 1990s,* London: The Vincent Wildlife Trust

Birks J.D.S. (1986) *Mink,* Oswestry: Nelson

Birks J.D.S. (1993) *Return of the polecat,* British Wildlife **5**: 16-25

Briggs B. (1995) *A survey of bats in Hertfordshire by use of bat detectors,* Trans Herts Nat Hist Soc **32**, 3: 245-258

Briggs P. (1995) *Bats in barns,* Trans Herts Nat Hist Soc **32**, 3: 237-244

Bright P.W., Mitchell P. & Morris P.A. (1994) *Dormouse distribution: survey techniques, insular ecology and selection of sites for conservation,* Journal of Applied Ecology **31**: 329-339

Bright P.W. & Morris P.A. (1996) *Why are dormice rare? A case study in conservation biology,* Mammal Review **26**: 157-187

Bright P.W., Morris P.A. & Mitchell-Jones A.J. (1996) *A new survey of the dormouse* Muscardinus avellanarius *in Britain, 1993-4,* Mammal Review **26**: 189-195

British Trust for Conservation Volunteers (1985) *Waterways and wetlands - a practical conservation handbook* British Wildlife *(General references)*

Blakeborough J.F. & Pease A.E. (1914) *The life and habits of the badger,* London: Foxhound

Bradbury K. (1974) *The badger diet* in Paget R.J. & Middleton A.L.V. *Badgers of Yorkshire and Humberside,* York: Ebor

Brink F.H. van den. (1967) *A field guide to the mammals of Britain and Europe,* London: Collins

Britt D.P. (ed.) (1985) *Humane control of land mammals and birds,* Potters Bar: Universities Federation for Animal Welfare

Brown J. & Stoddart D. (1977) *Killing mammals and general post-mortem methods,* Mammal Review **7**: 2 Chapter 7 Mammal Society/ Blackwell

Buckley J. (1982) *A guide for the identification of British amphibians & reptiles,* London: British Herpetological Society

Burrows R. (1968) *Wild Fox,* Devon: David & Charles

Burton J.A. (1966) *The distribution of weasel, stoat, common shrew, roe deer, water shrew and mole in the London area,* London: London Naturalist **45**: 35-42

Burton J.A. (1967) *Notes on mammals in the London area,* London: The London Naturalist **46**: 40-43

Burton J.A. (1974) *The naturalist in London,* Devon: David & Charles

Burton M. (1969) *The hedgehog,* London: Andre Deutsch

Cadman A. (1966) *Dawn, dusk and deer,* Country Life

Carbery M. & Grey E. (1948) *Hertfordshire heritage,* London: Green

Carson R. (1962) *Silent spring,* Cambridge Mass: Riverside Press

Carlhoun J.B. (1962) *The ecology and sociology of the Norway rat,* US Dept. Health, Education & Welfare

Carrington J. *Diary* in Johnson W. (1973)

Carrington R. & Matthews L.H. (eds) (1970) *The living world of animals,* Reader's Digest Association

Catt J.A. (1978) *Quaternary history of the Hertfordshire area,* Trans Herts Nat Hist Soc **28**: (4), 27-54

Cecil D. (1973) *The Cecils of Hatfield House,* London: Constable

Chanin P. (1991) *The otter* in Corbet G.B. & Harris S. (eds.)

Chanin P. (1985) *The natural history of otters,* Kent: Croom Helm

Chanin P. & Jerreries D. (1978) *The decline of the otter* Lutra lutra *in Britain: an analysis of hunting records and discussion of causes,* Biological Journal of the Linnean Society **10**: 305-328

Chapman D.I. & Chapman N.G. (1975) *Fallow deer: their history distribution and biology,* Terence Dalton

Chapman N. & Chapman D. (1970) *Fallow deer,* British Deer Society

Chapman N.G. *The Chinese muntjac* in Corbet G.B. & Harris S. (eds.) (1991)

Chapman N.G. (1991) *Deer,* London: Whittet

Chapman N., Harris S. & Stanford A. (1994) *Reeves' muntjac* Muntiacus reevesi *in Britain: their history, spread, habitat selection and the role of human intervention in accelerating the dispersal,* Mammal Review **24**: 113-160

Churchfield S. (1990) *The natural history of shrews,* London: Christopher Helm

Churchfield S. (1991) *The common shrew* in Corbet G.B. & Harris S. (eds.)

Churchfield S. (1991) *The pygmy shrew* in Corbet G.B. & Harris S. (eds.)

Clark M. *Mammals* in Sage B. (ed.) (1966) *Northaw Great Wood,* Hertfordshire: Hertfordshire County Council

Clark M. (1968) *Fraying by muntjac,* Deer **1**: 272-3

Clark M. (1970) *The conservation of badgers in Hertfordshire,* Trans Herts Nat Hist Soc **27**: 2 39-47

Clark M. (1978) *Mammals, reptiles & amphibians* in Shirley D. (ed.) *Hertfordshire - a guide to the countryside,* Letchworth: Egon Publishers

Clark M. & Hancox M. (1992) *Longevity of a Hertfordshire badger* (Meles meles), Trans Herts Nat Hist Soc **31**: 3 198-200

Clark M. (1970-99) *The Survey of mammals, reptiles and amphibia in Hertfordshire,* distribution maps and progress reports: Trans Herts Nat Hist Soc **27**: 2, 37-38 (1970); **27**: 237-238 (1973); **27**: 265-270 (1974); **28**: 9-16 (1977); **29**: 1, 11-14 (1979-82); **29**: 382-389 (1986); **29**: 382-389 (1987)

Clark M. & Summers S. (1980) *Seasonal population movements of brown rats and house mice in east Hertfordshire,* Trans Herts Nat Hist Soc **28**: 3 17-19

Clarke M. (1974) *Deer distribution survey 1967-1972,* Deer **3**: 232-279

Clutton-Brock J. (1987) *A natural history of domesticated mammals,* London: British Museum (Natural History)

Cocks A.H. (1905) *Victoria County Histories* (Mammals) Buckinghamshire & Hertfordshire

CoEnCo (1987) *Wildlife and the law No 3: mammals,* London: Council for Environmental Conservation and Mammal Society

CoEnCo *Wildlife and the law No.2: reptiles and amphibians,* London: Council for Environmental Conservation and British Herpetological Society

Cooke A. (1994) in Massey M. & Welch R.C. (eds) *Monks Wood National Nature Reserve:*

*The experience of 40 years, 1953-1993,* Symposium Proceedings, Peterborough: English Nature

Cooke A. (1999) *Conservation, muntjac deer & woodland reserve management,* Journal of Practical Ecology & Conservation, Sheffield: Wildtrack

Cooke A. & Lakhani H. (1996) *Damage to coppice regrowth by muntjac deer* Muntiacus reevesi *and protection with electric fencing,* Biological Conservation 75: 231-238

Coope R. (1977) *Fossil coleopteran assemblages as sensitive indicators of climatic changes during the Devensian (Last) cold stage,* Philosophical Transactions of the Royal Society of London, (Series B) 280: 313-340

Cooper M.E. (1984) *The law* in Rudge A.J.B. (ed.) *Guidelines for the safe and humane handling of live deer in Great Britain,* Peterborough: Nature Conservancy Council

Cooper M.E. (1987) *An introduction to animal law,* London: Academic Press

Corbet G.B. & Harris S. (eds.) (1991) *The handbook of British mammals,* (3rd ed) Oxford: Blackwell

Corbet G.B. & Southern H.N. (1977) *The handbook of British mammals* (2nd ed) Oxford: Blackwell

Corbet G.B. (1978) *The mammals of the Palaearctic region: a taxonomic review,* London: Brit Mus (Nat Hist)

Corbet G.B. (1966) *The terrestrial mammals of Western Europe,* Foulis

Corbet G.B. (1971) *Provisional distribution maps of British mammals,* Mammal Review 1: 95-142. Mammal Society/Blackwell

Corbett K. (1989) *Conservation of European reptiles & amphibians,* London: Christopher Helm

Corke D. (1971) *The local distribution of the yellow-necked mouse* Apodemus flavicollis, Mammal Review, 1:62-66

Corke D. (1979) *The mammals of Epping Forest* in Corke D. (ed.) *The wildlife of Epping Forest,* Essex Field Club, London

Corke D. & Harris S. (1972) *The small mammals of Essex,* Essex Naturalist 33: 32-59

Cott H. (1975) *Looking at animals,* London: Collins

Cotton J. (1979) *Mammals in the London area 1978,* London: The London Naturalist 58: 71-73

Cotton J. (1980) *Mammals in the London area 1979,* London: The London Naturalist 59: 84-86

Cowan D.P. (1991) *The rabbit* in Corbet G.B. & Harris S. (eds.)

Cowan D. (1980) *The wild rabbit,* Mammal Society/Blandford Press

Cowlin R.A. (1972) *The distribution of the Badger in Essex,* Essex Naturalist 33: 1-8

Cresswell P., Harris S. & Jeffries D.J. (1990) *The history, distribution, status and habitat requirements of the badger in Britain,* Peterborough: Nature Conservancy Council

Croin Michielson N. (1967) *Intraspecific and interspecific competition in the shrews* Sorex araneus *and* Sorex minutus, Bull. Mammal Soc 28: 6-7

Crowcroft W.P. (1957) *The life of the shrew,* Max Reinhardt

Dansie O. (1970) *Muntjac,* British Deer Society

Daniel W.B. (1812) *Rural sports,* London

Dawes J. (1998) *The pond owner's handbook,* London: Ward Lock

Delany M. (ed.) (1985) *Yorkshire mammals,* Yorkshire: University of Bradford

Dent G. (1907) *Occurrence of the serotine bat* Vesperugo serotinus *in Essex,* Essex Naturalist 15: 96

Dobson J. (1999) *The mammals of Essex,* Lopinga Books

Dony J.G. (1967) *Flora of Hertfordshire,* Hitchin Museum

Dowsett J.M. (1942) *The romance of England's forests,* London: John Gifford

Drabble P. (1969) *Badgers at my window,* London: Pelham

Drabble P. (1977) *A weasel in my meatsafe,* London: Michael Joseph

Dunnet G. *et al.* (1986) *Badgers and bovine tuberculosis,* London: HMSO

Dunstone N. (1993) *The mink,* London: T. & A.D. Poyser

Edwards J. (1974) *Cheshunt in Hertfordshire,* Broxbourne Borough Council

Eldridge M.J. (1968) *Some observations on* Apodemus sylvaticus *and* Clethrionomys glareolus *using the method of live trapping,* Proceedings of the Zoological Society of London 155: 2

English Nature (1991) *Facts about amphibians,* London: Advisory leaflet

English Nature (1991) *Facts about reptiles,* London: Advisory leaflet

Ewer R.F. (1973) *The carnivores,* Weidenfeld & Nicolson

Fairley J.S. (1975) *An Irish beast book,* Blackstaff Press

Farming and Wildlife Advisory Group *Pond management and the conservation of frogs and toads,* information leaflets 15 and 8

Fauna and Flora Preservation Society & A.C.O. Polymer Products *Toads on roads,* booklet

Field D. (2000) *Cheshunt: its people past and present,* Cheshunt: Gaillet Press

Fisher J. (1975) *The black rat,* Rattus rattus, *in London,* London Naturalist 29: 136

Fitter R.S.R. (1975) *A check-list of the mammals, reptiles and amphibia of the London area, 1900-1949,* London Naturalist 28: 98-115

Fitter R.S.R. (1975) *Further records of mammals, reptiles and amphibians in the London area,* London Naturalist 39: 18-21

Fitter R.S.R. (1945) *London's natural history,* London: Collins

Flowerdew J.R. (1984) *Woodmice & yellow necked mice,* (The Mammal Society series) Oswestry: Nelson

Flowerdew J.R. (1993) *Mice & voles,* London: Whittet

Foster A.H. (1934) *Reptiles & amphibians* in Hine (ed.)

Frazer D. (1983) *Reptiles & amphibians in Britain,* London: Collins

Gibb R. & Foster J. (eds) (2000) *The Herpetofauna worker's guide,* Froglife

Glendining V. (1989) *Hertfordshire,* London: Weidenfeld

303

Gold K.A.J. (1974) *Mammals in the London area, 1972-1973,* London: The London Naturalist **53**: 100-104,

Gold K.A.J. (1975) *Mammals in the London area, 1974,* London: The London Naturalist **54**: 66-68.

Gold K.A.J. (1976) *Mammals in the London area, 1975,* London: The London Naturalist **55**: 58-61

Gosling L.M. & Baker S.J. (1988) *Planning and monitoring an attempt to eradicate coypus from Britain,* symposia of the Zoological Society of London **58**: 99-113

Gipps J.H.W. & Alibhai S.K. (1991) *The field vole* in Corbet G.B. & Harris S. (eds.)

Glue D.E. (1967) *Prey taken by the barn owl in England and Wales,* Bird Study **14**: 169-83

Glue D.E. (1974) *Food of the barn owl in Britain and Ireland,* Bird Study **21**: 200-10

Godfrey G.K. and Crowcroft P. (1960) *The Life of the mole,* London: Museum Press

Gorman M.L. & Stone R.D. (1990) *The natural history of moles,* London: Christopher Helm

Gotch A.F. (1979) *Mammals - their Latin names explained,* Blandford Press

Gover J., Mawer A. & Stenton F. (1938) *The place names of Hertfordshire,* Cambridge University Press

Green W.L. (1998) *A study of small mammals in the Parish of Kimpton,* Trans Herts Nat Hist Soc **33**: 3, 239-242

Green W.L. (1998) *Water voles on the Hertfordshire River Mimram,* Trans Herts Nat Hist Soc **33**: 3, 266-272

Green W.L. (1999) *The effects of climate change on water voles* (Arvicola terrestris) *in Hertfordshire, seen during a five-year study,* Trans Herts Nat Hist Soc **33**: 5, 479-481

Green W.L. (1999) *Harvest mouse* Micromys minutus *distribution within a Hertfordshire agricultural environment,* Trans Herts Nat Hist Soc **33**: 5, 421-424

Green W.L. (1999) *Some observations of Hertfordshire's stoats* Mustela erminea *& weasels* Mustels nivalis, Trans Herts Nat Hist Soc **33**: 5, 425-427

Greenaway F. & Hutson A.M. (1990) *A field guide to British bats,* Bruce Coleman Books, Uxbridge

Griffiths R. (1987) *How to begin the study of amphibians,* London: Richmond

Griffiths R. (1996) *Newts & salamanders of Europe,* London: Poyser

Grzimek B. (1972) *Animal life encyclopedia: mammals,* Vols **10-13,** Van Nostrand Reinhold

Gurnell J. (1979) *Woodland mice,* London: HMSO

Gurnell J. & Flowerdew J.R. (1982) *Live trapping small mammals,* Reading: Mammal Society

Gurnell J. (1987) *The natural history of squirrels,* London: Christopher Helm

Gurnell J. (1991) *The grey squirrel* in Corbet G.B. & Harris S. (eds.)

Gurnell J. & Pepper H. (1993) *A critical look at conserving the British red squirrel,* Mammal Review **23**: 127-137

Hager P. (1955) *Slowworm,* Trans Herts Nat Hist Soc **24**: 4, 161

Hager P. (1956) *Melanic grey squirrels near Berkhamsted* and *Notes on mammals,* Trans Herts Nat Hist Soc **24**: 5, 198-199

Hall D.G. (1978) *Mammals in the London area 1976,* London: The London Naturalist **57**: 92-95

Hall D.G. (1978) *Mammals in the London area 1977,* London: The London Naturalist **57**: 96-97

Halliday T. & Adler K. (1986) *The encyclopedia of reptiles & amphibians,* London: Guild

Harris C.J. (1968) *Otters: a study of the recent* Lutrinae, Weidenfeld & Nicolson

Harris R.A. and Duff K.R. (1970) *Wild deer in Britain,* David & Charles

Harris S. (1986) **Badgers in law,** BBC Wildlife **4**: 232

Harris S. (1973/74) *The history and distribution of squirrels in Essex,* Essex Naturalist **33**: 64-78

Harris S. (1979) *Secret life of the harvest mouse,* London: Hamlyn

Harris S. (1980) *The harvest mouse,* Blandford Press

Harris S. (2000) *Rise of the reds,* BBC Wildlife **18**: 5, 48-55 Bristol: BBC Wildlife Magazine

Harris S. (1986) *Urban foxes,* London: Whittet

Harris S. & Lloyd H.G. (1991) *The fox* in Corbet G.B. & Harris S. (eds.)

Harris S., Morris P., Wray S. & Yalden D. (1995) *A review of British mammals,* Peterborough: JNCC

Harris S. & Trout R.C. (1991) *The harvest mouse* in Corbet G.B. & Harris S. (eds.)

Harrison Matthews L. (1952) *The British amphibia and reptiles,* London: Methuen & Co.

Hart-Davis D. (1992) *Eileen Soper's book of badgers,* London: Robinson Publishing

Harting J.E. (1880) *British animals extinct within historic times,* London: Trubner

Hawker J. (1961) *A Victorian poacher: James Hawker's journal,* Oxford University Press

Heath C. (1992) *The book of Hertford,* Northampton: Baron Birch.

Herbert C. (1992) *Notes on the occupancy of a suburban bat box project at Oak Hill Woods Nature Reserve, 1986-1991,* Trans Herts Nat Hist Soc **31**: 3, 180-184

Herter K. (1965) *Hedgehogs,* London: Phoenix House

Hertfordshire Countryside *(General reference, summer 1946 Vol.1, No.1 to date),* Letchworth

Hertfordshire Past *(General reference),* Hertfordshire Archaeological Council

Hills D. (1991) *Ephemeral introductions and escapes* in Corbet G.B. & Harris S. (eds.)

Hilton-Brown D. & Oldham R.S. (1991) *The status of the widespread amphibians & reptiles in Britain, 1990, and changes during the 1980s,* Peterborough: Nature Conservancy Council

Hine R. (ed.) (1934) *The natural history of the Hitchin region,* Hitchin: Hitchin & District Regional Survey Association

Hingston F. (1988) *Deer parks & deer of Great Britain,* Buckingham: Sport & Leisure

HMSO (1911) *Protection of Animals Act,* London

HMSO (1981) *Wildlife & Countryside Act,* London

Hodson D. (1974) *Printed maps of Hertfordshire,* London: Dawson

Hooper J.H.D. (1976) *Use of the Holgate ultrasonic receiver to obtain bat distribution data in the Thames Valley and adjacent areas to the west of London,* The Middle-Thames Naturalist, **29**: 4-13

Holm J. (1087) *Squirrels,* London: Whittet

Horwood M.T. and Masters E.H. (1970) *Sika deer,* British Deer Society

Hurrell E. (1962) *Dormice,* Animals of Britain No. 10, Sunday Times Publications

Hurrell E. (1963) *Watch for the otter,* Country Life Books

Hurrell E. (1980) *The common dormouse,* Mammal Society & Blandford Press

Hurrell H.G. (1963) *Pine martens,* Animals of Britain No.22, Sunday Times Publications

Hurrell H.G. (1968) *Pine martens,* London: HMSO

Hurrell H.G. (1968) *Wildlife: tame but free,* Newton Abbot: David & Charles

Hutchings M.R. & Harris S. (1996) *The current status of the brown hare* Lepus europaeus *in Britain,* JNCC, Peterborough

Jarvis N. & Marshall I. (1987) *Report of the Hertfordshire pond survey 1986,* Hertford: Hertfordshire County Council

Jefferies D., Wayre P., Jessop R. & Mitchell-Jones A. (1986) *Reinforcing the native otter* Lutra lutra *population of East Anglia: an analysis of the behaviour and range of development of the first release group,* Mammal Review **16**: 65-79

Jefferies D. (1989) *The changing otter population of Britain 1700-1989,* Biological Journal of the Linnean Society **38**: 61-69

Jefferies R. *The gamekeeper at home,* Murray (1914)

Johnson L. & Ingham J. *Chemicals in humans,* Article in The Express newspaper 6th Jan. 2000

Johnson W. (1973) *'Memorandoms for...' the Carrington diary,* London: Phillimore

Johnson W. (1952) *Companion into Hertfordshire,* London: Methuen

Jones J. (1995) *The distribution of bats in Hertfordshire,* Trans Herts Nat Hist Soc **32**: 3, 259-269

Jones J. & Molloy L. (1997) *The water vole: its status and habitat preference in Hertfordshire,* Trans Herts Nat Hist Soc **33**: 1, 85-90

Jones M., Rotherham I.D. & McCarthy A.J. (eds.) (1999) *Deer or the new woodlands?* Journal of Practical Ecology and Conservation, Special Publication 1. Sheffield: Wildtrack

Jones-Baker D. (1977) *The folklore of Hertfordshire,* London: Batsford

Kenward R.E. & Holm J.L. (1989) *What future for British red squirrels?* Biological Journal of the Linnean Society **38**: 83-89

King C.M. (1991) *The stoat* and *The weasel* in Corbet G.B. & Harris S. (eds.)

Kitchener A. (1991) *The natural history of the wild cats,* London: Christopher Helm

Kolb H. (1996) *Country foxes,* London: Whittet

Kourik S. (Force Wildlife Officer) (1991) *Wildlife law,* Hertfordshire Constabulary

Kruuk H. (1989) *The social badger - ecology and behaviour of a group-living carnivore,* Oxford: Oxford University Press

Lane M. (1946) *The tale of Beatrix Potter,* London: Warne

Lang A. (1994) *The suburban bat box project at Oak Hill Woods Nature Reserve - an update, 1992-1993,* Trans Herts Nat Hist Soc **32**: 1, 43-46

Langley P.J.W. & Yalden D.W. (1977) *The decline of the rarer carnivores in Great Britain during the nineteenth century,* Mammal Review **7**: 95-116

Langton T. (1989) *Snakes & lizards,* London: Whittet

Langton T. (1991) *Distribution and status of reptiles and amphibians in the London area,* London: The London Naturalist, No. 70

Laver H. (1898) *The mammals, fishes and reptiles of Essex,* Essex Field Club

Lawrence M.J. and Brown R.W. (1973) *Mammals of Britain, their tracks, trails and signs,* Blandford Press

Leech J. (1853) illustrations in *Mr Sponge's sporting tour,* London: Bradbury & Evans

Lenton E.J., Chanin P.R.F. & Jefferies D.J. (1980) *Otter survey of England 1977-79,* London: Nature Conservancy Council

Leighton G. (1901) *The life history of British serpents,* Edinburgh: Blackwood

Leighton G. (1903) *The life history of British lizards,* Edinburgh: Blackwood

Leutscher A. (1960) *Tracks & signs of British animals,* London: Cleaver-Hume

Lever C. (1977) *Naturalized animals of the British Isles,* London: Hutchinson

Linder L. (1971) *A history of the writings of Beatrix Potter,* London: Warne

Linn I. (1962) *Weasels,* Animals of Britain No. 14, Sunday Times Publications

Lloyd H.G. (1980) *The red fox,* London: Batsford

Lloyd H.G. (1983) *Past and present distribution of red and grey squirrels in Britain,* Mammal Review **13**: 69-80

Locker A. (1977) in *Animal bones and shellfish* pp160-162 in Neal D.S. *Excavations at the palace of Kings Langley, Hertfordshire 1974-1976,* Medieval Archaeology **21**: 124-165

Lockley R.M. (1965) *The private life of the rabbit,* London: Andre Deutsch

London Wildlife Trust *Frog facts,* leaflet

Long C.A. and Killingley C.A. (1983) *The badgers of the world,* Illinois: Charles C. Thomas

Lorenz K. (1952) *King Solomon's ring,* London: Methuen

Lorenz K. (1954) *Man meets dog,* London: Methuen

Lucas D. (1997) *Mammals in Carmarthenshire,* Andrew Lucas, Wales

Lydekker R. (1895) *A hand-book to the British Mammalia,* Allen's Naturalist's Library. London: W.H. Allen

Lydekker R. (1898) *The deer of all lands,* Rowland Ward

Lydekker R. (1909) *Hertfordshire,* Cambridge University Press

Mabey R. (1972) *Food for free,* London: Collins

Mabey R. (1983) *In a green shade,* London: Hutchinson

Mabey R. (1996) *Flora Britannica, (Project supported by Common Ground)* London: Sinclair-Stevenson

Macdonald D. (1995) *European mammals: evolution and behaviour,* London: Harper Collins

Macdonald D. (1988) *Running with the fox,* London: Unwin Hyman

Macdonald D. (ed.) (1984) *The encyclopedia of mammals,* 2 vols, London: Allen & Unwin

Macdonald D. & Barrett P. (1993) *Mammals of Britain and Europe,* London: Collins

Macgregor H. (1995) *Crested newts - ancient survivors,* British Wildlife **7**: 1, 1-8, Hampshire: British Wildlife Publishing

McKinley R. (1999) *The future for woodland deer,* Shrewsbury: Swan Hill

McNally L. (1975) *Year of the red deer,* Dent

Marsh A. (1999) *The national yellow-necked mouse survey,* London: The Mammal Society

Matheson C. *Brown rats,* Animals of Britain No.16 Sunday Times Publications (1962)

Matthews L.H. (1952) *British mammals,* London: Collins & 2nd ed (1960)

McBride A. (1988) *Rabbits & hares,* London: Whittet

Meads F. (1956) *They meet at eleven,* London: George Newnes

Meads J. (1979) *They still meet at eleven,* Tetbury: Standfast Press

Meads J. (1999) *My hunting world,* London: Quiller Press

Mellanby K. (1971) *The mole,* London: Collins

Mee A. (1940) *Hertfordshire,* London: Hodder & Stoughton

Mickleburgh S. (1987) *Distribution and status of bats in the London area,* London: The London Naturalist No.66

Middleton A.D. (1931) *The grey squirrel,* London: Sidgwick and Jackson

Millais, J.G. (1905) *The mammals of Great Britain and Ireland,* Vols 1-111, London: Longmans

Miller G. (1912) *Catalogue of the mammals of Western Europe,* London: Brit Mus (Nat Hist)

Mitchell-Jones A.J. *et al.* (1986) *Public concern about bats (*Chiroptera*) in Britain: an analysis of enquiries in 1982-83,* Biological Conservation **36**

Morgan E. (1972) *The descent of woman,* London: Souvenir Press

Morris P. (1966) *The hedgehog in London,* London: London Naturalist **45:** 43-49

Morris P.A. (1983) *Hedgehogs,* London: Whittet Books

Morris P.A. (1993) *A red data book for British mammals,* London: Mammal Society

Morris J. (ed.) (1976) *Domesday Book 12, Hertfordshire,* Chichester: Phillimore

Morris P.A., Bright P.W. & Woods D. (1990) *Use of nest boxes by the dormouse* Muscardinus avellanarius, Biological Conservation **51**: 1-13

Morris P.A. (1997) *The edible dormouse* (Glis glis), London: Mammal Society

Munby L. (1977) *The Hertfordshire landscape,* London: Hodder & Stoughton

Nature Conservancy Council (1979) *Wildlife introductions to Great Britain,* London: NCC

Nature Conservancy Council (1982) *Wildlife, the law and you,* London: NCC

Nature Conservancy Council (1983) *The ecology and conservation of amphibian and reptile species endangered in Britain,* Peterborough: NCC

Nature Conservancy Council (1984) *Focus on bats: their conservation and the law,* Peterborough: NCC

Nature Conservancy Council (1988) *Bats in roofs,* NCC

Nau B.S., Boon C.R. & Knowles J.P. (eds.) (1987) *Bedfordshire wildlife,* Ware, Hertfordshire: Castlemead

Neal E.G. (1962) *Otters,* Animals of Britain No. 8, Sunday Times Publications

Neal E.G. *The badger,* (1st ed 1948, 4th ed 1975), London: Collins

Neal E.G. (1977) *Badgers,* Poole Dorset: Blandford Press

Neal E.G. (1972) *National badger survey,* Mammal Rev. **2**: 55-64. Mammal Society/ Blackwell

Neal E.G. (1986) *The natural history of badgers,* London: Croom Helm

Neal E.G. & Cheeseman C.L. (1991) *The badger* in Corbet G.B. & Harris S. (eds.)

Newton R. (1989) *Observations on bats hibernating in an ice-house at Wormleybury, Hertfordshire,* Trans Herts Nat Hist Soc **30**: 3, 245-250

Niblett R. (1995) *Roman Hertfordshire,* Dorset: Dovecote

Norris J.D. (1967) *The campaign against feral coypus (*Myocastor coypus Molina*) in Great Britain,* Journal of Applied Ecology **4**: 191-199

Novick A. (1969) *The world of bats,* (with photographs by Nina Leen), Rinehart & Winston

Oakeley S.F. & Jones G. (1998) *Habitat around maternity roosts of the 55kHz phonic type of pipistrelle bat* Pipistrellus pipistrellus, London: J. of Zool. **245**: 222-228

Paget R.J. and Middleton A.L.V. (1974) *Badgers of Yorkshire and Humberside,* York: Ebor

Parkes C. & Thornley J. (1989) *Fair game - the law of country sports and the protection of wildlife,* Pelham

Pease A.E. (1898) *The badger,* Lawrence and Bullen

Page F.J.T. (ed.) (1971) *Field guide to British deer,* Blackwell, 2nd edn.

Pearce H., Baker M. & White G. (2000) *The River Mimram water vole, otter & crayfish survey,* St.Albans: Hertfordshire & Middlesex Wildlife Trust

Piechoki R. (1958) *Die Zwergmaus* Micromys minutus *Pallas,* Wittenberg Lutherstadt: Ziemsen (Translated by McCready R, Hertfordshire as *Harvest mouse*)

Pitt F. (1938) *Wild animals in Britain,* London: Batsford

Pirie M.D. & Goldsmith F.B. *Changes in Hertfordshire ponds, 1986-1997,* Trans Herts Nat Hist Soc **33**: 5, 482-494

Pollard E. & Cooke A.S. (1994) *Impact of muntjac deer* Muntiacus reevesi *on egg-*

laying sites of the white admiral butterfly Ladoga camilla *in a Cambridgeshire wood,* Biological Conservation **70**: 189-191

Potter B. (1901) *The tale of Peter Rabbit,* London: Warne

Prestt I. *An ecological study of the viper* Vipera berus *in southern Britain,* London: J. Zool., **164**: 373-418

Pring G. (1958) *Records of the Culmstock Otterhounds (c1790-1957),* Exeter: COH

Prior R. (1963) *Roe stalking,* Percival Marshall

Prior R. (1968) *The roe deer of Cranborne Chase: an ecological survey,* Oxford University Press

Rackham J. (1979) Rattus rattus: *the introduction of the black rat into Britain,* Antiquity **53**: 112-120

Rackham O. (1986) *The history of the countryside,* London: Weidenfeld and Nicholson

Rackham O. (1989) *The last forest,* London: J.M. Dent

Ransome R. (1990) *The natural history of hibernating bats,* London: Christopher Helm

Reid A. *Adder bites in Britain,* British Medical Journal, 17 July 1976, pp153-156

Richardson P. (1985) *Bats,* London: Whittet books

Robert R. (1968) *Historic Hertfordshire,* Letchworth: Hertfordshire Countryside

Roberts K.A. & Roberts P.L.E. (1978) *Postglacial deposits at Stanstead Abbotts,* London Naturalist **57**: 6-10

Ross J. & Sanders M.F. (1984) *The development of genetic resistance to myxomatosis in wild rabbits in Britain,* Journal of Hygiene, Cambridge **92**: 255-261

Rothschild M. (1983) *Dear Lord Rothschild,* London: Hutchinson

Ruby J. & Paine M. (1999) *The Commons Nature Reserve - a history,* Welwyn Garden City: Commonswood Community Arts Fund

Ryder S. R. (1962) *Water voles,* Animals of Britain No.4, Sunday Times Publications

Sage B. (1955) *The yellow-necked mouse* (Apodemus flavicollis) *in Herts,* Trans Herts Nat Hist Soc **24**: 4, 161

Sage B. (1954) *The slowworm* (Anguis fragilis) *and the red squirrel* (Sciurus vulgaris) *in south Hertfordshire,* Trans Herts Nat Hist Soc **24**: 2, 78

Sage B. (ed.) (1966) *Northaw Great Wood,* Hertfordshire: Hertfordshire County Council

Sage B. (1966) *Amphibians & reptiles* in Sage B. (ed.) *Northaw Great Wood,* Hertfordshire County Council

Saint-Girous M-C. (1973) *Les mammifereres de France et du Benelux,* Paris: Doin

Sawford B. (1982) *Wildlife of the Letchworth area,* Hertfordshire: Letchworth Naturalists' Society

Scruton R. (2000) *Animal rights and wrongs,* 3rd edn., London: Metro

Seaman K. (1995) *A demographic study of small mammals with special reference to* Micromys minutus *at two different habitats at Rye Meads Nature Reserve*

Sheail J. (1971) *Rabbits and their history,* Newton Abbot: David & Charles

Shorten M. (1954) *Squirrels,* London: Collins

Shorten M. *Grey squirrels,* Animals of Britain No.5, Sunday Times Publications

Shorten M. *Red squirrels,* Animals of Britain No.6, Sunday Times Publications

Slater F. (1992) *The common toad,* Buckinghamshire: Shire

Sleeman P. (1989) *Stoats & weasels; polecats & martens,* London: Whittet

Smith K.W., Dee C.W., Fearnside J.D., Fletcher E.W. & Smith R.N. (1993) *The breeding birds of Hertfordshire,* Hertfordshire: Hertfordshire Natural History Society

Smith M. (1951) *Amphibians and reptiles of the British Isles,* London: Collins

Soper E.A. (1955) *When badgers wake,* Routledge & Kegan Paul

Soper E.A. (1969) *Muntjac,* Longman

Soper T. (1965) *The bird table book,* Macdonald/David & Charles

Soper E.A. (1957) *Wild encounters,* London: Routledge and Kegan Paul

Southern H.N. (1968) *The handbook of British mammals,* (1st edn.) Oxford: Blackwell

Speakman F.J. (1965) *A forest by night,* London: Bell

Stafford P. (1987) *The adder,* Buckinghamshire: Shire

Staines B. (1980) *The red deer,* Mammal Society/ Blandford Press

Staines B.W. & Ratcliffe P.R. (1991) *The roe deer* in Corbet G.B. & Harris S. (eds.)

Stebbings R.E. (1988) *Conservation of European bats,* London: Christopher Helm

Stebbings R.E. (1970) *A bat new to Britain* Pipistrellus nathusii *with notes on its identification and distribution in Europe,* London: J. Zool. **161**: 282-6

Stephen D. (1963) *Watching wildlife,* London: Collins

Stephens M.N. (1957) *The otter report,* Potters Bar, Hertfordshire: UFAW

Steward J.W. (1969) *The tailed amphibians of Europe,* Newton Abbot: David & Charles

Stone R.D. & Gorman M.L. (1991) *The mole* in Corbet G.B. & Harris S. (eds.)

Stone R.D. (1992) *The mole,* Buckinghamshire: Shire

Strachan R. (1995) *Mammal detective,* London: Whittet

Strachan R. (1997) *Water voles,* London: Whittet

Strachan R. & Jefferies D.J. (1993) *The water vole* Arvicola terrestris *in Britain 1989-90: its distribution and changing status,* London: Vincent Wildlife Trust

Strachan R. & Jefferies D.J. (1996) *Otter survey of England 1991-1994,* London: Vincent Wildlife Trust

Stringer A. (1714) ed. *Fairley J.* (1978) *The experienced huntsman,* Belfast: Blackstaff

Sumption K.J. & Flowerdew J.R. (1985) *The ecological effects of the decline in rabbits* Oryctolagus cuniculus *due to myxomatosis,* Mammal Review **15**: 151-186

Swan M.J.S. & Oldham R.S. (1989) *Amphibian communities,* Leicester Polytechnic

Sykes L. & Durrant J. (1995) *The natural hedgehog,* London: Gaia

Tapper S.C. *et al.* (1982) *Effects of mammalian predators on partridge populations,* Mammal Review **12**: 159-167

Tapper S.C. (1992) *Game heritage - an ecological review from shooting and gamekeeping records*, Fordingbridge: Game Conservancy

Tapper S.C. & Parsons N. (1984) *The changing status of the brown hare* Lepus capensis *in Britain*, Mammal Review **14**: 57-70

Taylor K.D., Fenn M.G. & MacDonald D.W. (1991) *The brown rat* in Corbet G.B. & Harris S. (eds.)

Taylor K.D. (1991) *The ship rat* in Corbet G.B. & Harris S. (eds.)

Teagle W.G. (1962) *Mammal recording in 1961*, London: The London Naturalist No.41, pp88-89 (See also references in Appendix 6 for *LNHS* mammal records: Beames, Burton, Cotton, Gold, Hall, Morris, Roberts & Teagle)

Teagle W.G. (1963) *Mammals in the London area*, London: The London Naturalist No.42, pp42-58

Teagle W.G. (1964) *The harvest mouse in the London area*, London: The London Naturalist No.43, pp136-149

Teagle W.G. (1967) *The fox in the London suburbs*, The London Naturalist **46**: 44-68.

Teagel W.G. (1969) *The badger in the London area*, London: The London Naturalist No.48

Thomas Sir W.B. (1950) *Hertfordshire*, London: Hale

Thompson H.V. (1968) *British wild mink*, Annals of Applied Biology **81**: 345-349

Thompson H.V. & Worden A. (1956) *The rabbit*, London: Collins

Tittensor A.M. (1980) *The red squirrel*, The Mammal Society and Blandford Press, London and Dorset

Tittensor A.M. & Tittensor R.M. (1985) *The rabbit warren at West Dean near Chichester*, Sussex Archeological Collections **123**: 151-185

Tomkies M. (1991) *Wildcats*, London: Whittet

Tomkins M. (1975) *John Parnell's account of Arthur Young's farm*, Hertfordshire Past & Present **15**: 26-31

Toschi A. & Lanza B. (1959) *Fauna d'Italia Vol IV* Mammalia Generalita-Insectivora-Chiroptera, Bologna: Edizoni Calderini

Tree D. (1966) *Pig in the middle*, London: Joseph

Twigg G. (1984) *The Black Death*, London: Batsford

Twigg G. (1992) *The black rat* Rattus rattus *in the United Kingdom in 1989*, Mammal Review **22**: 33-42

Twigg G. (1975) *The brown rat*, David & Charles

Wacher J. (1978) *Roman Britain*, J.M. Dent & Sons

Wainwright M. (1998) *The Hertfordshire & Middlesex Badger Group database*, Trans Herts Nat Hist Soc **33**: 3, pp228-238

Walker E.P. (1975) *Mammals of the world*, 3 Vols. (3rd edn.), Johns Hopkins Press

Walton I. & Cotton C. (1926 edn.) *The compleat angler*, London: Bodley Head

Walton K.C. (1964) *The distribution of the polecat* Putorius putorius *in England, Wales and Scotland, 1959-62*, Proc Zool Soc Lond **143**: 333-6

Walton K.C. (1968) *The distribution of the polecat* Putorius putorius *in Great Britain, 1963-67*, Proc Zool Soc Lond **155**: pp237-240

Warner L.J. (1978) *Mammal photography and observation*, Academic Press

Warren S. (1912) *On a late glacial stage in the valley of the River Lea*, Quart J Geol Soc **68**: 213-51

Warren S. (1915) *Further observations on a late glacial or Ponders End stage in the valley of the River Lea*, Quart J Geol Soc **71**: 164-82

Wayre P. (1979) *The private life of the otter*, Batsford

Webb J. *Otter spraint analysis*, Mammal Society, Reading

Westell W.P. (1931) *Historic Hertfordshire*, Hertford: Stephen Austin

Whitaker J. (1892) *A descriptive list of the deer parks and paddocks of England*, London: Ballantyne, Hanson

White G. (1777) *The natural history of Selborne*, London: White *(Various modern editions)*

Whitehead G.K. (1950) *Deer and their management*, London: Country Life

Whitehead G.K. (1964) *The deer of Great Britain and Ireland: an account of their history, status and distribution*, London: Routledge and Kegan Paul

Whitehead G.K. (1972) *Deer of the world*, Constable

Whitlock D. (1961) *The Anglo-Saxon Chronicle*, London: Eyre & Spottiswoode

Whitmore R. (1987) *Hertfordshire headlines*, Newbury: Countryside Books

Whitmore R. (1983) *Mad Lucas*, Hertfordshire: NHDC

Whitmore R. (1975) *Of uncommon interest*, Buckinghamshire: Spurbooks

Williams D. (1959) *Pendley and a pack of hounds*, London: Hodder & Stoughton

Wilmore A. *et al.* (1925) *The natural history of Hertfordshire*, London: Bell

Wilson G., Harris S. & McLaren G. (1997) *Changes in the British badger population, 1988 to 1997*, London: People's Trust for Endangered Species

Wimsatt W.A. (1970 & 1977) *Biology of bats*, 3 Vols, Academic Press

Wisniewski P. (1989) *Newts of the British Isles*, Buckinghamshire: Shire

Yalden D.W. (1993) *Identification of remains in owl pellets*, London: Mammal Society

Yalden D.W. (1977) *Small mammals and the archaeologist*, Bulletin of the Peakland Archaeological Society **30**: 18-25

Yalden D.W. (1982) *When did the mammal fauna of the British Isles arrive?* Mammal Review **12**: 1-57

Yalden D.W. (1992) *Changing distribution and status of small mammals in Britain*, Mammal Review **22**: 97-106

Yalden D.W. (1999) *The history of British mammals*, London: T. & A.D. Poyser

Yalden D.W. and Morris P.A. (1975) *The lives of bats*, David & Charles

Young A. (1804) (1971 re-print) *General view of the agriculture of Hertfordshire*, Newton Abbot: David & Charles

# Index